Penguin Book 2520
African Writing Today
Edited by Ezekiel Mphahlele

AFRICAN
WRITING
TODAY

EDITED BY
EZEKIEL MPHAHLELE

PENGUIN BOOKS

Penguin Books Ltd, Harmondsworth
Middlesex, England
Penguin Books Inc., 3300 Clipper Mill Road,
Baltimore 11, Md, U.S.A.
Penguin Books Australia Ltd, Ringwood,
Victoria, Australia

First published by Penguin Books 1967
Copyright © Ezekiel Mphahlele, 1967

Made and printed in Great Britain by
Hazell Watson & Viney Ltd
Aylesbury, Bucks
Set in Linotype Juliana

Contents

Acknowledgements

For permission to publish or reproduce the material in this anthology, acknowledgement is made to the following copyright holders:

For CHINUA ACHEBE: 'Captain Winterbottom' from *Arrow of God*, to William Heinemann Ltd, and the author; for CHRISTINA AMA ATA AIDOO: 'The Message', to the author; for GEORGE AWOONOR-WILLIAMS: 'Rediscovery', to the author; for SYLVAIN BEMBA: 'The Dark Room', to *Preuves*, Paris (with Jean Pliya's 'L'arbre fétiche' 'La Chambre Noire' won the *Preuves*, 'Prix de la Nouvelle Africaine, 1964'); for ANTOINE-ROGER BOLAMBA: 'A Fistful of News', to *Présence Africaine*, Paris; for KWESI BREW: 'The Harvest', to the author; for DENNIS BRUTUS: 'Let not this plunger be misconstrued', to Mbari Publications, Ibadan; for BIRAGO DIOP: 'The Wages of Good' from *Tales of Amadou Koumba*, to Oxford University Press; for DAVID DIOP: 'To the Mystery-mongers', to *Présence Africaine*; for MBELLA SONNE DIPOKO: 'Love', to *United Asia* and the author; for SARIF EASMON: 'Bindeh's Gift', to the author; for CYPRIAN EKWENSI: 'Night of Freedom', to the author; for LUIS BERNARDO HONWANA: 'Dina', to the author; for PAULIN JOACHIM: 'Burial', to the author; for JOSEPH KARIUKI: 'New Life', to the author; for MAZISI KUNENE: 'Universal Love', to the author; for ALEX LA GUMA: 'Blankets', to the author; for CAMARA LAYE: 'Akissi' from *The Radiance of the King*, to William Collins Sons and Co. (first published as *Le Regard du Roi* by Librairie Plon, Paris); for AKÉ LOBA: 'A Justice of the Peace' from *Kocoumbo, l'étudiant noir*, to Flammarion et Cie, Paris; for TODD MATSHIKIZA: 'The Party' from *Chocolates for my Wife*, to Hodder and Stoughton Limited; for EZEKIEL MPHAHLELE: 'Remarks on Negritude' and 'On the Long Road' (first published in *Encounter*), to the author; for JEAN-BAPTISTE MUTABARUKA: 'Song of the Drum', to the author; for AGOSTINHO NETO: 'Friend Mussunda', to Mbari Publications; for ABIOSEH NICOL: 'Life is Sweet at Kumansenu', to the author; for LEWIS NKOSI: 'The Prisoner', to the author; for ONUORO NZEKWU: 'The Finger of God' from *Blade Among the Boys*, to Hutchinson and Co. Ltd and the author; for GRACE OGOT: 'Tekayo', to the author (first published in *Présence Africaine*); for FERDINAND OYONO: 'Waiting for a Medal' from *The Old Negro and the Medal* (to be published in 1967), to Heinemann Educational Books Ltd and John Reed (first published as *Le Vieux Nègre et la Medaille* by René Julliard, Paris); for LENRIE PETERS: After they put down their overalls', to Mbari Publications; for JEAN PLIYA:

'The Fetish Tree', to *Preuves*, Paris (with Sylvain Bemba's 'La Chambre noire' 'L'Arbre fétiche' won the *Preuves* 'Prix de la Nouvelle Africaine, 1964'); for RICHARD RIVE: 'Dagga-Smoker's Dream', to the author; for LÉOPOLD SÉDAR SENGHOR: 'Death of the Princess' from *Ethiopiques* and 'Negro Mask' from *Chants d'Ombre*, both to Éditions du Seuil; for OUSMANE SOCÉ: 'Karim at the Ball' from *Karim*, to Nouvelles Éditions Latines; for WOLE SOYINKA: Extract from *The Swamp-Dwellers*, and 'Requiem', to the author; for KULDIP SONDHI; 'Bad Blood', to the author; for FELIX TCHIKAYA U'TAM'SI: 'Presence' from *Feu de Brousse*, Mbari Publications, to the author; for CAN THEMBA: 'The Urchin', to the author; for AMOS TUTUOLA: 'My First Wedding' from *My Life in the Bush of Ghosts*, to Faber and Faber Ltd and the author; for JOSEPH ZOBEL: 'Flowers! Lovely Flowers!' from *Le Soleil Partagé*, to *Présence Africaine*, Paris.

Every effort has been made to trace copyright holders, but in a few cases this has proved impossible. The publishers would be interested to hear from any copyright holders not here acknowledged.

Introduction

This anthology is intended to give the intelligent reader a map of themes and styles of African writing in the metropolitan languages – English, French, and Portuguese. It is a young and still tender literature. Most of the authors represented here are between thirty and forty-five years of age. Of course it is impossible to be exhaustive, but the signposts are clear and speak out loud and bold. For purposes of economy, we have had, reluctantly, to discard seventeen authors whose work is widely known – for example Nigerian poets John Pepper Clark, Gabriel Okara and Christopher Okigbo; Ghana's playwright, Joe de Graft; Dahomey's novelist, Olympe Bhely-Quenum; Senegal's novelist, Sembene Ousmane; Cameroun's novelist, Mongo Beti; Ghana's poet, Francis Parkes; South Africa's playwright, Alfred Hutchinson; and Ivory Coast's poet, Bernard Dadie.

On the other hand, there are newer authors appearing for the first time in print or whose work has not yet been widely circulated, even in Africa. Among such authors are Dennis Brutus, Joseph Kariuki, Kuldip Sondhi, Grace Ogot; there are translations from the Portuguese of writing by the Moçambiquans, Louis Bernardo Honwana, José Craveirinha, Rui Nogar; from the French by West Africans like Jean Pliya, Sylvain Bemba, Paulin Joachim; the Rwanda poet, Jean-Baptiste Mutabaruka. There are also, of course, the much more familiar names, as Chinua Achebe, Wole Soyinka, Kwesi Brew, Tchikaya U'Tam'si, Cyprian Ekwensi, Sarif Easmon, Abioseh Nicol, Léopold Sédar Senghor, Birago Diop, Joseph Zobel, Richard Rive, Alex la Guma, Can Themba, Camara Laye, and so on. But even these are represented here by new and unfamiliar material from their work.

It may be asked why we have left out the white Africans, or non-Africans like William Plomer and Joyce Cary, in some of whose admirable work the African experience is an integral part.

Our intention is not to practise apartheid in reverse. It is a matter of cultural barriers. African writers, whether they use a metropolitan or an indigenous language, have assimilated many of the mannerisms and assumptions of their particular medium; to say nothing of the social, economic, and political systems and technology of the West which the African has absorbed. The reverse has not happened. No doubt, the black paint has rubbed off on to the white man in Southern, Central, and East Africa – more than he would be prepared to admit. But this is only subtly reflected in the literary style of white Africans.

It might be said that as they use the same languages blacks and whites already belong to the same literary culture. This is true, and there are places and times when a common literary culture is sufficient basis for an anthology. But this is not one of them. Black Africa is becoming more and more aware of itself and it is our aim, by limiting the anthology, to reflect this.

But you will find great variety in this collection; the rich imagery of French-language poetry; the austere, near-rhetorical English-language poetry; the well-controlled French prose and the cool and almost detached voice of the English-language prose; the highly-impassioned idiom of the South Africans; the voices of Moçambiquans that seem to float across the river that cuts them off from even their own fellow-men – voices that sound marooned, plaintive, throbbing with pain. There is here also the strong folk-loric tone of Sarif Easmon, Grace Ogot, Birago Diop, and Amos Tutuola.

The major universal concerns are here, although interpreted in African terms. But our writers are also products of a common history – that of colonialism, independence and its ecstasies, new self-awareness, and the burden of being unbound and becoming free while non-independent communities share a common yoke. There is the peculiarly African experience that is superimposed on that of the common denominator of world concerns. This results either in rich layers of meaning in any one writer or a varied pattern of meanings on a horizontal plane; depending on the emphasis an individual author may prefer to express one experience or another.

It might be reasonably argued that a European can also be committed to, say, British values that derive from a common history and culture, while at the same time he belongs to some world community. But then the continuity of Western thought has created a common broad front along which Western man moves. This has been absent in Africa. And even while we like to believe we have an identity of political aspirations like Pan-African unity, our countries are busy shrinking back into their pre-independence territorial nationalisms.

All these factors determine our literary themes and styles. We like to think, also, that Africans outside South Africa will soon feel the need to talk to their own immediate human environment, in their art, when the white-man-listen theme has exhausted itself: Ekwensi, Soyinka, and Clark of Nigeria and Awoonor-Williams and Aidoo of Ghana are already doing this. Nor has the drama of the black–white encounter yet played itself out, whether in Africa or outside. This is another dimension our literature will continue to display, either in its blunt or its subtle manifestations.

If some of the writing lacks humour, it is because we are tackling forms which are not native to Africa. As we learn to laugh at ourselves, we shall also be learning to handle words so as to make them echo laughter.

EZEKIEL MPHAHLELE

University College, Nairobi

Nigeria

Chinua Achebe

From Arrow of God

Arrow of God, Achebe's third and most ambitious novel, takes us back
to the setting of his first novel – the Ibo villages of Eastern Nigeria;
the time is 1921. Ezeulu, the Chief Priest of Ulu, the god of the villages,
is totally against a war that is brewing between his people of Umuaro
and a neighbouring people. He respects the white man's power and
sends his son to a mission school so that he may know the secret of the
white man's power. His son, with the zeal of a new Christian convert,
shuts a sacred python in a box in order to kill it. It is released before
he kills it. This attempt to kill a sacred snake does not improve relations
between Ezeulu and his enemies who already suspect that he has
become the white man's friend. Another incident that lowers his public
esteem is his detention by the white regional authority. In detention
he is offered the chieftainship, which he declines. This enforced stay
away from home has meant that Ezeulu has missed eating two of the
thirteen yams he had to consume, one at each new moon, before
the New Yam Festival at the end of the year. Thus, back home, when
he has three yams left to be eaten, he refuses to eat all at once, according to the advice from the elders. He sees himself as Ulu's whip with
which the people must be punished. For, to wait three moons before
the festival (it is only then that the people will be allowed to harvest
their yams) must lead to the destruction of the crops under the ground.
The Christians, taking advantage of the people's plight, succeed in
persuading them to bring offerings to the church which will give them
immunity and permit them to harvest their crops sooner. Ezeulu's power
declines and the death of his son deranges his mind. Thus the elders
are vindicated; for, according to them, Ulu has destroyed his own priest.
The extract below portrays two government agents and some of their
views on how to govern. Winterbottom is the senior of the two.

CAPTAIN WINTERBOTTOM

Captain Winterbottom was drinking brandy and ginger ale when Tony Clarke arrived.

'It's nice and cool today, thank God.'

'Yes, the first rain was pretty much overdue,' said Captain Winterbottom.

'I had no idea what a tropical storm looked like. It will be cooler now, I suppose.'

'Well, not exactly. It will be fairly cool for a couple of days, that's all. You see, the rainy season doesn't really begin until May or even June. Do sit down. Did you enjoy that?'

'Yes, thank you very much. I found it most interesting. Perhaps Mr Allen is a trifle too dogmatic. One could even say a little smug.'

Captain Winterbottom's Small Boy, Boniface, came forward with a silver tray.

'What Massa go drink?'

'I wonder.'

'Why not try some Old Coaster?'

'What's that?'

'Brandy and ginger ale.'

'Right. That's fine.' For the first time he looked at the Small Boy in his starched white uniform and saw that he was remarkably handsome.

Captain Winterbottom seemed to read his thought.

'He's a fine specimen, isn't he? He's been with me four years. He was a little boy of about thirteen – they've no idea of years. . . . They understand seasons, I don't mean that. But ask a man how old he is and he doesn't begin to have an idea.'

The Small Boy came back with the drink.

'Thank you very much,' said Mr Clarke as he took it.

'Yessah.'

Thousands of flying ants swarmed around the Tilley lamp on a stand at the far corner. They soon lost their wings and crawled on the floor. Clarke watched them with great interest, and then asked if they stung.

'No, they are quite harmless. They are driven out of the ground by the rain.'

The crawling ones were sometimes hooked up in twos at their tails.

'It was rather interesting what you said about Allen. A little smug, I think you said.'

'That was the impression I had – sometimes. He doesn't allow, for instance, for there being anything of value in native institutions. He might really be one of the missionary people.'

'I see you are one of the progressive ones. When you've been here as long as Allen has and understood the native a little more, you might modify some of your new theories. If you saw, as I did, a man buried alive up to his neck with a piece of roast yam on his head to attract vultures you might have second thoughts. We British are a curious people, doing everything half-heartedly. Look at the French. They are not ashamed to teach their culture to backward races under their charge. Their attitude to the native ruler is clear. They say to him : "This land has belonged to you because you have been strong enough to hold it. By the same token it now belongs to us. If you are not satisfied come out and fight us." What do we British do? We flounder from one expedient to its opposite. We do not only promise to secure old savage tyrants on their thrones – or more likely filthy animal skins, we not only do that, but we now go out of our way to invent chiefs where there were none before. They make me sick.' He swallowed what was left in his glass and shouted to Boniface for another glass. 'I wouldn't really mind if this dithering was left to old fossils in Lagos, but when young Political Officers get infected I just give up. If someone is positive we call him smug.'

Mr Clarke admitted whatever judgement he made was made in ignorance and that he was open to correction.

'Boniface !'

'Yessah.'

'Bring another drink for Mr Clarke.'

'No really, I think I've had . . .'

'Nonsense. Dinner won't be ready for another hour at least. Try something else if you prefer. Whisky?' Clarke accepted another brandy with great reluctance.

'That's a very interesting collection of firearms.' Mr Clarke had been desperately searching for a new subject. Then luckily he hit on a collection of quaint-looking guns arranged like trophies near the low window of the living-room. 'Are they native guns?' He had stumbled on a redeeming theme.

Captain Winterbottom was transformed.

'Those guns have a long and interesting history. The people of Okperi and their neighbours, Umuaro, are great enemies. Or they were before I came into the story. A big savage war had broken out between them over a piece of land. This feud was made worse by the fact that Okperi welcomed missionaries and government while Umuaro, on the other hand, has remained backward. It is only in the last four or five years that any kind of impression has been made there. I think I can say with all modesty that this change came after I had gathered and publicly destroyed all firearms in the place except, of course, this collection here. You will be going there frequently on tour. If you hear anyone talking about Otiji-Egbe, you know they are talking about me. Otiji-Egbe means Breaker of Guns. I am even told that all children born in that year belong to a new age-grade of the Breaking of the Guns.'

'That's most interesting. How far is this other village, Umuaro?' Clarke knew instinctively that the more ignorant he seemed the better.

'Oh, about six miles, not more. But to the native that's a foreign country. Unlike some of the more advanced tribes in Northern Nigeria, and to some extent Western Nigeria, the Ibos never developed any kind of central authority. That's what our head-quarters people fail to appreciate.'

'Yes, I see.'

'This war between Umuaro and Okperi began in a rather interesting way. I went into it in considerable detail. . . . Boniface! How are you doing, Mr Clarke? Fine? You ought to drink more; it's good for malaria. . . . As I was saying, this war started because a man from Umuaro went to visit a friend in Okperi one fine morning and after he had one or two gallons of palm wine – it's quite incredible how much of that dreadful stuff they can tuck away, anyhow, this man from Umuaro having drunk his friend's palm wine reached for his *ikenga* and split it in two. I may explain that *ikenga* is the most important fetish in the Ibo man's arsenal, so to speak. It represents his ancestors to whom he must make daily sacrifice. When he dies it is split in two; one half is buried with him and the other half is thrown away. So you can see the implication of what our friend from Umuaro did in splitting his host's fetish. This was, of course, the greatest sacrilege. The outraged host reached for his gun and blew the other fellow's head off. And so a regular war developed between the two villages, until I stepped in. I went into the question of the ownership of the piece of land which was the remote cause of all the unrest and found without any shade of doubt that it belonged to Okperi. I should mention that every witness who testified before me – from both sides without exception – perjured himself. One thing you must remember in dealing with natives is that like children they are great liars. They don't lie simply to get out of trouble. Sometimes they would spoil a good case by a pointless lie. Only one man – a kind of priest-king in Umuaro – witnessed against his own people. I have not found out what it was, but I think he must have had some pretty fierce tabu working on him. But he was a most impressive figure of a man. He was very light in complexion, almost red. One finds people like that now and again among the Ibos. I have a theory that the Ibos in the distant past assimilated a small non-negroid tribe of the same complexion as the red Indians.'

Winterbottom stood up. 'Now what about some dinner,' he said.

Cyprian Ekwensi

NIGHT OF FREEDOM

Chini was among them: the millions and millions who roamed the streets of a score of cities throughout the Federation that night – the night of freedom.

In this the capital city, all the streets were packed and milling with men, women, children; restless, floating, chattering, glum and silent, expectant, confused, drifting, banding together under the lights in awe of the unknown mysteries of Independence. Some were strangers who came from far corners where Africa meant darkness and now they clustered in solid groups at the Square over which the fireworks shot upwards and exploded in spectacular cascades. Freedom was here.

Krr . . a . . ka . . . toa! . . . Krraakkatooaa!

Chini drew near François and his protective arm tightened round her.

'It is romantic, *mon amour*? Too romantic, yes?'

'Oh, I want to die,' Chini whispered. 'I want to die – in your arms. I want to die for the new Nigeria!'

'*Mon chérie*, it would be good to die, and end it all. It would be good to die, now.'

She turned sharply and faced him. 'You mean that?'

He smiled. 'Why not? This is the climax, the end of Imperialism, the beginning of FREEDOM for Nigeria!' He pointed at the fireworks. Chini could recognize the quickly forming image. The glow resolved itself into the coronet of Queen Elizabeth the Second. 'I suppose Imperialism has played its part,' François sighed. 'A hundred years.'

Chini looked away, but the Queen's image still burned in her eyes. She was a Nigerian beauty, slim and bronzed, with a statuesque firmness of curve that always made the Frenchman marvel. Often she had accused François of being in love with her body, but he always said he could never bring himself to ignore its presence. Chini was breathing with a love ripeness in her eye. She was elegant, unselfconscious, wearing English clothes with sophistication, and Nigerian costume with charm. Her every movement stimulated a flow of poetry from François and an ebb of embarrassment from her. She called him 'My mad French lover'.

Suddenly she reached out and held him. 'Kill me, oh, kill me!' She was sobbing. From a million voices came the roar of the Nigerian National Anthem:

> NIGERIA WE HAIL THEE
> OUR OWN DEAR NATIVE LAND
> THOUGH TRIBE AND TONGUE MAY DIFFER
> IN BROTHERHOOD WE STAND
> NIGERIANS ALL AND PROUD TO SERVE
> OUR SOVEREIGN MOTHERLAND

The roar echoed and reverberated over the entire field and vapourized skywards into the stars and misty tropical night.

'I would have been so happy now, but why did I meet you? I would have been FREE! Now my country is free, but I . . . I am in chains.'

She felt his strong arms round her shoulders and she clung tightly to him. His face, bristly, grated against her tender skin.

'Chini, you are mine, *oui*?'

'Yours, François, yours.'

'You will come to Paris with me if . . .'

His grip was hurting her. He was pressing his lips on hers there in the Square with the mad crowds drifting about them.

'Oh, François, we're in public!'

'You don't mean that! No, you don't.'

His kisses smothered her sighs.

As the Dauphine sped towards Victoria Beach neither of them spoke. Chini looked straight ahead of her, her mind in a turmoil. Independence. François. Love. Marriage. Independence. Independence. Freedom! . . . Trees floated past. She sensed that other cars with lovers in them were flashing impatient lights behind them and passing by.

François drove past familiar places now glowing with an unfamiliar radiance. The Federal Palace Hotel loomed in stately grandeur. Even as late as midnight swarms of people still floated past the pavilions of the Nigeria Exhibition.

She remembered one afternoon when she had come near the site to meet François at work, putting up his own stand; and there were crowds as thick as the hairs on François' arm. That afternoon, having fought through the crowds, she found him in the basement of the stand. There he was, down among the workers who were cutting a steel bar with a lamp. The dazzling lights etched out his strikingly handsome face. He was dressed in a white shirt and white shorts, and on his face was an intense oily look of tiredness.

He turned just as she was about to steal away. 'Hey, Chini!' She almost jumped. François wiped his hands on the back of his shorts and spoke quickly to the two white men standing opposite. They looked like Americans in their narrow drip-dry pantaloons and soft cotton caps. One of them was chewing gum.

François came up to her in an easy swinging manner, just as the wind billowed out her skirt and she reached out a hand to keep it in place, holding on to her straw hat with the other.

'You look a picture, Chini,' he said. He took her hands and kissed them. Standing beside her he looked down at the stand and said: 'How do you like it?' His arm swept a wide arc, but Chini was looking into his eyes, instead. He returned her look and said, '*Chic*, eh?'

'The stand or me?'

He laughed. 'You, of course! Where shall we go, coffee?'

The way he talked she could not understand and it burned deep scars of pain in her heart. He would be going away in fourteen days, expelled from the country, so the rumour had said. Already it had leaked out among those who know that the Governor-General thought it would be 'conducive to the public good' for him to leave the country. Yet he had told her nothing. But did he really wish to marry her? Had she given up everything for nothing?

The coffee stand was built in the Espresso tradition. She could imagine this same stand crowded not by Teddy Boys or Beatniks but by the tough city slickers of Lagos, once known as the *Boma* Boys, but now very much more refined with stream-styled cars to help them . . . drifters, waiting to pick up a beating-up commission from some irate politician, only to change their loyalty when the victim increased their fee. She remembered how it had been in Chelsea on the cold nights, trying to read for the exam. Now she had achieved her ambition : she had become a secretary-typist, one of the best. Into her ears went the most secret dictations. And she had now fallen in love with this Frenchman who must leave the country.

'Well, and how's Independence, Chini?'

'Independence is fine, for those who are free !'

He did not say anything. He was smiling and she went on: 'Unity and Faith, and all that !'

'I love Nigeria. You Nigerians are the most moderate of all Africans.'

'All Africans are one, François, when it comes to that. When it comes to facing all white men.'

'You mean, I'm an outsider?'

She crossed her legs. A gleam of desire lighted up in François' eyes. Chini had the most marvellous legs. This afternoon's skirt was split and the splits were held together by decorative buttons five inches apart from waist to hem.

'You're in one of your moods, Chini.'

She stirred her coffee, but when she raised it to her lips it spilled on her dress. François sprang forward, handkerchief in hand. He dabbed the coffee pool on her skirt and on her breast, lingering on the splotch above the left breast.

For Chini the afternoon was ruined. She rose. He took her hand.

'I'm sorry, Chini.'

'It's my fault. I feel like crying.'

She walked. Head held high, she walked, flicking her heels and wiggling her hips with bitter malice. The car owners hooted and waved to her to come into their cars but she wanted none of them because she had her own car. François had his own car and she wanted none of them because they did not understand what it was like to be facing an impossible love affair; to be facing the condemnation of your own people, especially when you are in a position of confidence which you have fought so very hard to attain.

'I don't love this man . . . I love him . . . But he is a Frenchman . . . it doesn't matter . . . It does . . . Before Independence, it did not matter. But now, we're different. I must remain in my own country and work and build.'

Chini walked. There were two million people in Lagos, all milling about the bridge, but there were none as far as she was concerned, because she did not know anything about them.

She remembered now that her mother was to have come down for the celebrations but had so far sent no word. She might still come. Could it be that something had happened?

It would be best to tell her personally. One thing was certain. Nigeria independent was not Nigeria colonial. Women today were in a different position. Black and white, yellow or red, when love whispered, it was the same response. But WHY fall in love with a Frenchman?

Only that afternoon she and François had been arguing.

'Nigerian girls do not know the meaning of LOVE.'

'What is the meaning, François? I want to know.'

'It is not easy to explain.'

He was looking at the sea. She was looking at the sea too, but the water she saw was right there in her eyes.

'It is not easy to explain.' He was smoking. 'You see, love is all consuming, a personal affair between two people.'

'That's in Europe. In Africa it is a *public* affair. Everyone is concerned. My mother is concerned, so are my mother's people. My father is dead, but my uncle and his family must know. I did not drop from the sky, you know. Try and understand. You think I am weak.'

'Nigeria whispers,' he said, and tried to smile.

It was his way of teasing her, whenever she lost her temper. *Nigeria whispers.* It was his new phrase since Independence. 'You Nigerians will now know the difference between being protected, and being on your own. You will always – in your public life and in your private – have one choice to make : self or Nigeria. But always, Chini, Nigeria will always whisper. Nigeria is in you. Go on ! If you listen to yourself you will do one thing. It will not always be the same if you listen to Nigeria.'

'Have you finished teasing me?'

'Yes, my Beauty Queen.' He kissed her.

'You are very bitter, François.'

'Wouldn't you be? If you had to leave a country you love and the girl you love cannot make up her mind.'

'But François I love you.'

'Will you come with me then?'

'It is not easy,' Chini said. 'I love Nigeria at this time – but all I know is that I love you and that our fates are inexplicably bound up together.'

'What shall we do?' His voice was faint.

She saw his face now ferocious. He turned and pulled her close to him. Chini shut her eyes and felt his lips on hers, hungry for her.

'Woman of bronze, woman with the hot animal blood. In my nostrils is the smell of you, in my blood is the fire of you. Without you, my soul dies.'

Before such adoration Chini had no answer.

Lagos was gay and sweet. The buses rolled on along the roads, and the nurses at the General Hospital stood at the stops at the Marina, waiting before the gleaming white State House. The ferry shrieked and laboured homewards to Apapa, carrying the men to the Industrial Estates.

From the window of her office, Chini looked out and saw the Dauphine flash past. It was François.

The booming voice of her boss brought her attention back to the dictation. Her shorthand pen raced over the surface of the pad. In the wood-panelled room it was so silent that God seemed to be present.

'That will be all,' said her boss.

Chini rose. She gathered her things together but as she made for the door a piece of paper dropped and she bent down to pick it up.

'Chini,' said her boss.

'Sir.'

'Don't go for a moment.'

She saw the deep frown on his face. He was scanning the files before him. When he worked, he possessed the fantastic ability of complete concentration. She had often seen him like that, when, with a little black Bible in his hand he migrated – so to speak – into another world, away from the Press, the Radio, and the Critics, away from the physical boundaries.

Through her mind raced troubling questions. Did he know about François? He must know. Was he going to talk to her about it? No? Yes? Immediately she was on the defensive.

Without looking up he said, 'I shall be going on tour soon. And I want a good secretary-typist to come with me. You know Miss Wells has not been feeling well lately. Of the eighteen secretaries there's none that has a pleasanter manner than you. In any case, you have never come with me on tour. . . .'

She saw the face of François now, smiling *Nigeria whispers*. And she heard her boss talking. But what was he saying? Where was she standing? Why was he talking. Did he not know that François would deride her?

And then she realized that he had stopped. He was waiting for a reply. She was keeping him waiting.

'Will you come?'

'Sir?'

'Will you come?'

'I – I think so, Sir !'

She brushed aside the hibiscus bush. Dense and overhanging it reached out hands of destruction, ruffling her hair. In the windows the bright lights told her that François had not yet gone to bed. It was a hot evening and all day long she had searched in vain for him.

Jideh, his servant, met her on the steps.

'Master no well,' he said.

Her heart leapt. She pushed him aside and ran into the room.

François was lying on the bed, his face against the wall. She sat beside him, and took his hand.

'I love you, François.'

'Chini!'

How was she going to break the news to him?

She looked round the room and found that he had already started packing.

'Get me something to drink darling.'

She knew why he said that. He always admired the way she walked. When she walked to the fridge, she took her time and wiggled. She was dressed in 'native' and in the colour he liked. Blue.

She brought the drink on a tray and set it down and suddenly she felt his hot hand on her cheek.

His eyes were yellow with fire. She took off his hand quietly. 'You're ill.'

'You are my illness. I want to die in Nigeria, I want to die – with your love. Chini you have made up your mind?'

'To go to France with you?'

'Yes, will you come?'

'François you know I want to come, but –'

'*Nigeria whispers*, I know.'

She could not stand the sneer. 'Don't be cruel, François. Nigeria whispers, yes, but your voice is above a whisper. And I hear and listen. Because you talk love.'

Oh God, she thought, *how did I become so mad about this man? With all the young men who asked to marry me, how did I become so mad?*

She saw the young men now. In her first year at the University, Abiade fawned on her with all the devotion of a dog. She was flattered. It was her first year, and her last. She had been unable to continue her education. She wanted quicker results, more glamour. She went to England to study at Pitmans, and although Abiade wrote love to her, she learnt that he sustained himself with the flesh of the girls who drifted round Oke-Ado in Ibadan and the Marina in Lagos. They were legion.

She returned from England on a bright afternoon. Lagos lay somewhat in a haze of *siesta*. As Chini saw the towers of the Power House and the old familiar landmarks, she was filled with a choking nostalgia. Abiade. Only last night she had been reading his letter . . . There he was, waiting patiently and waving. He had come to see her.

She embraced him, but his face was a mask. Later on she was to know why. Meantime she kept his letters tied together with string and now she wondered what to do with them . . . Post them to him at his home address so that the pretty girl would be embarrassed, so that she might know that the happiness she found was at the expense of another's happiness? She carried the letters to the office, but could not get herself to re-read them. One evening she walked along the Marina.

Looking at the lights in the harbour, the ships from all parts of the world, she thought of her love affair. Then on an impulse she dropped the letters into the lagoon.

In her first job, a young doctor always called to take her back to the lodgings. She had not got the little Fiat then, and she lived at the YWCA Hostel. It was a great thing to have a man to call to see her. The girls always looked out of the window and told her that Long Pipe was here, because this doctor was always chewing a pipe.

The pieces of the broken heart seemed to be mending. The feeling of elatedness, the lightness of step, all began to return. One evening she was looking out of the YWCA window, when a girl shouted: 'Chini, quick. Come and see Long Pipe.'

The car had parked at the petrol station opposite. She could see that Long Pipe had tried to park it so that he would not be easily seen from the window. Chini saw him seated at the wheel and beside him a woman. In the rear seat were three children: two boys in striped singlets, and a pretty little girl with two red ribbons in her hair.

In the office she could not work. Promptly at ten minutes to two, she left and caught a bus. She would not let herself be caught at the office and she would not see him at home. But one evening he surprised her.

She met him in the sitting-room. 'You did not tell me you were already married,' she said.

He had no explanation. 'You are my girl-friend,' was all he said. And she could read the implication : that it was nothing unusual.

'Do I strike you as the girl-friend of a married man?'

'I meant no harm, Chini.'

She burst into tears. 'You were deceiving me !'

They had told her jokingly – the knowledgeable ones – that in Nigeria a girl had one of two choices. They told her that if she did not find a man before the end of her training in Britain, when she returned to Nigeria, she would meet men who were already settled, but who would want to take advantage of her desire to get married. She had laughed when they said this.

She looked down now at the warm hand on her lap. She studied the intent eyes of François. Her meeting with him had been something stiff and odd. Of all places they had met at an international seminar on African Culture.

François found it soothing, healing almost, to sit in the air-conditioned room where books, paintings and sculptures by Africans were displayed.

Chini with two ear-phones smartly clipped to her ears, sat at the horse-shoe-shaped table while the men talked. The interpreters talked at a somewhat slower pace, translating freely. François was speaking with so much animation that at one point the translator seemed to hang in mid-air. She pressed her fingers together so as to split out the precise shade of meaning, but François rattled onwards without a break spouting out the words with real enthusiasm.

'. . . That is why one must be led to the conclusion, that the Imperialist powers have left us with a doubtful legacy. The lace-doyley *petit bourgeois* atmosphere of the educated class in Africa and other once dependent territories, is a sad commentary on the Imperialist's belief that African culture, or indeed, any other culture, can look after itself.

'. . . The time has come now, when. . . .'

During the tea break, the delegates split into a handful of

animated groups. They talked of the paper François had just read. They fingered the books and art works on display. Chini went over with them to see the books.

He spoke with a strange French-English, a musical language rendered all the more charming by his delicacy of feeling. She was to associate this particular brand of English with François. Half of what he said she did not understand but it coincided with her present yearnings. At the same time, it would not be good manners not to understand what was being discussed at the conference to which she had been sent as a verbatim reporter.

They drifted from books to coffee and from coffee to themselves. François must be about six feet in height. At this conference he wore a red shirt rolled up to the elbows, displaying a fine down of brown hairs on his forearms. A perpetual smile curled the corners of his mouth, as though he knew what they knew about the professors, critics, anthropologists, and observers who were gathered to talk about *African Culture*.

Most of the people who came to the conference were oddly dressed. Chini had taken the trouble to be superbly groomed. Her hair was gathered into a little pig-tail at the back and she floated the extra yards of delicate print over her arm. For some reason her scrupulousness seemed to be a burden now. She felt out of place until glancing across the table she caught sight of a dazzling young woman who also appeared to be taking notes. She wore a pale blue transparent nylon material, lighter than the wind and twice as clinging. Her face was made up in a manner Max Factor would have approved, even for an African woman. Chini learnt later that this woman was a reporter from Radio Nigeria.

'I am a secretary–typist,' Chini said, answering François' question. She smiled. 'One of eighteen secretaries.'

'You have always spoken English?'

'Yes.'

'You write?'

'No. But I read what they write. I was sent here to report. No, I don't write. I read : mainly love stories.'

His face flushed. She felt she had said something out of place, and tried to rectify it. 'The first love story I really enjoyed was *When Love Whispers*.'

'I see ! . . . I've never heard of it.'

'A long time ago. I was in the convent then.' She remembered the story clearly, and promptly began to tell him about it. But somewhere in the middle she realized that the tone of this conference was set too high for glib talk, and she kept quiet so suddenly that an emptiness descended on them in the large hall, though everyone seemed to be babbling away.

At this point the bell rang and they resumed their seats.

Chini still works in Lagos. They will tell you about her – those who know, and sigh and shake their heads. You do not need to look too closely to see why she was the flash-point of that international controversy. But she is very cool now, very calm, very collected. She is so efficient that sometimes her boss calls her to his inner office and says, 'Look, Chi . . . you are working too hard. Take some rest.'

And she smiles, that mysterious smile of hers and says : 'Am I? . . . I like to work hard for my country.'

When she talks in this manner her boss hastily stubs his cigarette and frowns in silence. It seems she has touched something very deep.

'May I go now?'

A slow smile grows on her employer's face and he talks without paying any attention to her.

'We have all had misfortunes, you know. You must not live with your own all your life. François is dead through no fault of yours. It's true you loved him. . . . But that was unfortunate.'

Already she is crying. She is unable to stand up any more and she looks round and slumps into a seat. Her employer is talking to her now as a friend; as a man who knows her worth and realizes that her efficiency is bound up with her personal happiness.

'Can't you find some other young man? Look, Chi. You do not go out nearly enough. You – oh, what's the use?'

He was exasperated. This man who could sway multitudes with

his soft persuasive voice was exasperated before her, before Chi –
his own typist.

When he had talked and talked she knew that he was talking
from the other side of the wall. Her feminine stubbornness was
standing between her and him and she could not see him – or even
hear him.

Wole Soyinka

From The Swamp Dwellers

The following extract comes from *The Swamp Dwellers*. IGWEZU, son of ALU and MAKURI (father), has just come from the city where his wealthy twin-brother stole his wife from him. Disgust with city life and with his brother has driven him back home where he hoped to find his plot of land in good condition, ready to yield a good crop. Instead, he finds the land one mass of mud left behind by the floods. His parents have been paying their dues to the KADIYE, priest of the Serpent cult, as a normal devotional exercise, and IGWEZU feels bitter against the priest whose god has not saved the crops. The KADIYE has come to IGWEZU's home for him to shave him, and present in the house also is a blind BEGGAR who has come from the north and wants shelter.

> *The* KADIYE's *party arrive at the door.* MAKURI *runs to hold the matting aside, and the party enters as before.* ALU *comes out again and curtseys.*

KADIYE: Is he back? Ah, Igwezu, it is good to see you again. [IGWEZU *rises unhurriedly. The* KADIYE *tries to bless him but* IGWEZU *avoids this, as if by accident.*] I am glad to see you safe and well . . . [*Seats himself in the chair*] Ah, what an affair that was. The child was crying loud enough to drown all the frogs in the swamp. . . .

MAKURI [*leaning down to him. With fiendishness on his face*]: Did it happen, Kadiye? Did the child take his revenge?

KADIYE: Oh yes, he did. He drenched the healer with a sudden gush !

> [MAKURI *dances delightedly, laughing in his ghoulish manner.*]

KADIYE: And that wasn't all. The foolish mother ! She heard the cries and tried to get to her son from where she had been locked.

MAKURI: And pollute her own son !

KADIYE: Amazing, is it not? The mothers can never be trusted. ... And to think that she did succeed in the end!

MAKURI [*snapping his fingers over his head*]: The gods forbid it!

KADIYE: She did. I had to purify the boy and absolve him from the crime of contamination. That is the fourth circumcision where I have known it to happen.

MAKURI: The best thing is to send the mother out of the house.

KADIYE: Do you think that hasn't been tried. It is harder to shift them than to get the child to stay still.

MAKURI: Ay. That is true enough. All women are a blood-thirsty lot. They love to hear the child wailing and crying out in pain. Then they can hug themselves and say, Serve you right, you little brat. Now you'll know what pains I went through, giving birth to you.

KADIYE: Ah, that is the truth of it. ... Anyway, it is all over now ... all over and done with ... [*hems with pomposity and turns to* IGWEZU] And how is the city gentleman? Have you been making a lot of money, Igwezu?

IGWEZU: None ... where must I shave, Kadiye?

KADIYE [*puzzled*]: Where?

IGWEZU: Is it the head or the chin?

[KADIYE's *face freezes at once.*]

MAKURI [*gasps, then tries to force a casualness in his tone*]: Pay no attention, Kadiye. It is only the humour of the townsmen.

KADIYE: A-ah ... The chin, Igwezu. Shave off the beard.

IGWEZU [*begins to prepare the instruments*]: Did you make other vows, Kadiye? Were there other pleasures from which you abstained until the rains abated?

KADIYE: Oh, yes. Oh, yes indeed. I vowed that my body would remain unwashed.

IGWEZU: Ah. Did you keep within doors?

KADIYE: No. I had my duties. ... People still die, you know. And mothers give birth to children.

IGWEZU: And it rained throughout? Almost without a stop?

KADIYE: Yes, it did.

IGWEZU: Then perhaps once or twice you were out in the rain ...?

MAKURI [*quickly*] : Igwezu . . . you . . . you . . . you were going to tell Kadiye about the big town.

IGWEZU: Was I?

KADIYE: Ah, yes. Tell me about the place. Was business as good as they say?

IGWEZU: For some people.

KADIYE: And you? Did your business thrive?

IGWEZU: No more than my farming has done.

KADIYE: Come now, Igwezu. I am not trying to obtain the promise of an ox for sacrifice. . . . You did make some money?

IGWEZU: No.

KADIYE: I see he must be coaxed. . . . Admit you've made enough to buy this village – men, livestock and all.

IGWEZU [*slips the* agbada *over the* KADIYE's *head*]: No, Kadiye. I made none at all.

KADIYE: A-ah, they are all modest. . . . Did you make a little then?

IGWEZU: No, I made none at all.

KADIYE [*looks hard at him. He is obviously disturbed by* IG-WEZU's *manner. Speaks nervously*]: Well, never mind, never mind. To some it comes quickly; to others a little more slowly. But your own turn will come soon, Igwezu; it will come before long.

IGWEZU: I'm afraid I have had my turn already. I lost everything; my savings, even my standing as a man. I went into debt.

KADIYE: Impossible !

IGWEZU: Shall I tell you what I offered as security? Would you like to know, Kadiye?

KADIYE: Not your pretty wife, I hope [*guffawing*]. I notice you had to come without her.

IGWEZU: No, holy one. It was not my wife. But what I offered had a lot in common with her. I put down the harvest from my farm.

MAKURI: Ha?

ALU: Igwezu. My poor Igwezu.

KADIYE [*laughing*] : Now what do you take us for? As if anyone in the city would lend money on a farm which he had never even seen. Are they such fools – these businessmen of yours?

IGWEZU: No. They are not fools; my brother least of all. He is anything but a fool.

ALU: Awuchike!

MAKURI: My own son? Your own flesh and blood?

[ALU *remains staring at* IGWEZU *for several moments. Then, shaking her head in complete and utter bewilderment, she turns round slowly and goes into the house, visibly more slouched than ever before.*]

IGWEZU [*in the same calm relentlessness*]: Wait, mother . . . I have not told you all. [*He begins to lather the* KADIYE's *face.*]

ALU: I know enough [*she has stopped but does not turn round*]. But I no longer understand. I feel tired, son. I think I'll go to sleep.

IGWEZU: Don't you want news of my wife? Have you no interest in the simple and unspoilt child whom you wooed on my behalf?

[ALU *goes slowly out of the room.* IGWEZU *begins to shave the* KADIYE. *There is silence.*]

IGWEZU [*without stopping*]: Father. Tell me, father, is my brother a better man than I?

MAKURI: No, son. His heart is only more suited to the city.

IGWEZU: And yet we are twins. And in spite of that, he looked at my wife, and she went to him of her own accord. . . . Tell me father, are women so easily swayed by wealth? Are all women the same?

MAKURI: Alu was different. She turned their heads but she kept her own.

IGWEZU: Thank you, father. Now where is the stranger who would be my bondsman?

BEGGAR: Here, master.

IGWEZU: You sightless ones are known to be gifted with more than human wisdom. You detected from the Kadiye's voice that he was fat. . . . Keep still, priest of the swamps; this razor is keen and my hand is unsettled. . . . Have I still your attention, bondsman? You have listened to me. Is there anything in my voice which tells you what is lacking? Does something in my voice tell you why the bride of less than a season deserts her husband's side?

BEGGAR: I must seek that answer in the voice of the bride.

IGWEZU: That was wisely spoken. You have all the makings of a true bondsman.

MAKURI: You talk strangely, Igwezu. What is running in your head?

IGWEZU: It is only a game of children, father. Only a game of riddles and you have answered yours. So has my bondsman. Now it is the turn of the Kadiye.

KADIYE: I am prepared.

IGWEZU: With you, holy one, my questions must be round-about. But you will unravel them, because you speak with the voice of gods...?

KADIYE: As I said before, I am ready.

IGWEZU: Who must appease the Serpent of the Swamps?

KADIYE: The Kadiye.

IGWEZU: Who takes the gifts of the people, in order that the beast may be gorged and made sleepy-eyed with the feast of sacrifice?

KADIYE: The Kadiye.

IGWEZU [*his speech is increasing in speed and intensity*]: On whom does the land depend for the benevolence of the reptile? Tell me that, priest. Answer in one word.

KADIYE: Kadiye.

IGWEZU: Can you see my mask, priest? Is it of this village?

KADIYE: Yes.

IGWEZU: Was the wood grown in this village?

KADIYE: Yes.

IGWEZU: Does it sing with the rest? Cry with the rest? Does it till the swamps with the rest of the tribe?

KADIYE: Yes.

IGWEZU: And so that the Serpent might not vomit at the wrong season and drown the land, so that He might not swallow at the wrong moment and gulp down the unwary traveller, do I not offer my goats to the priest?

KADIYE: Yes.

MAKURI: Igwezu, sometimes the guardians of the air are hard to please. . . .

IGWEZU: Be quiet, father! . . . And did he offer them in turn to the Serpent?

KADIYE: He did.

IGWEZU: Everything which he received, from the grain to the bull?

KADIYE: Everything.

IGWEZU: The goat and the white cockerel which I gave before I left?

KADIYE: Every hair and feather of them.

IGWEZU: And he made it clear – that the offering was from me? That I demanded the protection of the heavens on me and my house, on my father and my mother, on my wife, land and chattels?

KADIYE: All the prayers were repeated.

IGWEZU: And ever since I began to till the soil, did I not give the soil his due? Did I not bring the first of the lentils to the shrine, and pour the first oil upon the altar?

KADIYE: Regularly.

IGWEZU: And when the Kadiye blessed my marriage, and tied the heaven-made knot, did he not promise a long life? Did he not promise children? Did he not promise happiness?

[IGWEZU *has shaved off all except a last smear of lather. He remains standing with one hand around the* KADIYE's *jowl, the other retaining an indifferent hold on the razor, on the other side of his face.* KADIYE *does not reply this time.*]

IGWEZU [*slowly and disgustedly*]: Why are you so fat, Kadiye? [*The two members of the* KADIYE's *train have sat unobtrusively beside the right door all this time. At this stage, they rise one after the other, and stare fearfully at the two men.* KADIYE *is rigid, afraid to bat even an eyelid.*]

IGWEZU: I think perhaps you did not slay the fatted calf. . . .

MAKURI: Unsay it, my son. Unsay that at once.

IGWEZU: Kadiye, perhaps you did not slay the fatted calf. . . .

[*The drummer stares, hesitates, and runs out. The servant moves nearer the door.*]

MAKURI [*snapping his fingers round his head*] : May heaven forgive what has been uttered here tonight. May earth reject the folly spoken by my son.

IGWEZU : You lie upon the land, Kadiye, and choke it in the folds of your flesh. . . .

MAKURI : Son, listen to me. . . .

IGWEZU : If I slew the fatted calf, Kadiye, do you think the land might breathe again? If I slew all the cattle in the land and sacrificed every measure of goodness, would it make any difference to our lives, Kadiye? Would it make any difference to our fates?

[*The servant runs out also.*]

KADIYE [*in a choking voice*] : Makuri, speak to your son. . . .

BEGGAR : Master . . . master. . . .

[IGWEZU *suddenly shaves off the final smear of lather with a rapid stroke which makes the* KADIYE *flinch. Releases him and throws the razor on the table.* KADIYE *scrambles up at once, tearing the cloth from his neck. Makes for the door.*]

KADIYE [*panting*] : You shall pay for this. . . . I swear I shall make you pay for this. . . . Do you think that you can make an ass of the Kadiye? Do you think that you can pour your sacrilege into my ears with impunity?

IGWEZU : Go quickly, Kadiye [*sinks into the chair*]. And the next time that you wish to celebrate the stopping of the rains, do not choose a barber whose harvest rots beneath the mire, one who can read the lie in the fat of your eyes !

KADIYE : You will pay, I swear it . . . you will pay for this [*flings off the sheet and goes out*].

MAKURI : Son, what have you done?

IGWEZU : I know now that the floods can come again. That the swamp will continue to laugh at our endeavours. I know that we can feed the Serpent of the Swamp and kiss the Kadiye's feet – but the vapours will still rise and corrupt the tassels of the corn.

MAKURI : I must go after him or he'll stir up the village against

us [*stops at the door*]. This is your home, Igwezu, and I would
not drive you from it for all the world. But it might be best for
you if you went back to the city until this is forgotten. [*Exit.*]
   [*Pause*]

BEGGAR [*softly*]: Master . . . master . . . slayer of serpents.

IGWEZU [*in a tired voice*]: I wonder what drove me on.

BEGGAR: What, master?

IGWEZU: Do you think that my only strength was that of despair? Or was there something of a desire to prove myself
worthy?

   BEGGAR [*remains silent.*]

IGWEZU: Your fat friend is gone. But will he stay away?

BEGGAR: I think that the old man was right. You should go back
to the city.

IGWEZU: Is it of any earthly use to change one slough for
another?

BEGGAR: I will come and keep you company. If necessary, I will
beg for you.

IGWEZU [*stares at him, slowly shaking his head*]: What manner
of man are you? How have I deserved so much of you that you
would beg for me?

BEGGAR: I made myself your bondsman. That means that I must
share your hardships.

IGWEZU: I am too tired to see it all. I think we all ought to go to
bed. Have they given you a place to sleep?

BEGGAR: Will I return with you to the city?

IGWEZU: No, friend. You like this soil. You love to scoop it up in
your hands. You dream of cleaving ridges under the flood and
making little balls of mud in which to wrap your seeds. Is that
not so?

BEGGAR: Yes, master.

IGWEZU: And you have faith, have you not? Do you not still
believe in what you sow? That it will sprout and see the harvest
sun?

BEGGAR: It must. In my wanderings, I think that I have grown
a healer's hand.

IGWEZU: Then stay. Stay here and take care of the farm. I must go away. [*He crosses the room as if to go into the house. Hesitates at the door, then turns round and walks slowly away.*] Tell my people I could not stop to say good-bye.

BEGGAR: You are not going now, master?

IGWEZU: I must not be here when the people call for blood.

BEGGAR: But the water is high. You should wait until the floods subside.

IGWEZU: No. I want to paddle as I go, like a little child.

REQUIEM

1

You leave your faint depressions
Skim-flying still, on the still pond's surface.
Where darkness crouches, egret wings
Your love is as gossamer.

2

Hear now the dry wind's dirge. It is
The hour of lesson, and you teach
Painless dissolution in strange
Disquietudes
Sadness is twilight's kiss on earth.

3

I would not carve a pillow
Off the clouds, to nest you softly.
Yet the wonder, swift your growth, in-twining
When I fold you in my thorned bosom.
Now, your blood-drops are
My sadness in the haze of day
And the sad dew at dawn, fragile
Dew-braiding rivulets in hair-roots where
Desires storm. Sad, sad
Your feather-tear running in clefts between

Thorned buttresses, soon gone, my need
Must drink it all. Be then as
The dry sad air, and I may yield me
As the rain.

4

So let your palm, ridge to ridge
Be cupped with mine
And the thin sad earth between will nurture
Love's misfoundling – and there it ended.
Storm-whispers swayed you outward where
Once, we cupped our hands. Alone I watched.
The earth came sifting through.

5

I shall sit often on the knoll
And watch the grafting.
This dismembered limb must come
Some day
To sad fruition.

I shall weep dryly on the stone
That marks the gravehead silence of
A tamed resolve.

I shall sit often on the knoll
Till longings crumble too
O I have felt the termite nuzzle
White entrails
And fine ants wither
In the mind's unthreaded maze.

Then may you frolic where the head
Lies shaven, inherit all,
Death-watches, cut your beetled capers
On loam-matted hairs. I know this
Weed-usurped knoll. The graveyard now
Was nursery to her fears.

6

This cup I bore, redeem
When yearning splice
The torn branch.

This earth I pour outward to
Your cry, tend it. It knows full
Worship of the plough.
Lest burning follow breath, learn
This air was tempered in wild
Cadences of fire.

No phoenix I. Submission
To her cleansing flames fulfilled
Urn's legacy.

Yet incandescing was the roar alone
Sun-searing haze pools lit the kilns
That bronzed me.

It is peace to settle on life's fingers
Like bran; illusive as the strained meal's
Bloodless separateness.

Be still. And when this cup would crush
The lightness of your hand, build no shrine
Strew the ashes on your path.

Amos Tutuola

From My Life in the Bush of Ghosts

Tutuola's hero begins as an innocent boy of seven (narrator of the story). At this age, he does not yet know the meaning of 'good' but knows quite well the meaning of 'bad' – owing to his experiences at home where his father's wives are always quarrelling. He is separated from his brother while they and the rest of the town are on the run just before a slave raid. At this time he runs into the Bush of Ghosts, entering through a hole in a mound. He is transformed into several things in the bush: a cow, a ju-ju stuck in the neck of an enormous pot, a horse, a camel and a monkey. He is often a slave or just an outsider as he travels. Among his many adventures, he marries a ghostess (the episode chosen for this excerpt), later a Super Lady. After twenty-four years in the Bush, having adopted its way of life, he returns to his people to live normally. In the place of innocence in the young man is knowledge.

MY FIRST WEDDING

Before the wedding day was reached my friend had chosen one of the most fearful ghosts for me as my 'best man' who was always speaking evil words, even he was punished in the fire of hell more than fifty years for these evil talks and cruelties, but was still growing rapidly in bad habits, then he was expelled from hell to the 'Bush of Ghosts' to remain there until the judgement day as he was unable to change his evil habits at all. When the wedding day arrived all the ghosts and ghostesses of the town, together with the father of the lady whom I wanted to marry, my friend and his mother, my best man and myself went to the church at about ten o'clock, but it was the ghost's clock that said so. When we reached their church I saw that the Reverend who preached or performed the wedding ceremony was the 'Devil'. But as he was preaching he reached the point that I should tell them my name which is an earthly person's name and when they heard the name the whole of them in that church exclaimed at the same time – 'Ah! you will be baptized in this church again before you will marry this lady.'

When I heard so from them I heard so, not knowing that Rev. Devil was going to baptize me with fire and hot water as they were baptized for themselves there. When I was baptized on that day, I was crying loudly so that a person who is a distance of two miles would not listen before hearing my voice, and within a few minutes every part of my body was scratched by this hot water and fire, but before Rev. Devil could finish the baptism I regretted it. Then I told him to let me go away from their church and I do not want to marry again, because I could not bear to be baptized with fire and hot water any longer, but when all of them heard so, they shouted, 'Since you have entered this church you are to be baptized with fire and hot water before you will go out of the church, willing or not you ought to wait and complete the baptism.' But when I heard so from them again, I exclaimed with a terrible voice that – 'I will die in their church.' So all of them exclaimed again that – 'You may die if you like, nobody knows you here.'

But as ghosts do not know the place or time which is possible to ask questions, so at this stage one of them got up from the seat and asked me – 'By the way, how did you manage to enter into the "Bush of Ghosts", the bush which is on the second side of the world between the heaven and earth and which is strictly banned to every earthly person to be entered, and again you have the privilege to marry in this bush as well?' So as these ghosts have no arrangements for anything at the right time and right place, then I answered that I was too young to know which is 'bad' and 'good' before I mistakenly entered this bush and since that time or year I am trying my best to find out the right way back to my home town until I reached the town of 'burglar-ghosts' from where I came with my friend to this town. After I explained as above, then the questioner stood up again and asked me whether I could show them my friend whom I followed to that town. Of course as my friend was faithful, before I could say anything, he and his mother whom we came to visit got up at the same time and said that I am living with a burglar-ghost in the town of the burglar-ghosts. But when my friend and his mother confirmed all that I said and as all the rest of the ghosts are respecting all the burglar-ghosts most because they were supplying them the earthly properties, so they overlooked my offence, then Rev. Devil continued the baptism with hot water and fire.

After the baptism, then the same Rev. Devil preached again for a few minutes, while 'Traitor' read the lesson. All the members of this church were 'evil-doers'. They sang the song of evils with evils' melodious tune, then 'Judas' closed the service.

Even 'Evil of Evils' who was the ruler of all the devils and who was always seeking evils about, evil-joking, evil-walking, evil-playing evil-laughing, evil-talking, evil-dressing, evil-moving, worshipping evils in the church of evils and living in the evil-house with his evil family, everything he does is evil, attended the service too, but he was late before he arrived and when he shook hands with me on that day, I was shocked as if I touch a 'live electric wire', but my friend was signalling to me with his eyes not to shake hands with him to avoid the shock but I did not understand.

Having finished the marriage service, all of us went to my in-laws' house where everybody was served with a variety of food and all kinds of ghosts' drinks. After that all the ghosts and ghostesses started to dance. Also all the terrible-creatures sent their representatives as 'Skulls', 'Long-white creatures', 'Invincible and invisible Pawn', or 'Give and take' who fought and won the Red people in the Red-town for the 'Palm-Wine drinker', 'Mountain-creatures', 'Spirit of prey' whose eye's flood of light suffocated Palm-Wine Drinker's wife and also the 'hungry-creature' who swallowed Palm-Wine Drinker together with his wife when returning from Deads-town came and saluted my wife's father and they were served immediately they arrived. But at last 'Skull' who came from 'Skull family's town' reported 'Spirit of prey' to my wife's father who was chief secretary to all the terrible and curious creatures in all dangerous bushes, that the spirit of prey stole his meat which the skull put at the edge of the plate in which both were eating as both were served together with one plate, because plates were not sufficient to serve each of them with a plate. But before my wife's father who was their chief secretary could have a chance to come and settle the matter for them, both of them started to fight fiercely so that all the ghosts and all the other representatives came nearer and surrounded them, clapping hands on them in such a way that if one of these fighters surrenders or gives up it would be very shameful to him.

Some of these scene-lookers were clapping, and an old Ape who was a slave and inherited by my wife's father from his first generation since uncountable years was beating a big tree under which both these terrible creatures were fighting as a drum which had a very big sound. But as this old slave ape was beating the tree as a drum in such a way that all the scene-lookers who stood round them could not bear the lofty sound of the tree which was beaten as drum and wait or stand still in one place, so all the ghosts, evils, terrible creatures, my friend, my wife and her father and myself started to dance at the same time. But as I was intoxicated by the drinks which I drank on that day, so I mistakenly smashed drinks ghost to death who came from the '9th town of ghosts' to enjoy the merriment of the marriage with us as I was staggering about.

At last I was summoned to the court of evil for wilful killing a small ghost, but as a little mistake is a serious offence as well as big offence in the 'Bush of Ghosts', so the 'Evil judge' judged the case at one o'clock of the judgement day and luckily I was freed by a kind lawyer whose mother was the native of the 'Bottomless Ravine's town', the town which belongs to only 'triplets ghosts and ghostesses'. But if it was not for this incognito lawyer who was very kind to me without knowing him elsewhere I would be imprisoned for fifty years as this is the shortest years for a slightest offence.

After I freed the case then I returned to my in-laws' town and lived there with my wife for a period of about three months and some days before I remembered my mother and brother again, because I did not remember them again when I married the lady. So one morning, I told the father of my wife that I want to leave his town for another one, but I did not tell him frankly that I want to continue to find the way to my home town which I left since I was seven years old. So I told him that I should leave with his daughter who was my wife, he allowed me to go or to leave, but disallowed his daughter to go with me. Of course, when I thought over within myself that however an earthly person might love ghosts, ghosts could not like him heartily in any respect, then I alone left his town in the evening after I went round the town and bade good-bye to the prominent ghosts.

Onuora Nzekwu

From Blade Among the Boys

Blade Among the Boys, Nzekwu's second novel, treats of the conflict between Christianity and African traditional rites. Patrick, Mr Nzekwu's hero, is born of a nominally Catholic family, but his uncle insists that he share in the traditional religious rites of his people. Patrick obeys. When he decides to become a Catholic priest, his mother is horrified: she cannot conceive of her son, the spiritual head of his dead and living family, committing himself to a life of celibacy. She regards it as an insult to the ancestors, and pleads with him to give up the idea. In this chapter Patrick is resisting, in a rather haughty manner, the suggestions of his elders to assume his traditional title. His mother is also trying to save him from the priesthood.

THE FINGER OF GOD

When the offices closed on the day of the bribery incident Patrick went to the Catholic mission to see the parish priest. He was convinced that his Maker had called upon him to receive the Sacrament of Holy Order and that any delay or any action taken by him which was contrary to it would be tempting God himself.

'Could you arrange for me to go to Confession?' he asked the parish priest after they had exchanged greetings.

'"There is joy in heaven over one sinner doing penance",' the priest quoted.

'I have been a very bad Christian for so very long and now I want to make my peace with God.'

'When do you want the Confession?'

'Now, if it is possible. I don't think it is useful postponing it.'

'Wise man,' the priest commented. 'Come with me to the church.'

They walked side by side to the church, with Patrick talking most of the way. At the entrance to the church building they parted. Patrick went into the church to prepare himself for Confession and the priest went into the sacristy. That evening he felt like one off whom a whole weight has been lifted. The next morning he went to early morning Mass and received Holy Communion for the first time since he left for Lagos ten years before. A week went by and he applied for admission into the Seminary of the Resurrection at Uchi through the parish priest at Umuahia. The priest forwarded the application to the seminary authorities. Time passed and he got no reply. But just as he was beginning to think his application had been rejected, the parish priest visited him one evening and handed over to him an envelope. It contained a formal application form which he wasted no time in filling and returning to the priest who was to advise on Patrick's suitability for the priesthood. During the period of waiting he had impressed the priest very favourably, and he wrote him an excellent recommendation. Not long after that, a letter came from the seminary telling him of his acceptance as a student for the priesthood, and allowing him six weeks within which to get his personal affairs straightened out.

As soon as he received the letter he told his mother his leave would start during the week, and that he would travel to Ado to spend part of it. She was happy to hear this, for it was going to be the first time he had visited Ado since he started working. The day before they both travelled home, Patrick paid in a month's salary in lieu of one month's notice which he was supposed to give his employers if he should decide to end his appointment.

About five days after his arrival home, the male members of his lineage sent a delegation of ten men to discuss with him the question of his retiring from service to assume the office of *okpala*. He was prepared for the delegation when they arrived and after the usual preliminaries their spokesman, Ononye, greeted everyone present and turned to him.

'We have been sent to discuss with you the vital office of *okpala* of the lineage which has fallen to you. As you know, it is a key office in our society, one on which depends the welfare and prosperity of the lineage. We should like to know what your stand is with regard to your assuming office.'

Patrick thanked the delegation for honouring him with their visit. Then he went on to speak on the issue which had brought them.

'I made my stand clear,' he said, 'on this issue of *okpala* to my uncle, Ononye, before I left Ado to seek my fortune far away from home. I told him, when we discussed it then, that I was a Christian and had no intention whatsoever of assuming the office. My answer now still remains what it was then.'

A deep silence fell on the gathering and all but he looked as if they had been hit by a terrible plague.

'One day you will perish in your own foolishness,' Ononye said, when he recovered from the shock given him by his nephew's statement. 'Ike, Etuka and Akudo are respected leaders of the Christian community among us, but still they make charms and consult diviners. Only last year Ike bore the cost of his grandmother's traditional funeral rites and Akudo sponsored his brother for the *ozo*-title. Mark you, these men were in the Church before you were born and they've got more Christian teachings in them than you've ever had. How can you, of all people, let the Church make a senseless woman of you? Why can't you apply a bit of common sense in pursuing your own ruin?'

'I do not gauge my faith by other people's standards,' Patrick replied haughtily, 'no matter in what regard the society holds them. I did not become a Christian to impress the society in which I live.'

'Do not let Christianity make you blind to the truths of life,' said one of the elders. 'You can't say you have failed to read any meaning into every event that has taken place round you recently.'

'You've got to mellow down,' another pleaded, 'and find a place in your heart for that which is dearest to your own kith and kin. We fail to understand how you can become so obsessed with a foreign way of life as to utterly neglect your own – your own which distinguishes you from all other peoples, which we are all proud of, which sustained your ancestors and which means life and death to us.'

'Man, the office of *okpala* is yours by right,' a young member of the delegation put in. 'You have built yourself a house. It now remains for you to marry and take the ozo-title to qualify for the office. You've got the means to face these responsibilities squarely. I cannot understand why you are being so unnecessarily difficult.'

'Brethren,' Patrick said, wishing to end the whole interview. 'You cannot move me with your arguments. My mind is made up and you cannot make me change it no matter what you say or do.'

Patrick had originally declined to assume office on the grounds that he was a Christian. Christianity to him, as to many other people, was synonymous with education, with progressive ideas and with modern thought. He would therefore have nothing, directly or indirectly, to do with an aspect of his traditional culture so conspicuously heathenish. He didn't care whether the life of the whole society depended on his acceptance of the office or not. What he cared about most was the salvation of his own soul. Now, as he faced the delegation, he had an added reason for not wanting to take up the office, but he feared to tell them this other reason.

One after another the people spoke, trying to convince him. They pleaded with him to no avail. They threatened him without success. Then Ononye went on to cite for him examples of people who had perished because of their obstinacy in refusing to accept the inevitable. He reminded him of Lucia Ezekamba, the Christian lady who, just before he left Ado, had run amok in the market place because, as everyone said, she had refused to succeed as the priestess of her lineage on the grounds that her Christian faith forbade the holding of such 'pagan' offices. A few days after she was taken home from the market she disappeared from her house, leaving no trace whatsoever of her whereabouts. And, though the police were quickly called in, she had never been found.

Much as Patrick feared to meet with a similar fate, he was unbending in his will. He was feeling uncomfortably hot inside him when Ononye lost his temper and shouted at him to respect the wishes of his relations.

'I won't!' he shouted back, a strong desire welling up in him to send them away. 'You respect my wishes. Must I for ever be a slave to your desires so as to promote harmony within the lineage when God has endowed me with a free will? When I was young you made me do things which I shouldn't have done, simply because you were caring for your selfish ends. When I started to earn a salary you made me give a large portion of my earnings to you, under the pretext that when I am old others will look after me. What guarantee is there that they will do it, now that our economy is fast changing into a cash economy. Now you want me to share out over seven hundred pounds to you as *ozo*-fees and, not only that, you want me to come home and spend the rest of my life spilling blood on carvings and offering pieces of food to inanimate objects. I am sick of this forced loyalty to the lineage and I am going to have no more of it.'

'Who are you shouting at?' Ononye asked menacingly.

'I'm shouting at all you who won't let a man live the way he pleases; at all of you who want to ruin my life for me.'

Ononye rose to his feet and spat, with a hissing sound like a cobra's. 'Curse be upon you,' he began. 'From this day on –'

'Don't,' shouted all the elders present.

'How dare you curse your own?' one of the elders sitting beside him asked. 'Already he has condemned himself to grapple with the gods. Why waste valuable power?'

'Leave him,' shouted Patrick, trembling with anger where he stood. 'The curses of the likes of him are never potent.'

'Stop tempting the old man,' Izualor shouted from behind him, and hit him a hammer-like blow which knocked him out. As soon as this happened the delegates began to sneak away, for much as they wanted the issue of *okpala* resolved, they hated a rough-house.

When Patrick woke up Ononye alone was with him.

'How do you feel?'

'Better,' Patrick answered.

'You were rash, talking to us the way you did. You should have been more prudent in your language.'

'I'm sorry.'

'Now be warned. The people you'll serve are ready waiting for you to take your rightful place among them. Remember that one false move will land you with a crisis on your lap. The odds will be against you, for you will be only one against an angry mob of relatives.'

'Rather than do what you ask I'll hang myself,' Patrick answered, determined to carry out his threat if the need arose.

After a total of two weeks at Ado he returned to Umuahia, and remained there until it was time for him to go to the seminary. He had disposed of all his possessions and put his money in a bank, where he left standing orders as to what allowance should be made his mother every month. At last the day came when he was to report at the seminary, and after bidding his friends farewell he took a mammy waggon bound for Uchi on his way to the Seminary of the Resurrection.

It was not until two months later that his relations got to know that he was no longer working, and was no longer at Umuahia. It was another month before they knew his whereabouts. As soon as his mother got the information she travelled to Uchi without a definite plan, but intent on coming home with her son. A few inquiries at the motor park at Uchi put her on the right road to the seminary. Arrived there, she was shown the principal's office by the porter at the gate. The principal was in and she told him her problem.

'No man is ever forced to become a priest,' the principal explained when he had listened to her. 'Your son made his own decision to come here. However, you will understand that he is mature. He knows what he wants and he is responsible for his own actions.'

'He is my son,' she insisted. 'No matter how old he claims to be, to me he is still a child and needs a mother's care and guidance. I should have been consulted on this but I was not. I want to make it clear that neither I nor his relations approve of his becoming a priest.'

'But you said you are a Catholic; baptized, confirmed and married in the church. How can you not give him to God?'

'You are a white man and cannot understand the values which we place on certain issues.'

'I think I do. I have lived here for fifteen years.'

'No. No white man ever does. Because your culture is entirely different from ours, you cannot understand the fear which right now is eating out my heart, a terrible fear that there is going to be no issue in the family. He is my only child and God made him a son so that the family will continue. He is not a eunuch as people are beginning to say in Ado, even to my face. You cannot understand what terrible anguish such statements cause a mother. If you were a woman perhaps you would understand a little of the torment it is to see your son slowly waste away under your very eyes.'

'But God gave His only Son to die for your salvation,' the priest argued.

'Yes He did. He could do it because He was God. I am only human and, what is more, a woman.'

'You seem to forget Mary. Jesus was her only son and she was a woman like you.'

'She knew beforehand that a sword was going to pierce her heart and that had prepared her for what was going to happen. Moreover, being a Jew, her culture and her sense of values were quite different from mine.'

'Did Patrick tell you all about the train accident at Gerti?' the priest asked, changing his line of argument. 'Did he tell you about the robbery and the bribe incident?'

'Yes, he did.'

'And you did not see in them the finger of God guiding your son towards the role He meant him to play?'

'His uncle would have told you that the gods and ancestors were employing these incidents to warn him that he should take up the office of *okpala* of his patrilineal lineage,' she answered. 'But that is beside the point. Right now I implore you,' and she fell on her knees, 'to release him. I beg you and that which you hold most dear; by the Blessed Sacrament; in the name of God; to pity a poor widow whose only hope is in her one child.'

'Well, why not talk to Patrick first and after that you can see me again?'

This seemed a reasonable proposition and she agreed.

Sierra Leone

Abioseh Nicol

LIFE IS SWEET AT KUMANSENU

The sea and the wet sand to one side of it; green tropical forest on
the other; above it the slow tumbling clouds. The clean round
blinding disc of sun and the blue sky, covered and surrounded the
small African village, Kameni.

A few square mud houses with roofs like helmets, here thatched
and there covered with corrugated zinc where the prosperity of
cocoa and trading had touched the head of the family.

The widow Bola stirred her palm oil stew and thought of nothing
in particular. She chewed a Kola nut rhythmically with her strong
toothless jaws and soon unconsciously she was chewing in rhythm
with the skipping of Asi, her grand-daughter. She looked idly at
Asi as the seven-year-old brought the twisted palm-leaf rope
smartly over her head and jumped over it, counting in English each
time the rope struck the ground and churned up a little red dust.
Bola herself did not understand English well, but she could count
easily up to twenty in English for market purposes. Asi shouted
six and then said nine, ten. Bola called out that after six came seven.
And I should know, she sighed. Although now she was old and
her womb and breasts were withered, there was a time when she
bore children regularly every two years. Six times she had borne
a boy child and six times they had died. Some had swollen up and
with weak plaintive cries had faded away. Others had shuddered
in sudden convulsions, with burning skins, and had rolled up
their eyes and died. They had all died. Or rather he had died, Bola
thought, because she knew it was one child all the time whose
spirit had crept up restlessly into her womb to be born and to mock
her. The sixth time Musa, the village magician whom time had
transformed into a respectable Muslim, had advised her and her
husband to break the bones of the quiet little corpse and mangle it
so that it couldn't come back to torment them alive again. But she

held on to the child, and refused to let them handle it. Secretly she had marked it with a sharp pointed stick at the left buttock before it was wrapped in a mat and they had taken it away. When, the seventh time she had borne a son, and the purification ceremonies had taken place, she had turned it slyly to see whether the mark was there. It was. She showed it to the old woman who was the midwife and asked her what that was, and she had forced herself to believe the other who said it was an accidental scratch made whilst the child was being scrubbed with herbs to remove placental blood. But this child had stayed. Meji, he had been called. And he was now thirty years of age and a second-class clerk in Government offices in a town ninety miles away. Asi, his daughter, had been left with her to do the things an old woman wanted a small child for, to run and take messages to the neighbours, to fetch a cup of water from the earthenware pot in the kitchen, to sleep with her and be fondled.

She threw the washed and squeezed cassave leaves into the red boiling stew, putting in a finger's pinch of salt, and then went indoors, carefully stepping over the threshold to look for the dried red pepper. She found it, and then dropped it, leaning against the wall with a little cry. He turned round from the window and looked at her with a twisted half smile of love and sadness. In his short-sleeved, open-necked white shirt and grey gaberdine trousers, a gold wrist watch and brown suede shoes, he looked like the pictures in African magazines of a handsome clerk who would get to the top because he ate the correct food, or regularly took the correct laxative, which was being advertised. His skin was greyish brown and he had a large red handkerchief tied round his neck.

'Meji, God be praised,' Bola cried. 'You gave me quite a turn. My heart is weak and I can no longer take surprises. When did you come? How did you come? By lorry, by fishing boat? And how did you come into the house? The front door was locked. There are so many thieves nowadays. I'm so glad to see you, so glad,' she mumbled and wept, leaning against his breast.

Meji's voice was hoarse, and he said: 'I am glad to see you too, Mother,' beating her back affectionately.

Asi ran in and cried 'Papa, Papa,' and was rewarded with a lift and a hug.

'Never mind how I came, Mother,' Meji said, laughing, 'I'm here, and that's all that matters.'

'We must make a feast, we must have a big feast. I must tell the neighbours at once. Asi, run this very minute to Mr Addai, the catechist, and tell him your papa is home. Then to Mami Gbera to ask her for extra provisions, and to Pa Babole for drummers and musicians. . . .'

'Stop,' said Meji raising his hand. 'This is all quite unnecessary. I don't want to see *anyone*, no one at all. I wish to rest quietly and completely. No one is to know I'm here.'

Bola looked very crestfallen. She was proud of Meji, and wanted to show him off. The village would never forgive her for concealing such an important visitor. Meji must have sensed this because he held her shoulder comfortingly and said: 'They will know soon enough. Let us enjoy each other, all three of us, this time. Life is too short.'

Bola turned to Asi, picked up the packet of pepper and told her to go and drop a little into the boiling pot outside, taking care not to go too near the fire or play with it. After the child had gone, Bola said to her son, 'Are you in trouble? Is it the police?'

He shook his head. 'No,' he said, 'it's just that I like returning to you. There will always be this bond of love and affection between us, and I don't wish to share it. It is our private affair and that is why I've left my daughter with you,' he ended up irrelevantly, 'girls somehow seem to stay with relations longer.'

'And don't I know it,' said Bola. 'But you look pale,' she continued, 'and you keep scraping your throat. Are you ill?' She laid her hand on his brow. 'And you're cold, too.'

'It's the cold wet wind,' he said, a little harshly. 'I'll go and rest now if you can open and dust my room for me. I'm feeling very tired. Very tired indeed. I've travelled very far today and it has not been an easy journey.'

'Of course, my son, of course,' Bola replied, bustling away hurriedly but happily.

Meji slept all afternoon till evening, and his mother brought his food to his room, later took the empty basins away. Then he slept again till morning.

The next day, Saturday, was a busy one, and after further promising Meji that she would tell no one he was about, Bola went off to market. Meji took Asi for a long walk through a deserted path and up into the hills. She was delighted. They climbed high until they could see the village below in front of them, and the sea in the distance, and the boats with their wide white sails. Soon the sun had passed its zenith and was half way towards the west. Asi had eaten all the food, the dried fish and the flat tapioca pancakes and the oranges. Her father said he wasn't hungry, and this had made the day perfect for Asi, who had chattered, eaten, and then played with her father's fountain pen and other things from his pocket. They soon left for home because he had promised they would be back before dark; he had carried her down some steep boulders and she had held on to his shoulders because he had said his neck hurt so and she must not touch it. She had said: 'Papa, I can see behind you and you haven't got a shadow. Why?'

He had then turned her round to face the sun. Since she was getting drowsy, she had started asking questions, and her father had joked with her and humoured her. 'Papa, why has your watch stopped at twelve o'clock?' 'Because the world ends at noon.' Asi had chuckled at that. 'Papa, why do you wear a scarf always round your neck?' 'Because my head would fall off if I didn't.' She had laughed out loud at that. But soon she had fallen asleep as he bore her homewards.

Just before nightfall, with his mother dressed in her best, they had all three, at her urgent request, gone to his father's grave, taking a secret route and avoiding the main village. It was a small cemetery, not more than twenty years or so old, started when the Rural Health Department had insisted that no more burials take place in the backyards of households. Bola took a bottle of wine and a glass and four split halves of Kola, each a half sphere, two red and two white. They reached the graveside and she poured some wine into the glass. Then she spoke to the dead man softly and caressingly. She had brought his son to see him, she said. This son whom God had given success, to the confusion and discomfiture of their enemies. Here he was, a man with a pensionable clerk's job and not a farmer, fisherman or a mechanic. All the years of their married life people had said she was a witch because her children had died young. But this boy of theirs had shown that she was a good woman. Let her husband answer her now, to show that he was listening. She threw the four Kola nuts up into the air and they fell on the grave. Three fell with the flat face upwards and one with its flat face downwards. She picked them up again and conversed with him once more and threw the Kola nuts up again. But still there was an odd one or sometimes two.

They did not fall with all four faces up, or with all four faces down, to show that he was listening and was pleased. She spoke endearingly, she cajoled, she spoke sternly. But all to no avail. Then she asked Meji to perform. He crouched by the graveside and whispered. Then he threw the Kola nuts and they rolled a little, Bola following them eagerly with her sharp old eyes. They all ended up face downwards. Meji emptied the glass of wine on the grave and then said that he felt nearer his father at that moment than he had ever done before in his life.

It was sundown, and they all three went back silently home in the short twilight. That night, going outside the house near her son's room window, she found, to her sick disappointment, that he had been throwing away all the cooked food out there. She did not mention this when she went to say goodnight, but she did sniff and say that there was a smell of decay in the room. Meji said he thought there was a dead rat up in the rafters, and he would clear it away after she had gone to bed.

That night it rained heavily, and sheet lightning turned the darkness into brief silver daylight, for one or two seconds at a time. Then the darkness again and the rain. Bola woke soon after midnight and thought she could hear knocking. She went to Meji's room to ask him to open the door, but he wasn't there. She thought he might have gone out for a while and been locked out by mistake. She opened the door quickly, holding an oil lamp upwards. He stood on the verandah, curiously unwet, and refused to come in.

'I have to go away,' he said hoarsely, coughing.

'Do come in,' she said.

'No,' he said, 'I have to go, but I wanted to thank you for giving me a chance.'

'What nonsense is this?' she said. 'Come in out of the rain.'

'I did not think I should leave without thanking you.'

The rain fell hard, the door creaked and the wind whistled.

'Life is sweet, Mother dear, good-bye, and thank you.'

He turned round and started running.

There was a sudden diffuse flash of lightning and she saw that the yard was empty. She went back heavily, and fell into a restless sleep. Before she slept she said to herself that she must see Mr Addai next morning, Sunday, or, better still, Monday, and tell him about this in case Meji was in trouble. She hoped Meji would not be annoyed. He was such a good son.

But it was Mr Addai who came instead, on Sunday afternoon, quiet and grave, and saw Bola sitting on an old stool in the verandah, dressing Asi's hair in tight thin plaits.

Mr Addai sat down and, looking away, he said: 'The Lord giveth and the Lord taketh away.' And soon half the village were sitting round the verandah and in the yard.

'But I tell you, he was here on Friday and left Sunday morning,' Bola said. 'He couldn't have died on Friday.'

Bola had just recovered from a fainting fit after being told of her son's death in town. His wife, Asi's mother, had come with the news, bringing some of his property. She said Meji had died instantly at noon on Friday and had been buried on Saturday at sundown. They would have brought him to Kameni for the burial. He had always wished that. But they could not do so in time as bodies did not last much after a day.

'He was here, he was here,' Bola said, rubbing her forehead and weeping.

Asi sat by quietly. Mr Addai said comfortingly, 'Hush, hush, he couldn't have been, because no one in the village saw him.'

'He said we were to tell no one,' Bola said.

The crowd smiled above Bola's head, and shook their heads. 'Poor woman,' someone said, 'she is beside herself with grief.'

'He died on Friday,' Mrs Meji repeated, crying. 'He was in the office and he pulled up the window to look out and call the messenger. Then the sash broke. The window fell, broke his neck and the sharp edge almost cut his head off; they say he died at once.'

'My papa had a scarf around his neck,' Asi shouted suddenly.

'Hush,' said the crowd.

Mrs Meji dipped her hand into her bosom and produced a small gold locket and put it round Asi's neck, to quieten her. 'Your papa had this made last week for your Christmas present. You may as well have it now.'

Asi played with it and pulled it this way and that.

'Be careful child,' Mr Addai said, 'it was your father's last gift.'

'I was trying to remember how he showed me yesterday to open it,' Asi said.

'You have never seen it before,' Mrs Meji said, sharply, trembling with fear mingled with anger.

She took the locket and tried to open it.

'Let me have it,' said the village goldsmith, and he tried whispering magic words of incantation. Then he said, defeated, 'It must be poor-quality gold; it has rusted. I need tools to open it.'

'I remember now,' Asi said in the flat complacent voice of childhood.

The crowd gathered round quietly and the setting sun glinted on the soft red African gold of the dangling trinket. The goldsmith handed the locket over to Asi and asked in a loud whisper: 'How did he open it?'

'Like so,' Asi said and pressed a secret catch. It flew open and she spelled out gravely the word inside. 'ASI'

The silence continued.

'His neck, poor boy,' Bola said a little wildly, 'that is why he could not eat the lovely meals I cooked for him.'

Mr Addai announced a service of intercession after vespers that evening. The crowd began to leave quietly.

Musa, the magician, was one of the last to leave. He was now very old and bent. In times of grave calamity, it was known that even Mr Addai did not raise objection to Musa being consulted.

He bent over further and whispered in Bola's ear: 'You should have had his bones broken and mangled thirty-one years ago when he went for the sixth time and then he would not have come back to mock you all these years by pretending to be alive. I told you so. But you women are naughty and stubborn.'

Bola stood up, her black face held high, her eyes terrible with maternal rage and pride.

'I am glad I did not,' she said, 'and that is why he came back specially to thank me before he went for good.'

She clutched Asi to her. 'I am glad I gave him the opportunity to come back, for life is sweet. I do not expect you to understand why I did so. After all, you are only a man.'

Sarif Easmon

BINDEH'S GIFT

'THIS IS KAILONDO'S ROCK,' Kallon shouted into Mr Brass-foot's ear, stamping on the granite boulder on which they stood looking down on the Mea Falls. 'It was on this very rock that he used to punish those "war boys" – this was in the 1860s – whose nerve had failed them in battle.'

Kallon and his friend Banky Vincent went on to demonstrate for old Bob Brassfoot how a coward was trussed up and, in the presence of the army assembled by the riverside, swung between two stalwarts and tossed into the thundering, boiling falls below. The former concluded:

'No single body was ever recovered. And, naturally, no "war boy" who witnessed an execution ever forgot the lesson.'

White, the black dwarf, stood at Mr Brassfoot's elbow grinning.

All four sat down on the boulder and for several minutes watched the river endlessly gathering itself in three vast, green serpent coils to their right to leap and thunder into the falls below. Now and again the wind would blow into their faces, damping them with spray; or it would catch the spray, fine as vapour, up-stream or down, and waft rainbows evanescently in the sunshine. Death in this cauldron that boiled with violence and not with heat, must be particularly ghastly, thought Bob Brassfoot. For such was the rush of waters over the centuries it had blasted the granite in the river bed: the rocks exposed down there at this dry season were gouged and scalloped in basins several inches deep; and for three hundred yards downstream there was not a square inch of water that was not boiling, leaping and tortured.

'But in the first place,' resumed Kallon, 'the idea of using the Falls to perfect his war-machine was not Kailondo's.' He paused awhile, trying to order his thoughts. He was the Native Administration Clerk and, a keen local historian, knew the history of

Kailahun like the palm of his hand. 'A generation before him, a night scene had been enacted at this very spot which makes everything that Kailondo did in that line almost amateurish.'

As Kallon paused again Mr Brassfoot oared in with his reedy voice : 'Yes, Kallon my boy?'

'In the incessant inter-tribal wars of those days,' Kallon took up the story in earnest, 'heroes were as thick as the flies that throve on the battlefields they created for their glory. And the war-leaders, like dogs, had their day and passed away. Kai Borie was one such leader, and *his* day spread over many a bloody year, ending on that ghastly night I am telling you of. He was no ordinary man. . . .'

Kai Borie stood on the great boulder by the Moa Falls, big, black, and magnificent, a human almost as charged with energy as thunder and lightning bursting out of black, nimbus clouds.

'Bring Bensali here,' he roared above the thunder of the waterfalls. 'He is my sister's child and, therefore, by tribal custom and fact, more precious to me than my own would be. But if in the attack he did behave like a coward, he shall die as other cowards have died before him.'

A movement like a shock-wave passed through the concourse of men assembled on this side of the river. Overhead the stars, numberless and brilliant in a moonless heaven, looked down on a river scene as brilliant and certainly more colourful than themselves. For five hundred palm-oil flambeaux were blazing on the Moa's near bank, making the stretch of water look like a hungry, roaring river of blood. Black men held the torches up, and they lined the rocks right down to the water's edge; men as thick as palisades right up to the forest roots, perched on trees – all fearful, all expectant of the horror that might have been the individual lot of any one of them. Upstream, downstream ten thousand 'war boys' awaited this royal execution. The light picked out their bodies like statues carved in ebony, here in chiaroscuro, there as clear as day – while here and there spear points glinted like stars answering the stars overhead.

From the river bank to the forest behind, the King's command was passed from mouth to mouth. It made a murmur from the ranks of men, a sound indefinite and eerily moving — as if the earth on which they stood had grumbled in protest.

The prisoner, sitting under guard by a fire in the forest, trembled as the shaft of a spear touched him on the shoulder, and he was ordered to rise.

Two soldiers, their bodies mirrored in the firelight, helped Bensali to rise — for his hands were bound behind his back. He set his teeth with the pain as they pulled him up: there was a wound festering high up on his right arm, on the inner side.

'Courage, Bensali!' whispered the man on his left.

'I am not afraid to die,' Bensali answered back, briefly.

They marched him down through the forest, from the fireside down the shadow of death ablaze with torches, to the destiny awaiting him by the Moa Falls.

Although bound, Bensali's brown body moved with rhythm, beautifully muscled. He towered a head above his guards. He moved steadily and firmly, not like a man walking the earth for the last time, and knowing Death to be but a few minutes away.

He jumped from rock to rock unaided, never losing his balance, halted below the boulder on which his uncle stood.

'Bensali,' Kai Borie shouted down to him, 'even at this last moment let me hear your story again. Perhaps God in his wisdom has hidden something from our senses that may yet save me from executing my favourite sister's child. Though I hate and will punish cowardice in anyone, I, having no son of my own, hate even more the thought of drowning my own heir.'

'There is nothing new to tell, Uncle,' said the bound man wearily.

'Nevertheless I must hear it,' the war-chief ordered. The right side of his face was twitching with emotion; the left was hideous and expressionless, eyeless also, being occupied by a four-pronged scar that twisted the mouth to one side.

'It was as I have said,' Bensali returned, raising his voice in that valley of death, that as many as possible of his fellows might hear him. 'A week today, Kai Borie, you ordered us to attack Gbaserie

in his wartown. I was honoured, grateful, and proud that you put
me in command.

'We lay in the forest all afternoon, not approaching the town
till we were sure that the guards would be weary, and sorely
tempted to sleep in the lateness of the night.

'All went well with us. In four groups we scaled the mud walls
around the town, and set fire to the crowded houses in different
parts of the town at once.

'But Uncle, Gbaserie was as old a hand at war as you. No doubt,
he had his spies among us: he must have known of the coming
attack. Our spies were not as good. It was only when we had set
fire to a quarter of the town that we realized it was deserted – and
that *we* were trapped in it.

'Yes, trapped, my Uncle! For Gbaserie had hidden his men in
the forest too. From whatever wall-gate we attempted to make a
sortie and burst out, we were greeted with a hail of spears. Only
later we found that those who had been left to guard our rear and
lines of communication outside the town had been slaughtered to
a man. O Lord – the horror and blood inside the town! Torture by
fire blazed behind us, certain death by an untold number of enemy
hands in front – these two, or surrender and slavery. An impossible
choice – so we could not help but fight. And bravely too, I think.
Only our bodies must have stood out with fatal clearness for our
enemies against the firelight: more spears found their mark
among us than I know is common in war.

'Still, we fought hardily, and as best we could. My younger
brothers died bravely beside me. I loved those two – as my mother
– your sister – loved them. It is a poor thought now that we could
have taken a thousand slaves in Gbaserie's town. Slaves come every
day, brothers not. Slaves, ten thousand slaves or their equivalent
in gold – a sorry exchange for two brothers dead! Oh Uncle,' he
cried in agony, 'I am sick of war – and do not mind to die. . . .'

Looking like drops of blood in that light, tears trembled on
Bensali's lids. His head fell forward on his chest, his shoulders
stooped, his grief ground him down to silence.

But Kai Borie, no less tortured than the man below the boulder,
called down to him relentlessly:

'I am listening!'

'There is little more to tell,' the young man resumed, his voice sick with weariness and heartbreak. 'We fought. We lost. I myself with my young arm ran my spear through Gbaserie's heart. At least, Kai Borie, that old enemy of yours is dead. The Peace he has for years driven out from our land may yet come back to us. So I, emboldened by this deed of blood, was fool enough to hope. But I gloried too soon. My spear was still stuck in Gbaserie's chest when his men roared like thunder all over the field . . . and closed in in a wall of death. But Gbaserie's death had put new life into us. We did not yield an inch. Thick as the enemy came, we cut our way right through. And when at last it seemed that safety, so dearly bought, was now within our grasp – then it happened.

'I had been striking with my sword till my arm had grown weary and ached. Suddenly sword and weariness disappeared from my hand. I felt no pain. But blood gushed from my arm, warm and soothing down to the fingers – and coursed like a brook washing the dead at my feet. I gazed, feeling foolish, at the hand at my side; gazed at my good right arm. Foolish! They were still mine, fingers and hand. But no longer could I move them. The nerves had gone, cut in the wound in my arm. The arm is almost quite dead now – and now my body follows. I tell you, Uncle, I could do no more, no more – no more. . . .'

'And so you ran away!' Kai Borie shouted in agony.

Bensali died many deaths at the accusation, his head falling in shame on his chest.

'Bensali! Bensali!' Kai Borie cried again. No man alive there by that river of death had ever seen the seasoned old warrior in such agony. 'We are all death's children, Bensali, and cannot escape her. She comes at her own will, but better in honour than in disgrace; she may come in action, she may come in peace – but there is no choice, she *must* come. Yet not even in death must a young man give up his hold on life, on honour. Look at your uncle, boy, this one-eyed Borie. Look at this scarred face, this sightless hole that was once an eye.

'I see my own one-eyed ugliness in the glass, and my age rejoices with pride in it. I had your beauty once, and was your age when hunting in the forest. Fate willed that a leopard and I should hunt the same deer. I killed the game, closed in on the trail – only to feel the full-grown leopard tearing at my back. I smelt and saw and felt death then, all over me – furry, savage, tearing me in pieces. But it never entered my head to admit it. As you see the beast tore my face to shreds. But by the mercy of God and the will to live, I wrapped my legs round the beast's body, and got my right arm round its throat. By the sheer will to live – the will to face the danger and dare live beyond it – I hung on. I was strong then, but no more than you are now. By holding on and refusing to die, in the end I throttled the beast. I bore him on my shoulders to the town – only to fall fainting at my father's door. Had I died then, it would have been better than to live to see this night. Ah Bensali! ... Ah, Bensali! ...'

Kai Borie stopped and turned towards the forest behind him. A voice had echoed his. In that place where no woman had a right to be, a woman was wailing; without restraint of grief, at the top of her voice:

'Ah, Bensali! ... Ah, Kai Borie. ... Ah, Bensali! ... Ah, Kai Borie! ...' ceaselessly in the night.

Kai Borie stared towards the boles of trees shadowed against the blaze of the many camp fires in the forest. Other trees beyond the fires were lit up like gold. In between, leaves made whispering traceries both against the fires and the stars over the warriors' heads. From the heart of this setting the woman's dirge issued most eerily for a man not yet dead in fact, yet as surely dead as anything can be sure in human life. Her anguished calls brought a murmur from the soldiers up and down the river – an incantation without words that set the hair of every mortal there standing on end.

At last the weeping woman came through the forest. The ranks of soldiers parted and made way for her. And two young warriors helped from rock to rock the other woman who followed her; and though it was she who carried the basket, she was doubly bent over with her burden and with age.

Weeping all the time, the young woman at last jumped up the great boulder, and threw herself prostrate at Kai Borie's feet.

'Ah, Kai Borie,' she shrilled in agony, and twined her arms round his ankles, 'I have come at this last minute to beg for my husband's life. My Bensali must not die. These five years he has served you well. . . .'

'Stop, woman !' Kai Borie shouted. 'You should not have come here. Do you think what *you* feel for Bensali can compare with the love I have for my sister's first-born? You soft and foolish thing ! What can a woman know of the agony I suffer this night?'

'If you truly suffer,' the woman wailed and beat her hands on the rock, 'then you must save him !'

'Foolish Bindeh ! In war, men are nothing if they are not men. And manhood means courage, a willingness to sacrifice life itself for the common good. Tonight Bensali is not Kai Borie's nephew but a soldier in his army. And what shall men say of Kai Borie hereafter, or of Bensali, if Kai Borie tonight shall gloss over a crime for which he has ruled death for other men's nephews, other women's husbands?'

'What do I care for wars or armies? I've hated them, as my mother and grandmother hated them, even before they made me suffer so.' The woman's words shrilled into the forest, and men felt their blood turning into water : for Bindeh was speaking with the voice of all their mothers, all their wives. 'Kai Borie, has war left no mercy in you? These six months I have been Bensali's wife. Only six months ! Ah, Kai Borie – you were young once – have mercy on me. Look !'

In an instant she was on her feet before him. With swift, nervous movements of her wrists she tore off the small native cloth tied round her chest, leaving only the *lappa* tied at her waist, reaching down to midleg.

She was tall, deep-brown of skin, a beautiful woman. Her breasts, with the aureolae deeply pigmented, gave incontestable proof of her pregnancy.

'These three months,' she cried in agony, 'I have been carrying Bensali's child. His first baby. . . . Kai Borie, must you make a widow of me and an orphan of my child? No – *mercy* – NO! . . .'

At this revelation Kai Borie buried his face in his hands and burst into tears.

Again a murmur rose eerily from the soldiers. They knew, vaguely, they had unitedly created in Kai Borie's army a monster whose code each of them hated as an individual; yet as an army they were powerless in its creed. Not one of them was not sorry for Bensali, distressed for Bindeh. Yet, though each saw Bensali in himself crucified at second hand, not one could have raised his voice to save him.

Kai Borie was too strong a man to weep for long. Swiftly his tears ended in an outburst of anger with himself. With jerky, angry movements he wiped his tears away. Firmly he told Bindeh:

'Woman, I cannot help it.'

Though Bensali was not afraid of death, he trembled with horror to see his wife in such a scene.

'Bindeh,' he called up to her, 'Kai Borie is right. My Uncle, see that my wife and child are cared for. And now, Uncle, let Bindeh be led away – or she'll unnerve me . . . my wife – Oh, my dear ! – God take care of you and our child. In God's name, then, Bindeh . . . go !'

'Not yet, Bensali – not yet !' She had started violently at the sound of his voice. Having called his name, she stuffed the cloth she had torn from her chest into her mouth – her face darkened and twitched as though she was choking herself to death. Kai Borie wrenched the cloth from her – she staggered back from him.

'Forgive – Sir – forgive – I don't know what I am doing . . . Oh . . . O God. . . .' Her features twitched a little more, her hands trembled at her sides. She was truly going through hell. And yet, out of the mystery of that thing men call character, she managed to find strength to pull herself out of the hell of her sufferings, to order her thoughts.

'Kai Borie,' her voice quavered, but she managed to control it, 'I have one more prayer that may yet move you. Grandmother, the basket !'

The old woman, standing at the base of the boulder below them, handed up the big raffia basket. Bindeh clutched it desperately to her chest, and turned again to the old warrior :

'Kai Borie, I have brought a gift for you. For sometimes gifts move kings where prayers fail. But I shall give it to you only as a last resort.' On her bended knees again, falling down at his feet for the last time, 'I beg you for my husband's life.'

'Rise woman!' He spoke to her in a gentle voice, so that in the roar of the falls only she heard him. 'You are brave. . . .Your son shall be my heir – for I grieve no less than you that Bensali must die. . . .'

The woman leapt up from the rock, transformed. She was so rapt and tensed up she looked as if she had passed beyond pain and agony. She looked, indeed, like the Goddess of Vengeance.

'Grandmother,' Kai Borie called down to the old woman, 'take her home.'

'I'll go Kai Borie,' Bindeh screamed so frenziedly her voice echoed back from the forest. 'But first you'll take my gift!'

Swiftness enhanced her every little movement with grace – she moved so swiftly in the next few seconds no one could stop her.

Bensali, understanding too late what she *would* do, shouted up to her: 'No, Bindeh – the child!'

The young woman did not even hear him.

With a lightning movement of her hand she tore the lid off the basket. She swung the basket in the air and, bringing it down very swiftly, covered Kai Borie's head like a hood. At once she turned to face the river, bent her knees, raised her arms above her head – took a flying leap into the seething violence of the Falls.

It all happened so swiftly that the multitude barely had time to shout – 'Ha-ah-HAH!' – momentarily renting the night with their united astonishment, drowning the river noises. But each remained rooted to the spot where he stood, paralysed with wonder. . . .

For an instant or two they saw the rush of waters bear the woman down a few yards – heard her shout: 'Bensali! Bensali!' – no more. The waters had choked and battered her, and she vanished from their view. . . .

'You crazy woman!' Kai Borie's voice came muffled from inside the basket.

He wrenched the basket off his head, tossed it down on the rock – from which it rolled off slowly, down into the river, and was frenziedly borne downstream.

Feeling something cold above his eyes, Kai Borie raised a hand to his forehead.

Bensali turned a face petrified with despair from the river to his Uncle on the boulder above him.

'My God . . . UNC . . .' the words froze in his throat.

For Kai Borie was turbaned with a brown deadly snake which, in soft undulations, was swiftly adjusting itself like a bandeau around his brow. A second snake was coiled round his neck. And the largest of the three was spiralling up the forearm he had raised to his head.

At the sight the two war boys who stood on the nearest boulder to their Chief leapt down in terror to where the old woman sat, sobbing to herself.

But for the eternal rush of the falls, not a sound broke the death-liness of the night.

The moment Kai Borie touched the coldness on his forehead he felt two intense needle-stabs on his brow, one on his throat, one in his arm.

He grasped the snake on his head, tore it off. Bending over the boulder he brained it on the rock. He wrenched the other off his throat, horsewhipped it to death with its own body against the granite. The third reptile fell from his forearm. Without hesitation Kai Borie stamped on its back. The snake looped back and struck back ten times with incredible swiftness at his leg. He bent down, gripped the vicious band in his hand – and crushed it to death between his fingers.

Unhurried, he sat down on the rock.

'Kai Borie is dying !' he called loudly to his men below. 'Unbind Bensali ! . . . Quick, my men – *quick* : I have so little time to live. . . .' The sweat was already pouring profusely from his face. 'Swear, soldiers, swear that Bensali shall be your King. . . .'

Sworn by their fathers' gods. The oath rose grandly, eerily in that Death's valley, drowning the river noises.

'She was a brave woman, Bensali. . . . For her sake and mine – swear . . . swear to be . . . a true heir . . . to me. . . .'

Bensali, unbound, ran up the boulder and held his dying uncle against his chest.

'What do I want with a kingdom, my Uncle?' Sobbing like a woman, Bensali's tears ran down his face, and joined with the sweat that had burst out all over his uncle's heaving chest. *His* father had died when he was but a boy – Kai Borie had been more than father to him all his life. 'Uncle, without you and Bindeh I do not wish to live. . . .'

'Courage goes – beyond life. . . . Swear, Bensali – quick lad – swear! . . .' the words rattled in the old warrior's throat. Already he was finding it difficult to breathe. The air rasped painfully, irregularly into his chest. 'I willingly – exchange my life – for yours, Bensali. . . .' He had lived by violence, he died with violence, his ribs moving gigantically against the pressure of Death, to get the words out. Already his eyes were glazing over. 'It was – hidden from – a man's wit. . . . Only the weakness of women . . . sometimes sees the truth: better the old . . . should die . . . rather . . . than the young!' His eyes shut wearily. But his vast body convulsed with one final effort to get his last wish in the word: 'S-S-SWEAR!'

It was the last word he spoke.

At last, Bensali took the oath, crying, crying.

Whereupon, sacred and moving, a prayer burst from ten thousand throats:

'*Long live Bensali!*'

Kai Borie nodded, and leaned back heavily on his nephew's chest. In five minutes he was completely paralysed – in ten he was dead.

'Oh Bindeh! Oh, my Uncle! . . . Oh Bindeh! . . .'

But still ten thousand soldiers hailed; '*Bensali! Long live Bensali!*' He looked down on them and shook his head. Only then he realized that life was at best a sham, but must go on.

'*Long live Bensali!*'

Ghana

Kwesi Brew

THE HARVEST

If this is the time
To master my heart
Do so;
Do so now !
As the clouds float
Home to their rain-drenched
Caverns behind the hills.

If this is the time
To master my heart
Let me fall an easy victim
To the pleasures that you hold to my lips
When the duiker
Lingers along the pool to drink
And the ailing leopard
Turns its dry unbelieving snout away;
When the dew-drops dry
Unnoticed on the sinews of the leaf
And the soft-paddling duck
Webs its way
Through the subtle
Entanglement of weeds
Along the River Prah.

Oh, I remember the songs
You sang that night
And the whirl of raffia skirts;
The speechless pulsation of living bones :

Oh I remember the songs you sang
Recounting what has gone before
And what is ours beyond
The tracks of our thoughts and feet.

You sang of beautiful women
Flirting with sportive spirits
Red-eyed, with red lips hoary-red
With quaffing of frequent libations;
You sang of feasts and festivals and
The red blood-line across the necks
Of sacrificial sheep;
Of acceptance and refusal of gifts;
Of sacrifices offered and withheld;

Of good men and their lot;
Of good name and its loss; of the die cast
And the loading of the dice;
Why the barndog barked
At the moon as she sang
And why the mouse dropped the pearl-corn
From its teeth and stood forced-humble
With the soft light of fear in its eyes.

I saw a sheen of light
On the soft belly of the leaves
Dream-worn in the night
Bright as the light
Defending day from night,
And palm-wine as clear
As the path of a spirit as water,
And her hair like the dark eyes of an eagle
Over the affairs of men.

And yet the river rolled on
And passed over rocks,
White sand in the bed
Bearing the burden of rotten wood
Twigs, grass – a flower – the breath
Of the soil and the bones of thousands
Who should have lived
To fight a war for this or that
And this or that a ruse
To deceive the mover of the move
And the mover of the move
Always moved by uncertainty.

And yet to fight
And yet to die or conquer
This was the badge we bore
On the pale texture
Of our hearts.
And yet to fight
And yet to conquer.

The sea-gulls blow
Like paper-pieces over the hard blue sea
And yet we live to conquer.
So we talk of wars
With their women
And yet they wept at the foot of the hills.

And the waters rolled on.
And what was old was new
And what was new never came to stay,
But to skim the gates of change;
Forever new; forever old and new:
Once-upon-a-time,
Never the same,
Always at last the same.

And her hair was dark
And her pride undimmed
By the dusty struggles
Of strong men over her shadow
And yet the river rolled on.
And the river rolled on.

Through the folds of her cloth
Her thigh slipped-slipped
As always, once-upon-a-time.
But those who slept with her
In those mud huts
(Arrows in their grips
And bows on their shoulders)
Have crawled away soft-bellied
Into hollow chambers
Along the road;
Lined their walls
With smooth white stones;
Abandoned the shade
That sheltered their peace
And call that peace of mind
Now floating away with the clouds
As peace –
That passes understanding.

And the clouds float home
To their rain-drenched
Caverns behind the hills
And that peace continues
To pass understanding.
   If this is the time
To master our hearts
Do so;
Do so now.

Christina Ama Ata Aidoo

THE MESSAGE

'Look here my sister, it should not be said but they say they opened her up.'

'They opened her up?'

'Yes, opened her up.'

'And the baby removed?'

'Yes, baby removed.'

'I say ! . . .'

'They do not say, my sister.'

– Have you heard it?

– What?

'This and this and this. . . .'

'A-a-ah ! that is it. . . .'

'Meewuo !'

'They don't say meewuo . . .'

'And how is she?'

'Am I not here with you? Do I know the highway which leads to Cape Coast?'

'Hmm. . . .'

'And anyway how can she live? How is it like even giving birth with a stomach which is whole . . . eh? . . . eh? . . . I am asking you. And if you are always standing on the brink of death who go to war with your stomach whole, then how would she do whose stomach is open to the winds?'

'Oh, poo, pity . . .'

'I say . . .'

– O, sometimes leave me alone, leave me alone . . . I thought now I would have peace, just a little peace.

'And I say, where is the little bundle I made? . . . Here, come to my back. You and I are going to Cape Coast today.'

– Cape Coast! how long ago it is when I went there. . . .You have pursued me all my life. What is it that I alone have done, that even now that I have grown very old you still pursue me? None of the three marriages I entered into worked for me. . . . But even that did not matter. If I had only got my little ones . . . but no. Would they allow them to grow up? How many were they? I have even forgotten but certainly more than ten . . . they snatched them up one by one, sleeping, playing, in the stream – the farm. . . . They wheeled around me day by day like kites . . . until, now I must make a journey to Cape Coast, which I have not seen for thirty years, because they have slit my little one up. She has eaten the knife, my child; oh I must not think about it. Did they cut her navel up too? I remember, it did not heal quickly at all, when her cord was cut and since a scar is a scar . . . perhaps it hurt her. Oh, my child. . . .

– I only hope they will give me her body. . . .

'My little bundle, come. You and I are going to Cape Coast to-day.' – I am taking one of her own cloths with me just in case. These people on the coast do not know how to do a thing and I am not going to have anybody mishandling my child's body. I hope they give it to me. Horrible things I have heard done to people's bodies. Cutting them up and using them for teaching others. . . . Even murderers still have decent burials. . . .

I see Mensima coming. . . . And there is Nkama too . . . and Adwoa Meenu . . . Now they are coming to . . . 'poo pity me . . .' witches, witches, witches . . . they have picked mine up while theirs prosper around them, children, grandchildren and great-grandchildren, theirs shoot up like mushrooms. . . .

'Esi, we have heard of your misfortune. . . .'

'That our little lady's womb has been opened up . . .'

'And her baby removed . . .'

'Thank you very much.'

'Has she lived through it?'

'I do not know.'

'Esi, bring her here, back home whatever happens.'

'Yoo, thank you. But get your things ready. If the government's people allow it, I shall bring her home.'

'And have you got ready your things?'

'Yes . . . No.'

– I cannot even think straight. It feels so noisy in my head. . . . Oh my little child . . . I mean the things which were ready for myself. There is the coffin which is in Kwame Hofo's room. Then there is a whole twelve-piece of silk-loin-cloth. Esi deserves something better for she lived on the coast all the time but the flour is already in the sand . . . I am wasting time. . . . And so I am going. . . .

'Yes, to Cape Coast. . . . No, I do not know anyone there now but do you think no one would show me the way to this big hospital . . . if I ask around? . . . Hmmmm . . . it's me has ended up like this. I was thinking that everything is all right now . . . Yoo. And thank you too. Shut the door for me when you are leaving. You may stay too long out if you wait for me, so go home and be about your business. I will let you know when I bring her in.'

'Maami Otua, where are you going?'

'My daughter, I am going to Cape Coast.'

'And what is our old mother going to do with such swift steps? Is it serious?'

'My daughter, it is very serious.'

'Mother, may God go with you.'

'Yoo, my daughter.'

'Eno, and what calls at this hour of the day?'

'They want me at Cape Coast.'

'Does my friend want to go and see how much Oguaa has changed since we went there to meet the new Wesleyan Chairman, twenty years ago?'

'My sister do you think I have knees to go parading on the streets of Cape Coast?'

'Is it heavy?'

'Yes, very heavy indeed. They have opened up my grandchild at the hospital, hi, hi, hi. . . .'

'Eno due, due due . . . I did not know. May God go with you . . .'

'Thank you Yaa.'

'Oh, the world?'

'It's her grandchild. The only daughter of her only son. Do you remember Kojo Amisa who went to Soja and fell in the great war, overseas?'

'Yes, it's his daughter. . . .'

'. . . Oh, poo, pity.'

'Kobina, run to the street, tell Draba Anan to wait for Nana Otua.'

'. . . Draba Anan, Draba, my mother says I must come and tell you to wait for Nana Otua.'

'And where is she?'

'There she comes.'

'Oh, just look at how she hops like a bird . . . does she think we are going to be here all day? And anyway we are full already . . .'

'Oh, you drivers! No respect for anybody. . . .'

'What have drivers done?'

'And do you think it shows respect when you speak in this way? It is only that things have not gone right but she is old enough, at least, to be your mother. . . .'

'But what have I said? I have not insulted her. I only think that only youth must be permitted to see Cape Coast, the town of the Dear and the Expensive. . . .'

'And do you think she is going on a peaceful journey? Her only granddaughter, child of her only son, has been opened up and her baby removed from her womb.'

Oh . . . God.

Oh . . .

Oh . . .

Oh . . .

Poo, pity.

'Me . . . poo – pity. I am right about our modern wives. I always say they are useless compared with our mothers.'

'You drivers !'

'Now what have your modern wives done?'

'Aren't I right what I always say about them? You go and watch them in the big towns. All so thin and dry as sticks – you can literally blow them away with your breath. No decent flesh anywhere. Wooden chairs groan when they meet with their hard exteriors.'

'Oh you drivers . . .'

'But of course all drivers . . .'

'What have I done? Don't all my male passengers agree with me? These modern girls. . . . Now here is one who cannot even have a baby in a decent way. But must have the baby removed from her stomach. Tchiaa !'

'What. . . .'

'Here is the old woman.'

'Whose grandchild . . .?'

'Yes.'

'Oh, Nana, I hear you are coming to Cape Coast with us.'

'Yes my master.'

'We nearly left you behind but we heard it was you and that it is a heavy journey you are making.'

'Yes my master . . . thank you my master.'

'Push up, please . . . push up. Won't you push up? Why do you all sit looking at me with such eyes as if I was a block of wood? It is not that there is nowhere to push up to. Five fat women should go on that seat but look at you ! And our old grandmother here is none too plump herself . . . Nana if they won't push, come to the front seat with me.'

'. . . Hei, scholar, go to the back.'

'. . . And do not scowl on me. I know your sort too well. Something tells me you do not have any job at all. As for that suit you are wearing and looking so grand in, you hired or borrowed it . . .'

'Oh you drivers !'

Oh you drivers. . . .

– The scholar who read this telegram thing said it was made about three days ago. . . . Three days . . . Oh God – that is too long ago. Have they buried her . . . where? or did they cut her up. . . . Oh I should not think about it . . . or something will happen to me. Eleven or twelve . . . Efua Panyin, Okuma, Kwame Gyasi and who else? It is so long ago. I cannot even count them now. . . . But they should have left me here. Sometimes . . . ah, I hate this nausea. But it is this smell of petrol. Now I have remembered I never could travel neatly in a lorry. I always was so sick. But now I hope at least that will not happen. These young people will think it is because I am old and they will laugh. . . . At least if I knew the child of my child was alive, it would have been good. And the little things she sent me. . . . Sometimes some people like Mensima and Nkansa make me feel as if I had been a barren woman instead of only a one whom death took away. . . .

– I will give her that set of earrings, bracelet and chain which Odwumfo Ata made for me. It is the most beautiful and the most expensive thing I have. . . . It does not hurt me to think that I am going to die very soon and have them and their children gloating over my things. After all what did they swallow my children for? It does not hurt me at all. If I had been someone else, I would have given them all away before I died. But it does not matter. They can share their own curse. Now, that is the end of me and my roots . . . Eternal death has worked like a warrior rat, with diabolical sense of duty, to gnaw at my bottom. Everything is finished now. The vacant lot is swept and the scraps of old sugar-cane pulp, dry sticks and bunches of hair burnt . . . how it reeks the smoke! . . .

'Oh, Nana do not weep. . . .'

'Is the old woman weeping?'

'If the only child of your only child died, wouldn't you weep?'

'Why do you ask me? Did I know her grandchild is dead?'

'Where have you been, not in this lorry? Where were you when we were discussing. . . .'

'I do not go putting my mouth in other people's affairs. . . .'

'So what?'

'So go and die . . .'

'Hei, hei, it is prohibited to quarrel in my lorry.'

'Draba, here is me, sitting quiet and this lady of muscles and bones being cheeky to me....'

'Look, I can beat you ...'

'Beat me ... beat me ... let's see.'

'Hei, you are not civilized, eh?'

'Keep quiet and let us think, both of you, or I will put you down....'

'Nana, do not weep. There is God above.'

'Thank you my master.'

'But we are in Cape Coast already.'

– Meewuo! My God, hold me tight or something will happen to me.

'My master, I will come down here.'

'Oh Nana. I thought you said you are going to the hospital.... We are not there yet.'

'I am saying maybe I will get down here and ask my way around.'

'Nana, you do not know these people, eh? They are very impudent here. Sit down, I will take you there.'

'Are you going there, my master?'

'No, but I will take you there.'

'Ah, my master, your old mother thanks you. Do not shed a tear when you hear of my death.... My master, your old mother thanks you.'

– I hear there is somewhere where they keep corpses until their owners claim them ... if she has been buried, I must find her husband.... Esi Amfoa, what did I come to do under this sky.... I have buried all my children and now I am going to bury my grandchild!

'Nana we are there.'

'Is this the hospital?'

'Yes, Nana. What is your child's name?'

'Esi Amfoa. His father named her after me.'

'Do you know her English name?'

'No, my master.'

'What shall we do? ...'

'... Er lady, we are looking for somebody.'

'You are looking for somebody and can you read? If you cannot you must ask somebody what the rules in the hospital are. You can only come and visit people at three o'clock.'

'Lady, please. She was my only grandchild . . .'

'Who? And anyway, it is none of our business . . .'

'Oh, Nana, you must be patient . . . and not cry. . . .'

'Old woman, why are you crying, it is not allowed here. No one must make any noise here !'

'My lady, I am sorry but she was all I had.'

'Who? . . . Oh, are you the old woman who is looking for somebody?'

'Yes.'

'Who is he?'

'She was my granddaughter – the only child of my son.'

'I mean, what was her name?'

'Esi Amfoa.'

'Esi Amfoa . . . Esi Amfoa. I am very sorry, we do not have anyone whom they call like that.'

'Is that it?'

'Nana, I told you they may know only her English name here.'

'My master, what shall we do then?'

'What is she ill with?'

'She came here to have a child. . . . And they say, they opened her stomach and removed the baby . . .'

'Oh . . . oh, I see.'

– My Lord, hold me tight so that nothing will happen to me now.

'I see. It is the Caesarean case . . .'

'Nurse, you know her?'

– And when I take her back, Anona Ebusuafo will say that I did not wait for them to come with me. . . .

'Yes. Are you her brother?'

'No. I am only the driver who brought the old woman.'

'Did she bring all her clan?'

'No. She came alone.'

– Strange thing for a villager to do.

– I hope they have not cut her up already.

'Did she bring a whole bag full of cassava and plantain and kenkey?'

'No. She has only her little bundle.'

'Follow me. But you must not make any noise. This is not the hour for coming here. . . .'

'My master, does she know her?'

'Yes.'

– I hear it is very cold where they put them . . .

It was feeding time for new babies. When old Esi Amfoa saw her young granddaughter Esi, the latter was all neat and nice. White sheets and all. She did not see the beautiful stitches under the sheets. 'This woman is a tough bundle,' Dr Gyamfi had declared after the identical twins had been removed, the last stitches had been threaded off and Mary Koomson, alias Esi Amfoa, had come to.

The old woman somersaulted into the room and lay groaning, not screaming, by the bed. For was not her last pot broken?

– So they lay them in state even in hospitals and not always cut them up for instruction?

The Nursing Sister was furious. Young Esi Amfoa spoke.

And this time Old Esi Amfoa wept loud and hard. Wept all her tears.

Scrappy nurse-under-training Jessy Treeson, second-generation Cape Coaster, said, 'As for these villagers,' and giggled.

Draba Anan looked hard at Jessy Treeson, her starched uniform, apron and cap . . . and then dismissed them all . . . 'Such a cassava stick . . . but maybe I will break my tongue if I licked at her buttocks . . .' he thought . . .

And by the bed the old woman was trying hard to rise and look at the pot which had refused to get broken.

George Awoonor-Williams

REDISCOVERY

When our tears are dry on the shore
and the fishermen carry their nets home
and the seagulls return to bird island
and the laughter of the children recedes at night,
there shall still linger the communion we forged
the feast of oneness whose ritual we partook of.
There shall still be the eternal gateman
who will close the cemetery doors
and send the late mourners away.
It cannot be the music we heard that night
that still lingers in the chambers of memory.
It is the new chorus of our forgotten comrades
and the halleluyahs of our second selves.

Kenya

Kuldip Sondhi

BAD BLOOD

It was hardly a village. Five mud huts in a clearing. In the day-time the women snoozed away the hours, gossiping under the shade till the evening, deglamourized, plain creatures. Later when darkness set in they dressed up. With moonlight dripping through the grove and lights glowing deep inside their huts the aspect changed. It was alluring with music and shrill laughter mingling with the murmur of male jests.

The women looked dark and viperish from this distance, purple-hued harpies, swaying, laughing, enticing strangers into their open doorways. Their chatter floated like a net over the grove. It set his pulses racing. The one he sought was among them. He had heard rumours of her – a fabulous creature lighting up the wilderness with her fair skin and flowing black hair. What luck if she actually existed! Thrusting aside the fistful of branches hiding him he walked over to a solitary hut set apart from the others. The old woman in its doorway looked up at his approach.

'Jambo Mama Mzee,' Manju said softly.

'Jambo,' she returned eyeing him. He stood before her smiling, allaying her fears.

'Have you been here before?' she asked presently, intrigued by his shy manner and good looks.

'No, this is my first visit,' he confessed, 'how far from town is it!' He sat down on the edge of her cot, a lean tall youth with frizzy, black hair. She accepted a cigarette from his pack and inhaled deeply. They smoked in silence for a while.

The grove looked bewitched, transformed by the alchemy of darkness into a night-world of flaring tapers and moving shadows heavy with the musk of tropical blooms.

'I wonder who this place belongs to?' he ventured after a while.

'To whom – to me of course.'

'All of it?'

'Yes. The coconut trees, the mangoes, everything you see on it. The girls pay me rent for using those huts,' she added meaningfully.

'You must be very rich.'

The old woman glanced at him, funnelling smoke through her lips. But he looked grave and properly attentive.

'Everyone thinks me rich,' she said with sudden bitterness, 'but of what good is this money while I live in the bush like any shenzi woman? If that girl were different we could live in Mombasa, and be respectable people. Have you ever seen Miriam?'

'No Mama!'

She cast away her cigarette. 'Miriam is so white bwana, so white she could be taken for a Mzungu! Miriam could marry a white man and advance in life, but instead she waits every evening for that black ape who comes here as he pleases and treats her like dirt! I do not understand that girl,' she rocked on her cot, 'the blood has turned out bad ... bad!'

'What kabila was her father?'

'What kabila!' the old woman looked angrily at him, 'a white man of course, a great lord who owned land everywhere. He gave me this shamba when he went away ... for years I was like a wife to him.'

'Does your daughter live with you then?'

'No, she lives there.'

'You mean –'

'Yes I mean that!' And as though in answer a loud wail shattered the tranquillity of the night. A lantern swayed, casting agitated shadows in the end hut. Its doorway filled out with the short, broad stature of a man.

'That's him,' hissed the old woman leaning forward.

'And that's Miriam?'

'Yes!'

Manju stared. It was true. She was every bit the woman he had imagined her: small, black-haired, and beautiful as the moon! The sight of the man stabbed him to the heart. 'Is he her husband Mama?'

'You fool – he means nothing to her !'

A crowd collected. The women came running out of their huts. Manju strode across the clearing and thrust his way to the front. His mop of black hair shook with anger. Seizing the stranger's arm he whirled him round and grabbed his shirt front, 'What do you mean by striking that woman? She is not your wife !'

A shocked murmur rippled through the crowd. 'Answer me,' he repeated, 'what –'

'Let go,' ordered the stranger coolly. He freed himself with a quick jerk. A warning glint came into his eye, 'You do not know me, boy – stand back !'

The crowd retreated, fearful of sudden violence. But Miriam barred his way, 'And what do you really know of me, you monkey?' she screamed. 'You think everyone is afraid of you because you are an inspector !'

'He had no right,' exclaimed a shrill voice from the crowd.

'She takes his money !' answered another. An altercation broke out. Partisans joined in. Words flew, infuriating, wounding, raising passions and exciting tempers. The stranger folded his arms. He stood at the centre of the storm, muscular and strong. There was a glistening blackness about him which was awesome to behold. His gaze rested finally on Manju. And Manju stared back with ill-concealed hatred.

'He thinks of me only in terms of money,' Miriam confided coming swiftly to her rescuer's side. 'I know that, well let him pay me then – let us understand each other !'

'What is there to understand about you?' said the man overhearing her. 'Money is all you know. Every wriggle, every thrust means another shilling to you, out of my way you whore !'

'Let him go,' hissed Manju pale with rage. He seized her arm and held her back, 'I will give you all you need and more.'

The stranger regarded him in silence for a moment. Then he strode off without another word.

His sudden departure dampened the excitement. Peace of a kind returned to the grove, and from her doorway the old woman watched a light sway again at the back of her daughter's hut. She shook her head in despair. Now there were two black men !

Manju followed Miriam into her room. 'Not your husband?' he repeated full of misgivings. 'But he acted like one – admit it Miriam!'

Miriam shrugged and gazed at herself in the mirror. Her dress was crumpled and she looked dishevelled, but she was beautiful. Nothing could change that. He sat down on her bed.

It was a small hot room with a wooden door and a high grating for ventilation. 'You are right, he acted like one but he isn't my husband,' she said picking up a comb and pulling it through her hair. 'Mwangi started coming here six months ago. At first he was nice and spoke kindly to me and I received him like I would anyone else. But then his visits became frequent and he began to get rough. I hate men who get rough and soon he began to demand me free of charge as though I were a drink of someone's beer!' She whirled, 'So I told that inspector to stop coming here any more and that's when he slapped me!'

'Is that what happened tonight?' Manju demanded, unable to take his eyes off her.

'Yes,' she shrugged, 'Mwangi thinks everyone is afraid of him . . . and women are all whores in his eyes –' she put in a centre parting, shaking her hair lightly and pinned a flower behind each ear. 'Did you not see the way he stands and struts,' she marched up and down the room holding her comb and blowing out her cheeks, 'but he knows I am not afraid of him . . . and I am not!' She opened her blouse and dabbed musk from a small grey bottle on her shoulders, 'I hate him!'

Manju sighed. She turned and studied him thoughtfully for a moment, suddenly concerned for his feelings. A childish smile transformed her face. She seized his hands and sat down next to him, 'You are much better than him, you are kind. I know what you think of me but you should not, you do not know me yet.' She laid her head on his shoulder and whispered, 'If a man comes to me just to quench his thirst why should he not pay? You are going to pay me and he is no different, so he should pay too!'

She nuzzled closer. Her breath stung his cheek. She put a hand on his knee. 'But your mother is rich,' he brought out, 'there is no need for you to do all this – she told me so!'

'My mother talked to you?' she exclaimed jumping up. 'What do you know of her, you fool – that old woman is the devil herself!'

'. . . I was only saying what she told me,' he stammered. 'Is she not your mother?'

'I hate my mother,' her pale blue eyes glittered in the lamplight, 'more than anyone else in the world!'

'How was I to know that?' he muttered wishing he had never brought up the subject.

'She wants me to marry a white man . . . my father was a white man so I should marry one too, any white man will do, even a sailor from one of the bars in Mombasa!'

Manju shook his head. He did not know which one to believe. This one who stood before him with half-naked breasts and flowers in her hair or that old crone grieving on her cot. 'My mother fights me all the time,' she went on angrily, 'so what am I to do – starve? Marry a man I would hate? None of them, because Miriam will do as she pleases, bwana!' But her anger subsided, as swiftly as it had flared. She gazed at him and nodded approvingly. Her teeth flashed in a smile. Dazed he drew her close. She placed both hands on his shoulders and kissed him, a long lingering kiss that sent shudders down his spine and drove ideas through his brain.

'Listen to me,' he whispered, 'you must give up all this and I will support you, I will give you all the money you need because . . . we are really of the same kabila!'

'What?' she looked at him in surprise.

'Yes. I never saw my father but my mother told me, he was a white man and I believe it to be true. I feel different to the others. Can you not see it?'

'Certainly you are not as black as the others . . .' she leaned back to survey him better, piqued by the reddish glow in his complexion, 'and your face too . . . yes I can see it!'

His heart sank. He glanced at her and knew that she was taunting him. She saw in him only what the others saw: an African with a touch of Arab perhaps, a coastal Swahili like the others on the coast. No more. In her eyes he was no different to any other man.

'My mother is a Mkamba and I have never called myself any

other,' he said bitterly, 'it is only in you that I have confided, I thought you would understand.'

'But I do,' she ran a consoling hand over his head and pouted, 'I do understand.'

He felt sick. Degraded. Then fierce youthful determination welled up in him. If she did not see the difference between him and the others who came to her then he would make her see it. By deeds not words! He pulled out his wallet. The feel of it gave him a moment's pause. It was all he had. Deprived of his pay a month's privation lay in store for him. But the thought of holding back anything now repelled him. He was not like the others – she had to see that. It would be all or nothing! He emptied his wallet fully. A hundred and eighty shillings in notes fell out. He pushed the heap over to her, 'There Miriam, you take this – but remember one thing –'

'Yes bwana?' she gazed wonderingly at him, frightened somewhat now. Giving her all his money like that!

'Promise me never to see him again,' he said slowly, 'him or any other. If you do that I will give you all the money I ever earn and we will live together in Mombasa. Forget this filthy existence. My pay is enough for both.'

'For both?' she looked at him in surprise, putting the money away in her skirt. 'I do not understand, are you asking me to live with you?'

'Yes.'

She opened her eyes, 'To be your wife?'

'Yes, that is it, to be my wife!'

'But . . . why?' she stared at him in amazement.

'I told you why only you do not understand, but you will one day. We will have children of our own and this life will be forgotten like a bad dream.'

'How different you are to Mwangi,' she sighed, 'he never talked to me like that.'

The hard light went out of his eyes. His face softened, 'You will learn that not all men are alike,' he said, 'I will look after you, Miriam.'

'We will live in our own house.'

'Yes.'

'And I will get all the clothes I want?'

'Yes, yes . . . everything I have will be yours – ha ! what is that?'

'What, where?' A panicky look shot into her eyes. She jumped up and peeped into the clearing outside, her face pressed tight against the grating.

'It's them, you must hide !' she jumped down and ran to the door slipping the crossbar into place. Voices boomed in the corridor. Footsteps sounded in its narrow confines.

'Let us in,' commanded a voice.

'There,' she pointed frantically under the four-poster bed, 'hide.'

'Open the door, Miriam !' shouted the law, her flimsy barricade shuddering under their hammering.

'Let them in,' said Manju quietly. She shot him an angry glance and raised the crossbar. Mwangi strode in. He was in police inspector's uniform. His companion, a tall thin askari in hobnailed boots, waited outside.

'We are on duty, let that be clearly understood,' said the inspector blandly looking about the room, 'we are carrying out a search for people who have not paid poll tax, that is all !'

Miriam turned away.

'You collect poll tax at night?' retorted Manju.

'Why not, is there an hour to catch criminals?'

'Do not waste your time, bwana,' called the askari from the corridor, 'it is an offence.' He poked his head in, tall as a giraffe. A grin split his big mouth, 'Produce your tax receipt and be done with it, man.'

Manju took out his wallet again and extracted some papers from it. He laid them on the bed and crossed his arms, 'There, have a good look, bwana mkubwa inspector !'

The inspector sat down and crossed his legs. He stroked his short black moustache and scrutinized the papers one by one. He was handsome, this brute of a man, Manju noticed with surprise. In close-fitting police uniform he looked the epitome of masculine power. His presence filled the room. 'Good,' he handed back the papers and twirled his swagger stick, 'anything else to show?'

'Why should there be?'

'Nothing else to show?'

'No.'

'In that case you can come and spend the night with us.'

'You will be the serikali's guest,' chuckled the askari, entering the room. There was a clink of iron as he took out a pair of hand-cuffs.

'I have not committed any crime,' said Manju slowly, 'why should I come with you?'

'Then show me this year's tax receipt,' rapped the inspector standing up, 'have you got it?'

'But it is not due yet! There is another month to go for those who live in Mombasa.'

'This is not Mombasa. You are five miles outside the municipal limits, on the other side of the ferry in the Likoni district. Here poll tax is overdue.'

He pulled out his own wallet and took out a yellow chit from it, 'See, I have paid, have you?'

'I will pay from next month's salary.'

'You cannot leave Likoni without paying your poll tax.'

'The serakali allows you to pay your tax immediately if you are caught,' suggested the askari helpfully, 'you can pay now if you have the money.'

'That is true.'

'I will pay,' said the woman coming out of her corner, 'how much is it?' she lifted her skirt and took out the money.

'Forty-five shillings,' chuckled the askari. The inspector watched her counting out the money in stunned silence, 'Why are you paying, Miriam?' he blurted out, 'this has nothing to do with you.'

'Why not, he has a good heart and would help me if I asked him.'

'But . . . I don't understand you,' he stammered.

'Don't pay,' said Manju huskily, 'don't pay him for me. I will go to jail and be happy if I know you are waiting for me.'

'Here,' she thrust the notes into the inspector's hand, 'forty-five shillings, take it and be off!' She turned away abruptly.

'She has saved him,' echoed the askari, 'did you see that bwana Mwangi, she gave this money from her own body!'

The inspector took off his cap and sat down. Lighting a cigarette he blew out the smoke and was silent a long while. None spoke when he raised his eyes and looked steadily at the woman. She blushed and looked back at him.

'Take this, Miriam,' he said softly, holding out his cigarette to her, 'it is all I have to offer you now.'

Manju glanced at them and left the room. The askari followed him out into the clearing. He was more than amused. 'She looks white enough to be a Mzungu,' he mused, 'what kind of blood does that woman have?'

'Bad blood, her mother says,' Manju sighed, and walked away.

Joseph E. Kariuki

NEW LIFE

It will rain tonight,
I smell it in the air,
And how we have waited.

My love said she would come with the rain.

A gentle knock at the door –
Palpable thudding in my breast.

A gust of wind blows out the tiny candle,
A momentary torrential outburst,
Then a flash that lights up
Scorching eyes.
A crack to end the world :
An unbearable brief eternity of silence
And then the rain.

It comes heaving, tearing, bearing down,
Surging in impatient billows to drain its source,
Till unable to bear its own forces
It settles to a timeless steady flow
Endless.

There is calm in the air,
And greater calm by my side.

Tomorrow the village women go planting
Their seed in the hungry ground :
And life is born anew.

Grace Ogot

TEKAYO

The period of short rains was just starting in a semi-arid part of the Sudan. The early-morning mist had just cleared, and faint blue smoke rose from the ground as the hot sun touched the surface of the wet earth.

'The people in the underworld are cooking !
People in the underworld are cooking !'

the children shouted as they pelted one another with wet sand.

'Come on, Opija,' Tekayo shouted to his son. 'Give me a hand, I must get the cows to the river before it is too hot.'

Opija hit his younger brother with his last handful of sand, and then ran to help his father. The cows were soon out of the village and Tekayo picked up the leather pouch containing his lunch and followed them.

They had not gone far from home when Tekayo saw an eagle flying above his head with a large piece of meat in its claws. The eagle was flying low searching for a suitable spot to have its meal. Tekayo promptly threw his stick at the bird. He hit the meat and it dropped to the ground. It was a large piece of liver, and fresh blood was still oozing from it. Tekayo nearly threw the meat away, but he changed his mind. What was the use of robbing the eagle of its food only to throw it away? The meat looked good : it would supplement his vegetable lunch wonderfully. He wrapped the meat in a leaf and pushed it into his pouch.

They reached a place where there was plenty of grass. Tekayo allowed the cows to graze while he sat under an *ober* tree watching the sky. It was not yet lunch time, but Tekayo could not wait. The desire to taste that meat was burning within him. He took out the meat and roasted it on a log fire under the *ober* tree. When the meat was cooked he ate it greedily with millet bread which his wife had made the previous night.

'My! What delicious meat,' Tekayo exclaimed. He licked the fat juice that stained his fingers, and longed for a little more. He threw away the bitter herbs that were the rest of his lunch. The meat was so good, and the herbs would merely spoil its taste.

The sun was getting very hot, but the cows showed no desire to go to the river to drink. One by one they lay down in shades, chewing the cud. Tekayo also became overpowered by the afternoon heat. He rested against the trunk and slept.

While asleep, Tekayo had a dream. He was sitting before a log fire roasting a large piece of liver like the one he had eaten earlier. His mouth watered as he watched rich fat from the roasting meat dripping into the fire. He could not wait, and although the meat was not completely done, he removed it from the fire and cut it up with his hunting knife. But just as he was about to take the first bite, he woke up.

Tekayo looked around him wondering what had happened to the meat! Could it be that he was dreaming? 'No, no, no,' he cried. 'It was too vivid to be a dream!' he sat upright and had another look around, as if by some miracle he might see a piece of liver roasting on the log fire beside him. But there was nothing. All he saw were large roots of the old tree protruding above the earth's surface like sweet potatoes in the sandy soil.

The cattle had wandered a long way off. Tekayo got up and followed them. They reached the river bank, and the thirsty cows ran to the river. While the cows drank, Tekayo sat on a white stone cooling his feet and gazing lazily at the swollen river as it flowed mightily towards the plain.

Beyond the river stood the great 'Ghost Jungle'. A strong desire for rich meat came back to Tekayo, and he whispered, 'The animal with that delicious liver must surely be in that jungle.' He sat there for a while, thinking. The temptation to start hunting for the animal bothered him. But he managed to suppress it. The afternoon was far spent and they were a long way from home.

The next morning Tekayo left home earlier than usual. When

his wife begged him to wait for his lunch, he refused. He hurried from home, taking his hunting spears with him.

Tekayo made it impossible for the cows to graze. He rushed them along, lashing at any cow that lingered in one spot for long. They reached the edge of the 'Ghost Jungle', and there he left the cows grazing unattended.

Tekayo could not see any path or track leading into the 'Ghost Jungle'. The whole place was a mass of thick bush and long grass covered with the morning dew. And except for the sounds of mating birds, there was a weird silence in the jungle that frightened him. But the vehement desire within him blindly drove him on, through the thick wet grass.

After walking for some time, he stood and listened. Something was racing towards him. He turned round to look, and sure enough a big impala was running frantically towards him. Warm blood rushed through Tekayo's body, and he raised his spear to kill the animal. But the spear never landed. He came face to face with a big leopardess that was chasing the impala. The leopardess roared at Tekayo several times, challenging him, as it were, to duel. But Tekayo looked away, clutching the spear in his trembling hand. There was no one to fight and the beast went away after her prey.

'What a bad start,' Tekayo said slowly and quietly, when his heart beat normally again.

'That wild cat will not leave me alone now.'

He started to walk back towards the plain, following the track he had made. The sight of the leopardess had taken the life out of him.

He saw another track that cut across the forest. He hesitated a little, and then decided to follow it, leaving his own. The track got bigger and bigger, and without any warning Tekayo suddenly came upon a baby wildebeest which was following a large flock grazing at the foot of the hill. He killed it without any difficulty. He skinned the animal and extracted its liver, leaving the rest of the carcass there.

Tekayo returned to the herd, and he sat down to roast the meat on a log fire. When the meat was cooked, he took a bite and chewed it hurriedly. But he did not swallow it : he spat it all out ! The liver was as bitter as the strongest green herbs given to constipated children. The back of his tongue felt as if it had been burned. Tekayo threw the rest of the meat away and took his cows home.

He arrived home tired and disappointed; and when his young wife set food before him, he refused to eat. He pretended that he had stomach-ache and did not feel like eating. That night Tekayo was in low spirits. He did not even desire his young wife who slept by his side. At dawn the young wife returned to her hut disappointed, wondering why her man did not desire her.

The doors of all huts were still closed when Tekayo looked out through his. A cold east wind hit his face, and he quickly shut himself in again.

It was getting rather late and the calves were calling. But it was raining so much that he could not start milking. He sat on the hard bed looking at the dead ashes in the fire-place. He longed to get out to start hunting.

When the rain stopped, Tekayo milked the cows in a great hurry. He then picked up the lunch that had been left near his hut for him, and left the village. The wife he had disappointed the previous night watched him till he disappeared at the gate.

When he reached the 'Ghost Jungle', it was drizzling again. The forest looked so lonely and wet. He left the cows grazing as usual, and entered the bush, stealing his way through the dripping leaves. He turned to the left to avoid the thick part of the jungle. Luck was with him. He spotted a family of antelope grazing not far from him. He crawled on his knees till he was quite close to them, and then threw his spear, killing one animal instantly. After skinning it, he extracted its liver, and also took some delicate parts for the family.

When he sat down under the tree to roast the meat, Tekayo was quite sure that he had been successful. But when he took the meat, he shook his head. The meat was tender, but it was not what he was looking for.

They reached the river bank. The cows continued to graze after drinking, and Tekayo, without realizing it, wandered a long way from his herd, still determined to discover the owner of that won- derful liver. When he suddenly looked round, the herd was nowhere to be seen. The sun was sinking behind Mount Pajulu, and Tekayo started to run, looking for his cows.

The cows, heavy with milk, had gone home without Tekayo. For one day when Tekayo's children got lost in the forest, the cows had gone without them, following the old track they knew well. On that day the whole village came out in search of the children in fear that the wild animals might harm them.

It was getting dark when Tekayo arrived home. They started to milk and Odipo remarked, 'Why Father, you are late coming home today.'

'It is true,' replied Tekayo thoughtfully. 'See that black bull there? He went to another herd across the river. I didn't miss him until it was time to come home. One of these days, we shall have to castrate him – he is such a nuisance.'

They milked in silence until one of the family girls came to fetch some milk for preparing vegetables.

At supper time the male members of the family sat round the log fire waiting and talking. One by one, baskets of millet meal and earthen dishes of meat and vegetables arrived from different huts. There was fish, dried meat, fried white ants, and herbs. A little food was thrown to the ground, to the ancestors, and then they started eating. They compared and contrasted the deliciousness of the various dishes they were having. But Tekayo kept quiet. All the food he tasted that evening was as bitter as bile.

When the meal was over, the adults told stories of war and the clans to the children, who listened attentively. But Tekayo was not with them : he was not listening. He watched the smoky clouds, as they raced across the sky.

'Behind those clouds, behind those clouds, rests Okenyu, my great-grandfather. Please ! Please !' Tekayo beseeched him. 'Please, Father, take this longing away from me. Give me back my manhood that I may desire my wives. For what is a man without this desire?'

A large cloud covered the moon giving the earth temporary darkness. Tears stung Tekayo's eyes, and he dismissed the family to sleep. As he entered his own hut, a woman was throwing small logs on the fire.

He offered many secret prayers to the departed spirits, but the craving for the mysterious liver never left him. Day after day he left home in the morning, taking his cows with him. And on reaching the jungle he left them unattended while he hunted. The rough and disappointed life that he led soon became apparent to the family. He suddenly became old and uninterested in life. He had nothing to tell his sons around the evening fire, and he did not desire his wives. The sons of Tekayo went to Lakech and told her, 'Mother, speak to Father – he is sick. He does not talk to us, and he does not eat. We don't know how to approach him.'

Though Lakech had passed the age of child-bearing and no longer went to Tekayo's hut at night, she was his first wife, and he loved her. She therefore went and asked him, 'Man, what ails you?' Tekayo looked at Lakech, but he could not look into her eyes. He looked at her long neck, and instead of answering her question he asked her, 'Would you like to get free from those heavy brass rings around your neck?'

'Why?' Lakech replied rather surprised.

'Because they look so tight.'

'But they are not tight,' Lakech said softly. 'I would feel naked without them.'

And Tekayo looked away from his wife. He was longing to tell Lakech everything, and to share with her this maddening craving that was tearing his body into pieces. But he checked himself. Lakech must not know: she would not understand. Then he lied to her.

'It is my old indigestion. I have had it for weeks now. It will soon pass.'

A mocking smile played on Lakech's lips, and Tekayo knew that she was not convinced. Some visitors arrived, and Lakech left her husband.

Tekayo hunted for many months, but he did not succeed in finding the animal with the delicious liver.

One night, as he lay awake, he asked himself where else he could hunt. And what animal would he be looking for? He had killed all the animals in the 'Ghost Jungle'. He had risked his life when he killed and ate the liver of a lion, a leopard and a hyena, all of which were tabooed by his clan.

A little sleep came to Tekayo's heavy eyes and he was grateful. But then Apii stood beside his bed calling: 'Grandpa, Grandpa, it is me.' Tekayo sat up, but the little girl was not there. He went back to sleep again. And Apii was there calling:

'Can't you hear me, Grandpa?'

Tekayo woke up a second time, but nobody was there. He lay down without closing his eyes. Again the child's fingers tickled the skin of the old man. Tekayo sat up a third time, and looked round in the room. But he was alone. The cock crew a third time, and it was morning.

And Lakech died without knowing her husband's secret, and was buried in the middle of the village, being the first wife. Tekayo sat at his wife's grave morning and evening for a long time, and his grief for her appeased his hunger for the unknown animal's liver. He wept, but peacefully, as if his craving for the liver was buried with his wife.

It was during this time of grief that Tekayo decided never to go hunting again. He sat at home and looked after his many grandchildren, while the younger members of the family went out to work daily in the fields.

And then one day as Tekayo sat warming himself in the early-morning sun near the granary, he felt slightly sick from the smell of grain sprouting inside the dark granary. The shouting and singing of his grandchildren attracted his attention. As he watched them playing, Tekayo wondered. . . . Was there a creature on earth whose liver he had not tasted? The old craving returned to him so that his body ached within.

Now among the children playing was a pretty little girl called Apii, the daughter of Tekayo's eldest son. Tekayo sent the other children away to play, and as they were going he called Apii and told her, 'Come, my little one, run to your mother's hut and bring me a calabash of water.'

Apii walked to her mother's hut for the water. While she was fumbling in a dark corner of the house, she was not aware that Tekayo had slipped in fast after her. She felt a pair of rough hands around her neck. The limp body of the child slipped from Tekayo's hands and fell on the floor with a thud. He looked at the body at his feet and felt faint and sick. His ears were buzzing. He picked up the body, and as he staggered out with it, the air seemed black, and the birds of the air screamed ominously at him. But Tekayo had to eat his meal. He buried the body of Apii in a near-by ant-hill in a shallow grave.

The other children were still playing in the field when Tekayo returned with the liver in his bag. He roasted it in his hut hastily and ate it greedily. And alas! it was what he had been looking for for many years. He sat lazily resting his back on the granary, belching and picking his teeth. The hungry children, back from their play in the fields, sat in the shade eating sweet potatoes and drinking sour milk.

The older people came back in the evening, and the children ran to meet their parents. But Apii was not amongst them. In great desperation they asked the grandfather about the child. But Tekayo replied, 'Ask the children – they should know where Apii is. They were playing together in the fields.'

It was already pitch dark. Apii's younger brothers and sisters sat in front of the fire weeping with their mother. It was then they remembered their grandfather sending Apii to fetch water for him. The desperate parents repeated this information to the old man, asking him if Apii had brought water for him that morning.

'She did,' Tekayo replied, 'and then ran away after the others. I watched her go with my own eyes. When they came back, I was asleep.'

The grief-stricken family sat near the fireplace, their heads in their hands. They neither ate nor drank. Outside the little crickets seemed to tell a sad tale. Tekayo felt they were singing much louder than usual.

For many days Apii's parents looked for their child, searching every corner and every nook. But there was no trace of her. Apii was gone. Months went by, and people talked no more about the disappearance of Apii. Only her mother thought of her. She did not lose hope of finding her child alive one day.

Tekayo forgot his deed. And when he killed a second child in the same way so as to satisfy his savage appetite, he was not even conscious of what he was doing. And when the worried parents asked the old man about the child, Tekayo wept saying, 'How could I know? The children play out in the fields – I stay here at home.'

It was after this that Tekayo's sons said among themselves, 'Who steals our children? Which animal can it be? Could it be a hyena? Or a leopard? But these animals only hunt at night. Could it be an eagle, because it hunts during the day? But no! Father would have seen the eagle – he would have heard the child screaming.' After some thought, Aganda told his brothers: 'Perhaps it is a malicious animal brought upon us by the evil spirits.'

'Then my father is too old to watch the children,' put in Osogo. 'Yes, father is too old, he is in danger too,' the rest agreed.

And from that time onwards the sons kept watch secretly on the father and the children. They watched for many months, but nothing threatened the old man and the children.

The sons were almost giving up the watch. But one day it was the turn for Apii's father to keep watch, he saw Tekayo sending away the children to play in the fields – all except one. He sent this child to fetch him a pipe from his hut. As the child ran to the hut, Tekayo followed him. He clasped the frightened child and dragged him towards the fireplace. As Tekayo was struggling with the child, a heavy blow landed on his old back. He turned round sharply, his hands still holding the child's neck. He was facing Aganda, his eldest son. The child broke loose from the limp hands of Tekayo and grabbed Aganda's knees. 'Father!' Aganda shouted.

Seeing that the child was not hurt, Aganda pushed him aside saying, 'Go to your mother's hut and lie down.'

He then got hold of the old man and dragged him towards the little windowless hut built for goats and sheep. As he was being dragged away, the old man kept crying, 'Atimo ang'o? Atimo ang'o?' – 'What have I done? What have I done?'

Aganda pushed the old man into the little hut and barred the door behind him, as you would do to the animals. He went to the child, who was still sobbing.

The rest of the family returned from the fields, and when Apii's father broke the news to them, they were frightened. The family wore mourning garments and went without food.

'Tho! Tho!' they spat towards the sun which, although setting on them, was rising on the ancestors.

'Great-grandfathers, cleanse us,' they all cried.

And they lit the biggest fire that had ever been lit in that village. Tekayo's eldest son took the old greasy drum hanging above the fireplace in his father's hut and beat it. The drum throbbed out sorrowful tunes to warn the clan that there was sad news in Tekayo's home. The people who heard the drum left whatever they were doing and ran to Tekayo's village following the sound of the drum. Within a short time the village was teeming with anxious-looking relatives.

'What news? What news?' they asked in trembling voices.

'And where is Tekayo?' another old man asked.

'Is he in good health?' asked another.

There was confusion and panic.

'Death of death, who will give us medicine for death? Death knocks at your door, and before you can tell him come in, he is in the house with you.'

'Listen!' someone touched the old woman who was moaning about death. Aganda spoke to the people.

'Men of my clan, we have not called you here for nothing. Listen to me and let our sorrow be yours. Weep with us! For several months we have been losing our children when we go to work on the fields. Apii my own child was the first to disappear.' Sobbing broke out among the women at the mention of the children's names.

'My people,' Aganda continued, 'the children in this clan get sick and die. But ours disappear unburied. It was our idea to keep watch over our children that we may catch whoever steals them. For months we have been watching secretly. We were almost giving up because we thought it was probably the wrath of our ancestors that was upon us. But today I caught him.'

'What man? What man?' the people demanded angrily.

'And from what clan is he?' others asked.

'We must declare war on his clan, we must, we must.'

Aganda stopped for a while, and told them in a quavering voice, 'The man is in that little hut. The man is no one else but my father.'

'Mayo!' the women shouted. There was a scuffle and the women and children screamed as if Tekayo was around them, and they were afraid of him. But the men kept quiet.

When the commotion died down, an old man asked, 'Do you speak the truth, man?'

The son nodded. Men and women now shouted, 'Where is the man? Kill him, kill him! He is not one of us. He is an animal!'

There was nothing said outside that Tekayo did not hear. And there in the hut the children he had killed haunted him. He lay his head on the rough wall of the hut and wept.

Outside the hut the angry villagers continued with their demand, shouting, 'Stone him now! Stone him now! Let his blood be upon his own head!'

But one of the old men got up and calmed the people. 'We cannot stone him now. It is the custom of the clan that a wicked man should be stoned in broad daylight, outside the village. We cannot depart from this custom.'

'Stone me now, stone me now,' Tekayo whispered. 'Take me away quickly from this torture and shame; let me die and be finished with.'

Tekayo knew by the angry shouting of the men and the shrill cries of frightened women and children that he was banished from society, nay, from life itself. He fumbled in his leather bag suspended around his waist to find his hunting knife, but it was not there. It had been taken away from him. The muttering and shouting continued outside. There was weeping too. Tekayo was now hearing them from afar as if a powerful wave was carrying him further and further away from his people.

At dawn the villagers got up from the fireplace to gather stones from near-by fields. The sun was not up yet, but it was just light enough to see. Everyone in the clan must throw a stone at the murderer. It was bad not to throw a stone, for it was claimed that the murderer's wicked spirit would rest upon the man who did not help to drive him away.

When the first rays of the sun appeared, the villagers had gathered enough stones to cover several bodies. They returned to the village to fetch Tekayo from the hut, and to lead him to his own garden outside the village. They surrounded the hut and stood in silence, waiting to jeer and spit at him when he came out.

Aganda and three other old men tore the papyrus door open and called Tekayo to come out. But there was no reply. They rushed into the hut to drag him out to the people who were demanding 'Come out, come out!'

At first it was too dark to see. But soon their eyes got used to the darkness. Then they saw the body of Tekayo hanging on a short rope that he had unwound from the thatched roof.

The men came out shaking their heads. The crowd peered into the hut in turns until all of them had seen the dangling body of Tekayo – the man they were preparing to stone. No one spoke. Such a man, they knew, would have to be buried outside the village. They knew also, that no new-born child would ever be named after him.

Congo (Brazzaville)

Felix Tchikaya U'Tam'si

PRESENCE

Having found no man
on my horizon
I played with my body
the ardent poems of death
I followed my river
to the cold and surging billows
I opened myself to the world
of sea weeds
where solitudes crawl
open the markets to solitudes
to the sun
open my flesh
to ripe blood and riots
the breath of sperm transfers me
into the yeast of leaves and storms

and my hair roughened by all the winds
stands on edge
my hands moist to all seeds
carry my feet deep into space
and I resemble slow death with its rich suns

faked presence I shall be unfaithful
for christ the god of armies
has betrayed me
when he allowed his skin to be pierced
treacherous christ
here is my flesh of bronze
and my blood closed

by the numberless – copper and zinc
by the two stones of my brain
eternal through my slow death

perfume of verbena and hind
torments me and I hear voices
born late in the day
day passes zenith
with a learned retinue of crickets
if I indulged myself this were the moment to take leave
but I still have no task

Sylvain Bemba

THE DARK ROOM

I didn't say I liked him: I said I was fascinated by him.
OSCAR WILDE

N'Toko liked taking his hairy face, the face of a bearded, grimacing faun, round the streets of Paris. He was conscious of his ugliness and he derived a sort of secret pleasure from displaying his repulsive features with calm effrontery. He was visibly amused by the shuddering amazement which he caused in the street when he passed other people who turned round to watch the huge Negro walking away. Baggy clothes gave him an outline which was vague, unfinished, blurred, almost ghostly. And yet, when people came to know him better, they were surprised to find that they no longer felt the slightest malaise in his presence. Then they recognized that he had a certain charm, an irresistible magnetism. . . .

N'Toko loved Paris. He still remembered his first days in the famous city. On his arrival he had been disappointed. He had expected to find a *de luxe* work in a handsome gilded binding. Instead, a dismal, dirty sky and sad-looking walls showed him Paris in the guise of an old book found in a box on the quays. The miracle occurred when he began leafing through the worn volume. On every page, at every line, he met the hypnotic gaze of the statues' vacant eyes. He lived again through those centuries of a history which he had learnt at school and whose tide still beat in foaming breakers against the cliffs of modern times.

The first joys N'Toko experienced in Paris were those of a conquistador. He was discovering a new world. In his imagination he deliberately mixed up the over-familiar monuments of the capital. He wanted to discover his own Paris. His first monument was five feet seven inches high; surmounted by a peaked cap, it was hand-

ing back to absent-minded passers-by the way they had lost. Soon
he rediscovered with the joy of an old inhabitant a familiar monument rising to a height of about five feet three inches, irrigated by
two great rivers, coffee and good wine, exporting on a generous
scale voluble words and sweeping gestures, and content with life.
Then he conceived a passion for the Metro. He saw it as a symbol
of physical love and pictured Paris in an indecent posture whenever the underground lament of the two frenzied lovers came
faintly to his ears. A little later, his monuments became talking
dolls which laughed idiotically at the slightest touch and repeated
the same things like a gramophone needle stuck in the groove of a
worn-out record. He amused himself by savaging these dolls, rather
like a child who will not stop until he has destroyed the new toy
whose mechanism he has been trying to understand. And in fact,
he regarded his temporary homeland as a gigantic toy which he
was trying to take to pieces with a vague feeling that he must
revenge himself. On whom, on what? The answer was sleeping
somewhere in his subconscious. . . .

Once again N'Toko stood up and walked unsteadily towards the
juke-box which was shining with all its chromium. He stopped in
front of the machine and began methodically turning out his
pockets. Seen from a distance, he seemed a defenceless figure con-
fronting some threatening animal. Finally he found a coin, examined it carefully and inserted it in a slot. A sort of vague din filled
the air. It reminded him of the dirges of the women mourners in
his own country. Out there, they offered their services free of
charge to bereaved families. Each mourner used the mental picture
of a dead relation to produce a tearful expression, praising the
merits of the deceased in a voice choking with sobs, and thus di-
verting her river of tears towards the family she was assisting.

This produced exactly the same result as the 'jam-session'
which seemed to be welling up from the bowels of the huge music
box.

Perched on stools, two women who looked like fashion models
exchanged a brief glance.

'That record is beginning to get on my nerves,' one of them said in a low voice. 'That's probably the fiftieth time he's played it this afternoon.'

'You know what I think?' replied the other, who had a more practical turn of mind. 'I think that the client is ripe to work on now. I wouldn't have spoken to him for anything when he came in here, he looked so fierce. But I think I'll try him now.'

'Be careful,' the first woman said in a confidential tone of voice; 'the fellow still doesn't strike me as easy to handle, and you risk working for nothing.'

Through a hazy screen N'Toko suddenly saw one of the two fashion-plates coming towards him. He had not paid the slightest attention to these creatures. Their immobolity had made him think that they formed an integral part of the setting. He gave a start when the fashion-plate stopped in front of him and began to speak. He replied with a selection of insults recited with the earnestness of a lesson well learnt. Out of breath, and faced with the woman's impassive smile, he shrugged his shoulders helplessly. He was not going to be able to get rid of this intruder. To hell with these leeches ! And he made a meaningful gesture with his hands. But she was still there. There was nothing left for him to do but capitulate. With a triumphant smile she sat down opposite him and summoned the waiter with a vulgar gesture. She ordered a complicated concoction and drank it with what looked like blissful pleasure.

'Darling,' she said a few moments later, 'I'm going to put on something livelier. Don't you want to dance, honey?'

Later on, when they were in his room, he became more and more disconcerting. His tousled beard and his jerky movements made him look like a broken-down clockwork puppet. He walked up and down, alternately eloquent and cynical. He waved his arms about to impart a certain rhythm to his words.

'You're probably wondering why I don't look at anything but your belly? All through my childhood I never saw anything but my mother's belly. She didn't buy her dresses at Dior's, and all she wore was a little pagne tied round her waist. I was the last child in a large family – I had thirteen brothers, unless I'm mistaken

– and for me my mother's belly was the haven where I took refuge every night, hanging on to the gourds which gave life. That belly warmed me and protected me from the outside world. Today, a woman's belly still has that sort of almost mystic significance for me. The belly, you see, is the seat of a great many social evils such as hunger, cold, fear, unsatisfied desire. You ought to see the bellies of the women in my country! We live in unimaginable poverty, and yet our women have lots of children. It's as if a fellow like me were like a by-product of poverty. Just now, in the bar, you were surprised to see me playing that jazz record over and over again. Why has jazz conquered the world? Because it comes from the very bowels of human suffering. Look, I'm a Catholic, and even if I don't practise my religion any more, I sometimes go into a chapel just to hear religious music. Only, that music was written to serve as a heaven for uplifted souls. What they need in church is music that can also express what bodies suffer. I was reading the other day that in Central Europe some priests have written scores inspired by jazz, to attract the young. What does it matter what their aim is? What interests me is the rehabilitation of Negro music. That's the stone Christ spoke about which is rejected by the builders but which becomes the chief cornerstone. Do you know that in my country, in Africa, black is presented as the colour of sin and evil, and the tom-tom as the instrument of the devil? But everything changes. The tom-tom has made a noisy entry into the African church. Nobody insists any more on the curse which was supposed to lie on the descendants of Ham. From now on, Easter is the colour of an Africa which has succeeded in tipping over the tombstone under which it was buried.'

He stopped to get his breath back, and the woman took the opportunity to say timidly:

'You talk too much, darling. Come and sit down by me.'

'I don't want the Cross to be the only symbol of universal suffering,' he went on without appearing to take any notice of the interruption. 'Why, look at that, there on the wall. What is it?'

The woman looked with a stupid expression on her face, and saw a simple figure in the shape of a hook.

'I can't think what it can be,' she stammered.

A snigger answered her.

'Well, well, we belong to the most intelligent race in the world, and we can't decipher symbols! You're the only exception then. It's true that we aren't in Africa. Out there, it's only the Whites who open the gates of the past. The Negroes can say: "Open, Sesame" as often as they like: nothing opens for them. What the Africans need is to find the magic word themselves which will enable them to move mountains. I would have liked to harness myself to that task, but unfortunately I can't. I've enough to worry about with myself. I'm a bit like that character in Tolstoy who says that he has become his own prison. So you don't know what that picture means? That picture is what I regard as the Cross of the Black world. That kind of hook, in fact, represents a Negro bending his back as a sign of deference or as a sign of suffering under the ill-treatment to which he is subjected. Did you know that the black man is descended from india-rubber?'

The woman no longer had any doubts. The man was mad. She had only one movement to make to reach the door and get out of the room. But she stayed where she was, unable to make much of all these extraordinary words, yet fascinated by such a flow of language.

'Yes,' the Negro went on, 'we are descended from india-rubber, and our great ancestor, if you like, was Michelin, or rather the fellow you see on the posters advertising that brand of tyres. That's why our forefathers and the slaves who were sent to America were able to adapt themselves to a situation that was new to them. Just imagine the deluge which fell on our primitive life for forty days and forty nights, drowning our beliefs and our idols – though only to put others in their place – and washing away everything which made up our world. You might say that the European flood "white-washed" our African life away. Why don't you laugh? Don't you think that's funny?'

He was beginning to calm down. It was always like that. Whenever he had one of his inexplicable depressions, he would get drunk first and then look for somebody to serve him as both audience and victim. For the others, the white man in the dock had long since been discharged. For him, the trial had only just begun, and was still going on; and he never missed a chance to pronounce his indictment, as he was doing at this moment.

'A terrible deluge,' he went on. 'Those who had stayed in the Ark threw themselves into the water to avoid being called savages. All those who were already spinning about, caught in the tumultuous current, were no longer anything but pieces of flotsam. The less they tried to swim against the current, the more they were considered to be civilized. We have your race to thank for that nice little tornado.'

'Hey!' protested the young woman. 'What are you looking at me like that for? I've never taken any interest in politics, I haven't.'

'Oh, because you think that colonization is politics, do you? You're even stupider than I thought. Never mind! Come along with me!'

She followed him passively, and they went into a small room.

'This is my dark room,' he explained. 'It's here that I develop my photographs. You look surprised, but I'm telling the truth. Thanks to some useful people I know, I do some work as a photographer for a leading paper. But what's the matter with you? You're trembling, honey. Don't tell me you're afraid of Bluebeard?'

'But I'm not trembling.'

'Yes, you are. Wait a minute. I'll turn on the light.'

The little room, which could not have been swept out for several months, was in a state of incredible disorder. Pieces of paper were strewn about, and there was a basin on the floor. On an old chest of drawers there were a few empty frames and a camera which was still in good condition. An indefinable smell took you by the throat, or rather you could detect a great many different smells in the room. N'Toko hurriedly rummaged about in the chest of drawers and brought out a thick wad of photographs.

'Look at these,' he said. 'Bluebeard's victims. Count them if you like. This collection consists of nothing but women – my mistresses of course. I've got other collections here on lots of other things, but you won't see those. Take a good look at the photos I've given you. That's how I, Bluebeard, kill you – with ridicule. In the colonies you are unbearable with your air of belonging to another planet, but in your own country . . .'

The woman looked, very much against her will, and blushed to the roots of her hair. In each photograph she discovered a more daring posture than in the last. How could these women have agreed to pose in such humiliating ways? It was some time before she came to the end of the collection. Her temples and her heart were pounding. Suddenly she saw nothing more. The room was plunged into darkness and the woman felt huge hands running over her body, like monstrous spiders . . .

'We had a rather stormy scene,' Bernard Quillet was saying on the telephone. (Bernard Quillet was the editor of the paper for which N'Toko, to use his own words, 'did some work as a photographer'.) 'In the end he walked out, slamming the door behind him and declaring that I would never see him again. I still haven't got over it. After all, I only sent for him to discuss his job. I told him that with his education it was madness to be satisfied with an irregular post which was badly paid into the bargain. Once again I offered him that post which was waiting for him on the staff of the paper, and which I mentioned to you a year ago, when you recommended this young man to me, saying that he was one of your former students. He rejected the offer and answered me in the most violent terms. The other day, his hotel rang me up to ask me if I had any news of him. Nobody had seen him since the very day we had . . . a few words. I began to feel worried and I even thought of phoning the police. It was then that I remembered you, Professor. You are or at least were his patron to some extent, and perhaps you have some news of him?'

'Alas, no,' replied the professor; 'but I don't think there's any cause for worry. N'Toko was a whimsical character. You might say that he was an armchair student, who regarded his work as fun. He was pathologically lazy, but he had a phenomenal memory. He was always absolutely unbearable with his air of listening to lectures with only half an ear. All the same, he was never stumped by a question and never failed a written examination. I even got

the impression that he came to the university just to while away
the time. Until what? I still ask myself that question. He not only
had an amazing memory, but also possessed a lively mind. And the
two of us fought a great many splendid word-duels. The fellow was
intelligent, but terribly disconcerting. A hundred times I thought
I had formed a mental picture of his true character. The next day,
I always had to admit to myself that the picture was inaccurate.
Something had escaped my notice. Today, I still miss the fellow.
I must tell you that I haven't seen him since the time when I
warmly recommended him to you. It's typical of him to accept
such a poor job, purely out of defiance. Yes, out of defiance. He
was the *enfant terrible* of the university. He got on the nerves of
all his fellow students and his teachers. He hadn't a single friend
in the place. He was the most resolutely antisocial animal I have
ever known. He didn't play games or go to the students' dances,
and he didn't go to the cinema or the theatre . . .'

'Do you think, Professor, that this was the behaviour of somebody with – how shall I put it? – anti-white sentiments?'

'Not particularly. To tell the truth, that had never occurred to
me. Generally speaking, the Africans who come to France can
exorcize the devils of colonialism themselves.'

'Well, that doesn't get us much further, Professor. I must say I
have what you might call presentiments.'

'I haven't,' declared the professor. 'All the same, to make quite
sure, I'll go to see him at his hotel, and I'll keep you informed.'

'Good. I'd have done that myself, but we parted on such bad
terms . . .'

'I quite understand. In any case I'll tell you how things stand.
Good-bye, old chap.'

The professor was in his library, like a sailor surrounded by a sea
of books. From his fifth floor, he had a magnificent view of Paris,
and particularly of the Eiffel Tower. Wearing his dressing-gown,
he was walking up and down, apparently deep in thought. He was
smoking nervously, throwing his cigarettes away when they were
only three-quarters smoked, and there was an absolute hecatomb of
cigarette-ends in the ashtray on his desk.

'Professor,' said a timid little voice beside him, 'your soup is going to get cold. It's after seven o'clock in the evening.'

He had not heard her coming. She belonged, he always thought jokingly, to the cat family. Her behaviour revealed a remarkable physical and moral equilibrium. Never a word louder than another, never a movement faster than another. She greeted each new day with an unshakeable serenity. The professor had known this good woman for seventeen years, and during this long period there had been established between them that economy of words and of displays of feeling which is to be found only in the case of old married couples and old friends. Yet she was nothing more than his housekeeper. He had engaged her as the result of a newspaper advertisement. He had just lost his wife and needed a servant to look after his flat. He had not remarried since.

'Oh, yes, the soup,' said the professor, with an absentminded expression. 'It can wait, Madame Bonnet.'

After these few words, he started slowly pacing up and down again. A few moments later, he stopped in front of Madame Bonnet and started speaking, though without addressing her in particular – something which did not surprise the good woman, who in any case had ceased to be astonished by anything which happened in this house.

'You see,' the professor was saying, 'this young fellow lived on nothing but a challenge flung down to himself and to those around him. He wanted to destroy the others, and perhaps in the end he has destroyed himself? Where the devil can he have taken refuge in this big city? I daren't leap to any tragic conclusions, but I can't see him accepting the hospitality of friends.'

The professor continued his monologue:

'Yes, I think that that young fellow suffered from persecution mania. Everybody knows that that mania is closely related to insanity. Those who suffer from it are convinced every minute of their lives that people are trying to harm them. Either they take cover behind a shield supposed to protect them against blows which exist only in their imagination, or else fear creates arrows which they shoot off at everybody who approaches them. Let's see, Madame . . .'

These last words were addressed directly to his housekeeper.

'Let's see, Madame. Supposing I went to see you at your home. You are out and I go away, but taking some knick-knack with me out of curiosity. Is that theft?'

'That depends, Professor. For you it would be a nondescript knick-knack, but for the owner it might be an object of great sentimental value...'

'Yes, obviously,' said the professor, with a far-away look in his eyes, 'this notebook bound in imitation leather which I am holding in my hands may have considerable value for its owner – one of my former pupils, an African. He disappeared from his hotel several days ago. I went to see him the other day, and I used my position as his former tutor to obtain permission to visit his room. That was where I found this little notebook. But I daren't open it yet. It seems to me that man is too quick to open all the doors he sees in front of him. My experience as an old professor makes me rather doubtful whether freedom enlightens the world. On the other hand, there is a case for thinking that curiosity enlightens the world. One of these days, man will open a door through which he won't be able to return. That's the point which I myself have reached. For several days I have been undecided as to whether or not to glance inside this notebook. On the other hand, I tell myself that it may contain some useful clues which would enable me to trace my former pupil.'

The professor plunged once again into a silent reverie. Madame Bonnet waited for a moment, then left the room as she had come in, without making the slightest noise.

The professor had the irritating impression that he was about to commit an act of sacrilege, but curiosity and uncertainty were too strong for him. With a hand which was trembling slightly he began turning the pages of his former pupil's private diary. He felt an unconquerable embarrassment as he read date after date followed by a woman's Christian name and the entry: 'Submitted to my will.' Will sometimes became law, caprice, or more prosaically desire. Only the first three words remained invariable: 'Submitted to my...'

It was clear that N'Toko led a very busy sex-life, but this was of little interest to the professor, who was looking for something else, though he was not sure what. He went through the notebook methodically, reading more dates, more women's Christian names; then, on one page, some writing in a regular script danced before his eyes. His heart missed a beat, and he concentrated his attention on what follows:

N'toko's Notebook

I have just arrived in Paris. What activity! What a change from Africa, where it is Time that circles round men who are indifferent out of fatalism or temperament. Here, everybody bustles around. Out there, we are condemned – or we were condemned – like Theseus, to remain in one place. That won't last. They are busy putting clockwork inside us, to be able to wind us up and make us move whenever they wish.

Punctuality, the politeness of civilized slaves. I can't see kings, real kings, putting themselves at its service or being dependent on it.

A comparison. The photograph, the field of vision of my fore-fathers. The 'advanced' nations: the ambitious gigantism of the cinema, with its hunger for vast spaces, vaster than its screens can contain. The photo modestly frames a backwater. The cinema tries to depict the whole ocean, though it can't show at the same time the streams and the rivers which run into that ocean.

The finest telescope in the world has only just discovered a satellite close to the earth, a suburban satellite which is not thousands of light-years distant, but only several thousand million francs away. Who will be the first astronaut to land on that planet?

If I were a big noise in the cinema world, what a message I would give this world! I would make a nonconformist film, floating out of the zone of gravity of threadbare concepts towards a sort of stratosphere in which time and space would be abolished. I have always dreamt of this allegorical film in a hundred different scenes.

The first scene would present two characters, one a photographer, the other a mere lens, slavishly obeying the former. Dialogue. The lens would say: 'I am blinded by the flashes of your camera.' The photographer: 'That's inevitable. The aim of my civilization is to blind you. Then you will wear the spectacles I am making for you.' – 'And what if I don't wear them?' – 'In that case, you will be condemned to grope your way in this new world which I am substituting for yours.' Another dialogue. The lens: 'You have taught me exposures, but you restrict my actions and gestures. Why?' – 'I can't trust you yet with the secret of movement. You would escape from my control. For the moment, my law remains unchanged: don't move!'

Tirelessly and implacably, the photographer would go on taking snapshots, progressively stripping the lens of everything it had previously possessed. The lens: 'Now I am completely naked.' – 'That was my aim: to reduce you to such a state of destitution that you can no longer do without me.'

The colonization of Africa by the West ought to be prosecuted for rape of a minor. It is not for nothing that that phenomenon is shamelessly referred to as penetration. For posterity, the nineteenth century will be the period in which Europe was swept by a wave of lust. It became a competition to see who could penetrate furthest. Who cared if the victim brutally robbed of her virginity remained marked for the rest of her life? And they call that making history!

The machiavellism and moral ugliness of the western world! It exports vices to Africa in pretty Pandora's boxes. Those boxes are naturally opened in Africa, and the inhabitants are amazed to see unknown scourges and diseases inexplicably appear.

Look for man here, and you will find only crowds. A terrible insult to God, who is implicitly accused of being nothing but a manufacturer of mass-produced men.

In the beginning, God made the Word. Men, for their part, made the word. These huge rivers of speech displace millions of cubic yards of promises and hopes, but never flow into the ocean of universal happiness. Their Spanish taste for battles of words, in which you keep hearing the same things without the face of the world changing one iota.

In our day, Galileo would say: 'The earth revolves all the same', and this 'all the same' would be full of meaning. It would mean: yes, but in what direction. Yesterday Africa was the kingdom of H.M. Idler the First, seated on his throne (a chaise-longue). Well, the industrialized West has never had as many idlers (rich men) as it has now. They are prolonging the Idler dynasty on their 'relaxing chairs'. The West in its turn is moving fast towards the law of minimum effort: reduction of the working week, supremacy of the machine, and so on.

How many ugly sights I have discovered since I arrived in Paris! A comforting thought. The god has fallen off his pedestal. To be sure of that, I must amass evidence. The idea of a film is too fanciful. As for a novel, I very much fear I lack the patience to write one. A book like that has to be written with everyday words, but words capable of destroying the so-called material power of that fallen god. With words charged with a 'demystifying' force. Alas, I am afraid of being unable to find such words. But photography would provide the answer. In the absence of a closer reality, I could at least have an accurate copy of this ugly life. I could take masses of photos of all those who have fallen into an abyss. After all, don't the Europeans use the same methods in my country? They never photograph anything but Africa in rags, a grimacing, painted Africa which is more photogenic, it seems.

The ideal: to bring off a composite photograph of this world in all its putrefaction.

I could go back to my country, once my studies were over, and find a high administrative position waiting for me. Instead of that, I have become a turncoat. Why? I think it is because I have never been able to adapt myself to circumstances. This sickly shyness of mine which I have to hide behind a mask of hardness. I am frightened. Am I a monster? I always experience a feeling of unusual *excitement and fierce joy every time I photograph a fatal accident. Those awful wounds, that horrible pulp, give me a vague feeling of revenge. It is terrible. Every time that has happened to me, I have had to drown that feeling in a flood of alcohol. There is a Mr Hyde in me who has Dr Jekyll completely in his power. There is nothing to be done, and it is impossible to make a move. It is like being in a dark room. I don't know where the door is. Paris is no longer anything but a prison for me and I am my own gaoler . . .*

The notes stopped there. Then, all of a sudden, light dawned on the professor. The words 'I am my own gaoler' whirled around in his head in a mad saraband. He realized that N'Toko had not 'disappeared from his room, and that on the contrary he must be there – probably rid for ever of the crushing burden of everything which had weighed upon his short life. A saying by the writer Zweg came back to him : 'To try to judge a human being carried away by passion would be as absurd as to call a storm to account or to bring a lawsuit against a volcano.'

                                    Translated by Robert Baldick

Congo (Leopoldville)

Antoine-Roger Bolamba

A FISTFUL OF NEWS

The hills hunch their backs
and leap above the marshes
that wash about the calabash
of the Great Soul

Rumours of treason spread
like burning swords
the veins of the earth
swell with nourishing blood
the earth bears
towns villages hamlets
forests and woods
peopled with monsters horned and tentacled
their long manes are the mirror of the Sun

they are those who when night has come
direct the regiments of bats
and who sharpen their arms
upon the stone of horror

the souls of the guilty
float in the currents of air
on the galleys of disaster
paying no heed to the quarrels of the earthbound
with fangs of fire
they tear from the lightning its diamond heart.

Surely the scorn is a goblet of smoking flesh
surely the spirits recite the rosary of vengeance
but like the black ear of wickedness
they have never understood a single word
of the scorpion's obscure tongue :
stubbornness

nor the anger of the snake-wizard
nor the violence of the throwing-knife
can do anything against it.

Translated by Gerald Moore

Ruanda

Jean-Baptiste Mutabaruka

SONG OF THE DRUM

Listen to the palpitations
     of the twice-wounded heart
     of the friend who rises up for your sake
beating in scarcely audible pulses,

Wilfully blind one with the soft look;
Touching your slender neck my hand closes
     in impotent clenchings;
Look at my lonely forehead furrowed
With the precocious wrinkles of the torment
     of a dream as deep as my faceless race;

Hear my hollow voice how it loses itself
     among the discordant echoes
     with my desperate cries
     of hobbled Hope
     Behind the high barrier
     In the face of my burning thirst;

See how they weigh on my bowed shoulders
     The years of brutalization
     When the awakening of the pattering mornings
     Sounded on the dusty roofs
     Of our burned huts ...

My countenance soiled with the salt ashes
Of destroyed riches, I bring it
To the limpidity of your look
To be washed clear of its traces of soot.

You girl with the graceful neck
Turn your face bewildered
By the reflecting fires
Of this country shining
        in its stolen jewels.

The sombre child of a luminous country
I ruminate on the sorrow of a shoulder
Which moved away when its warmth had animated me.

Who will blow on the embers
        long buried
under the cold of forgetfulness?

No one knows
And tomorrow's knowledge
Controls nothing in the present . . .

O neglected savage of the consumed hamlet.

Speak to me of your beauty
Of the original beauty rather
Of faces once known
And today bewildered
        in the great dispersion
            tear-stained, emaciated with hunger;
The star has failed, the signal has disappeared
        behind false pretences.

Speak to me, my friend, of the waters
        full of pearls, of silt,
            of ores;
The excavator has abstracted them
Do you know this my friend
In your dumbness of chastity?

Hear my cry, if from my gagged mouth
Or from my blocked nostrils
Can still issue
A warning note

A broken voice to pierce
The polite silence
A nasal and a nocturnal voice ...

And now I give you a song
        unlearned by time
Recaptured by time
In the time of our grandparents:

   'The hero has departed
   Chaste and noble beauty
   Child promised for the nuptials
   Of evenings singing the return
   Of your true-love
   Covered in glory and laurels.'

The hero has departed promised beauty
The morning call of the war-drum
        Has only ceased to hammer on the air
With the rending of hearts
        In the morning of farewells

The strangled sobs of the mothers
The rasped throats of the fathers
And the painful pigeon-throated mourning
        Of the old grandmothers.

Child promised for the evenings of dancing
In the widened circle of alliances
I celebrate the future path
Of him who shall return
Your lover my brother-in-arms.

When will the hero return
Stranded down there
Beyond the offices
Among tactful gestures
Both emptied and nourished
By decorated waiting?

Tell me, tell me
My journey is for today
My departure irrevocable,
For lands unknown
For lands buried
Under sand and mud,
The boundaries established on the graves
Of liquidated forefathers.
In the reddening West
The incandescent belfries
Announce from afar
The desecration of space.

Tell me, yes tell me
Your word of advice
The dull-witted pebble
Oh no, it's the uncertain step . . .
A swallow of creamy milk
A handful of narrow-leaved sprays
A little walk behind the house
A blow at the friendly fire
A quick touch of father's weapons . . .
Who will reawaken this long-smothered flame
To its burning?

Translated by Oliver Bernard

Senegal

Birago Diop

THE WAGES OF GOOD

Diassigue-the-Alligator, scraping the sand with his flaccid belly, was returning to the channel after sleeping all day long in the hot sun, when he heard the women coming back from drawing water, scouring calabashes and washing linen. These women, who had undoubtedly done more work with their tongues than with their hands, were still talking and talking. They were saying sorrowfully that the king's daughter had fallen into the water and been drowned, and that it was very likely – indeed it was certain, according to a woman slave – that at dawn the next day Bour-the-King would have the channel drained in order to find his beloved daughter's body. Diassigue, whose hole in the channel bank was close to the village, turned back the way he had come and went far into the interior in the dark night. The next day, sure enough, the channel was drained and, what is more, all the alligators that lived in it were killed; in the hole of the oldest of them all, they found the body of the king's daughter.

In the middle of the day, a child who was gathering dead wood found Diassigue-the-Alligator in the scrub.

'What are you doing there, Diassigue?' asked the child.

'I have lost my way,' answered the alligator. 'Will you carry me home, Goné?'

'There isn't a channel any more,' the child told him.

'Then carry me to the river,' said Diassigue-the-Alligator.

Goné-the-Child went to fetch a mat and some creepers. He rolled Diassigue up in the mat, which he fastened with the creepers. Then he put it on his head and walked until the evening, when he reached the river. Arriving at the water's edge, he put down his bundle, cut the creepers, and unrolled the mat. Then Diassigue said to him:

'Goné, my legs are all stiff from that long journey. Will you put me into the water, please?'

Goné-the-Child walked into the water until it came up to his knees, and he was about to put Diassigue down when the latter said to him:

'Go on until the water comes up to your waist, for I would find it hard to swim here.'

Goné did as he asked and walked on until the water encircled his waist.

'Go on until it comes up to your chest,' the alligator begged him.

The child went on until the water reached his chest.

'You might as well go on now until it comes up to your shoulders.'

Goné walked on until his shoulders were covered, and then Diassigue said to him:

'Now put me down.'

Goné obeyed. He was about to return to the river bank when the alligator gripped him by the arm.

'Wouye yayô! Oh, Mother,' cried the child. 'What are you doing? Let go of me!'

'I shan't let go of you, because I'm very hungry, Goné.'

'Let go of me!'

'I shan't let go of you. I haven't had anything to eat for two days and I'm too hungry.'

'Tell me, Diassigue, do you repay a kindness with another kindness or with a bad turn?'

'A good deed is repaid with a bad turn and not with another good deed.'

'Now it's I who am in your power, but what you say isn't true, and you must be the only person in the whole world to say it.'

'Oh! You really think so?'

'Well, let's ask a few people and we'll see what they say.'

'All right,' said Diassigue; 'but if we find three people who share my opinion, then you'll end up in my stomach, I promise you.'

He had scarcely finished uttering this threat when an old, old cow arrived to drink out of the river. When she had quenched her thirst, the alligator called her and asked her:

'Nagy, you who are so old and possess all wisdom, can you tell us whether a good deed is repaid with a kindness or with a bad turn?'

'A good deed,' declared Nagy-the-Cow, 'is repaid with a bad turn, and believe me, I know what I'm talking about. In the days when I was young, strong, and vigorous, when I came back from the pasture I was given bran, millet and a lump of salt, I was washed and rubbed down, and if Poulo, the little shepherd, happened to raise his stick against me, he was sure to receive a beating in his turn from his master. At that time I gave a lot of milk, and all my master's cows and bulls are offspring of mine. Now I am old and no longer give any milk or calves, so nobody takes care of me any more or takes me out to graze. At dawn every day, a blow from a stick drives me out of the park, and I go off on my own to look for my food. That is why I say that a good deed is repaid with a bad turn.'

'Goné, did you hear that?' asked Diassigue-the-Alligator.

'Yes,' said the child, 'I heard it all right.'

With her thin, bony buttocks swaying like a couple of sword-blades, Nagy-the-Cow went off, swinging her old tick-bitten tail, towards the sparse grass of the scrubland.

Then gaunt old Fass-the-Horse arrived on the scene. He was about to brush the water with his lips before drinking when the alligator called out to him:

'Fass, you who are so old and wise, can you tell us, this child and me, whether a good deed is repaid with a kindness or with a bad turn?'

'I certainly can,' declared the old horse. 'A kindness is always repaid by an evil deed, and I know something about it. Listen to me, the two of you. In the days when I was young, strong and high-spirited, I had three grooms all to myself; I had my trough filled with millet morning and night, and bran mash often mixed with honey at all hours of the day. I was taken for a bathe and a rub-down every morning. I had a bridle and a saddle made by a Moorish saddler and adorned by a Moorish jeweller. I used to go on the battlefields, and the five hundred prisoners my master took in the wars were brought back on my crupper. For nine years I carried my master and his booty. Now that I have grown old, all that they do for me is hobble me at dawn, and then, with a blow from a stick, they send me into the scrubland to look for my food.'

Having spoken, Fass-the-Horse brushed the scum from the surface of the water, took a long drink, and then went off, hampered by his hobble, with his jerky, limping walk.

'Goné,' said the alligator, 'did you hear that? Now I'm too hungry to wait any longer: I'm going to eat you.'

'No, Uncle Diassigue,' said the child. 'You said yourself that you would ask three people. If the next person who comes along says the same as those two, then you can eat me, but not before.'

'Very well,' agreed the alligator, 'but I warn you that we shan't go any further afield.'

Then Leuk-the-Hare came running up, his hindquarters twitching. Diassigue called him:

'Uncle Leuk, you who are the oldest among us, can you tell us which of us two is right? I say that a good deed is repaid with a bad turn, and this child declares that the price of a good deed is a kindness.'

Leuk rubbed his chin, scratched his ear, and then asked in his turn:

'Diassigue, my friend, do you ask a blind man to tell you whether cotton is white or whether a crow is really black?'

'Of course not,' admitted the alligator.

'Can you tell me where a child whose family you don't know is going?'

'Certainly not.'

'Then explain to me what has happened and I may be able to answer your question without much risk of making a mistake.'

'Well, Uncle Leuk, this is the position: this child found me in the interior, rolled me up in a mat and carried me here. Now I'm feeling hungry, and seeing that I have to eat, because I don't want to die, it would be stupid of me to let him go, to run after a dubious prey.'

'Indubitably,' said Leuk; 'but when words are sick, ears have to be healthy, and my ears, to the best of my knowledge, are perfectly well, thank God, for there are some of your words, Brother Diassigue, which don't strike me as being in very good health.'

'Which words are those?' asked the alligator.

'It's when you say that this little boy carried you in a mat and brought you all the way here. I can't believe that.'

'All the same, it's true,' declared Goné-the-Child.

'You're a liar like the rest of your race,' said the hare.

'He is telling the truth,' confirmed Diassigue.

'I can't believe that unless I see it,' said Leuk increduously. 'Get out of the water, both of you.'

The child and the alligator came out of the water.

'You claim to have carried this big alligator in that mat? How did you do it?'

'I rolled him up in it and then tied it up.'

'Well, I want to see how.'

Diassigue lay down on the mat, and the child rolled it up.

'And you say that you tied it up?'

'Yes.'

'Tie it up to show me.'

The child tied the mat up securely.

'And you carried him on your head?'

'Yes, I carried him on my head.'

'Well, carry him on your head so that I can see.'

When the child had lifted up mat and alligator and placed them on his head, Leuk-the-Hare asked him :

'Goné, are your family blacksmiths?'

'No.'

'So Diassigue isn't a relative of yours? He isn't your totem?'

'No, certainly not.'

'Then take your bundle home. Your father and your mother and all your relatives and their friends will thank you, since you can eat alligator at home. That is how to repay those who forget a good deed.'

Translated by Robert Baldick

David Diop

TO THE MYSTERY-MONGERS

Cynical monsters with cigars
Transported by flights of orgies
And trailing equality in an iron cage
You were the preachers of sadness chained to fear
Of the melancholy song and of renunciation
Mantled in folds of madness
You let fall death on the birth of every summer
And contrived the nightmare of rhythmical steps in the circus of
   Negroes
Today your forbidden cities
Open amid belated tears and solemn vows
And your words of sugar heap themselves up inexhaustibly
Among the accumulated ruins
Now is the time when your thinkers suddenly smitten with pangs
Are brought to bed of unity like a choir
And busily convert the lightning into a tinsel monotone
Which will give way to the invisible torpor
Of traps woven about the worm-eaten cradle
Which will give way to the trumpets of the baptism
When the cords break in the hard wind
And the masquerades die pecked from rock to rock.

The trembling of the maize flower
And the cry of the peanut pounding the hunger of Negroes are
   enough
To turn our steps towards where the light falls straight
And to your nights of intoxication by propaganda
To your nights crushed flat by automatic greetings
To your nights full of pious silence and endless sermons

We oppose the anthem with the springing muscles
Which celebrates the glittering departure
The uncalled-for anthem of Africa in tatters
Tearing the darkness of a thousand years.

Translated by Oliver Bernard

Ousmane Socé

From Karim

Karim, born, like the author, in Saint-Louis, goes to the city with his companions. They are typically Wolof (the principal ethnic group in Senegal and the surrounding territories), fond of brave and noble deeds and trials of strength. But the city, which marks one of the changes that have overtaken Africa, demands new goals, new ideals, new methods. Conflict rages round the hero: between men and between values of the past and present. Finally, Karim, harassed by debt from all sides as a result of an impulse to dazzle his girl-friends, goes back to the village, back to his *boubou*. The following is an account of one of Karim's city experiences.

KARIM AT THE BALL

Sunday.

Early in the morning, the old church of Gorea made the air tremble with the chimes of its bells.

Ladies and gentlemen, young and old, put on their finest clothes. Even the grandmothers draped themselves in their multicoloured pagnes which they kept carefully packed away all year in old Empire chests.

Young people in their Sunday best kept arriving from Dakar on the launch, invaded the town, and gradually increased the population.

And in the streets, usually so empty, there was nothing but new dresses, laughter, and gaiety.

Everywhere the festivities were beginning, champagne and wine were flowing, gramophones were singing.

Two o'clock in the afternoon.

Ding, dong! Ding, dong! Ding, dong!

The church was summoning the faithful with solemn notes. The animation of the morning, which had diminished at midday under the overpowering heat, had returned. From the houses which were still standing, and from under the ruins, there came a crowd which hurried to the church and disappeared inside.

'*Pange lingua gloriosi corporis mysterium . . .*'

Vespers were over; and this chant, lustily sung by a man's voice, marked the beginning of the procession.

Orphan girls, watched over by the nuns of the Immaculate Conception, in white coifs and blue robes, led the way, holding rich, brightly-coloured banners high in the air.

After them came the choir.

A loud solo arose, intoned by male throats which were soon joined in a superb duet by piping women's voices.

Then came the choir-boys, in red cassocks and white surplices. They advanced slowly, raising a bronze cross above the crowd.

An officiating priest was walking along under a canopy, in the middle of the procession. His golden cope was glittering; he was deep in contemplation, and was advancing solemnly, holding the monstrance in both hands, his eyes fixed in a stare as if he were hypnotized by the Holy Sacrament . . .

The onlookers brought up the rear, the women making an elegant show as they marched along in their pink and blue silk dresses.

The procession disappeared among the narrow, twisting streets lined with tumbledown houses; and the singing, which grew louder as it spread through the Gorean ruins, awakened them from their age-old sleep.

But they remained indifferent to this religious emotion, looking as if they were saying :

'We have seen your predecessors go by in procession with far greater pomp, and they rest now in nothingness; like them, you will be destroyed by the power of time.'

Along the way, at the ringing of the little bell, everybody would stop and the choir-boys would strew the sand with the flowers they were carrying in baskets hanging from their necks.

Suddenly there was a loud blowing of bugles which formed a striking contrast with the languid religious chants. The procession had reached a point between the Training College and the Military

Hospital. There a temporary altar had been erected, wreathed in rose-tree branches withered by the heat. Right at the back there danced the flames of huge candles, almost invisible in the daylight. All around, blazing red blossoms were scattered on the ground.

The clergy mounted the altar steps, still at the same solemn pace. The officiating priest put down his golden monstrance and wafted clouds of incense around it. Then the prayers continued . . .

Karim had followed the procession all the way to admire Marie N'Diaye who was the most beautiful girl he knew.

He took advantage of a movement of the crowd to go up to his friend.

'I'll see you tonight at the ball at Monsieur Fernand's house.'

They could not stay together for long. Marie was well known at Gorea; if she was seen in a young man's company, spiteful women would start backbiting straight away.

Nine o'clock at night.

The ball had just begun. Conspicuous among the guests were the Senegalese Catholics and the 'advanced' Moslems. They were wearing light lounge suits of impeccable cut, made of flannel, cream-coloured linen or white linen, ironed until they were as smooth as glass; silk-fronted shirts, expensive-looking ties and fine socks. Their hair, which had been patiently curled, rippled down over their necks in little waves.

Other Moslems, semi-conservatives who usually wore the bubu and the fez, had donned lounge suits that evening, to be able to dance without looking out of place.

Among the women and girls, who were all Catholics, two tendencies could be observed. Some had completely adopted the European style. Others had chosen hybrid outfits: they too wore silk dresses, but also pagnes, kerchiefs, and gold slippers.

'Riquetta, pretty Java flower,
Come and dance, come and kiss me!'

The orchestra (an accordion, a mandolin, a banjo, and a violin) played foxtrots, one-steps, and waltzes. The musicians, who had no scores, stylized the tunes in their repertoire, stressing the rhythm to make them easier to dance to.

'Oh, the poor little boy !
He looks like a broken toy !'

Some of the men danced in the classic style, while others swayed their hips, impelled by a violent need for a strong, swinging rhythm.

'China night, that lovely night I spent with you !
Night of love, that night you said you would be true !'

Midnight.

Karim had danced as little as possible with Marie. Now the older people were leaving. The young people remained behind, and most of them openly formed couples.

'Ramona, last night I dreamed I was in your lovely arms,
Ramona, last night I tasted your lovely charms.'

Marie whirled about gracefully, under the gentle impulse of Karim's arms, waltzing lightly and easily like a black sylph.

The young man held her in a loving embrace, carried away by the nostalgic strains of the accordion, the winged notes of the mandolin.

The couples spun around, bewitched by the accordion-player, an old salt who exhaled his regret for the countries he had known through the voice of his accordion. He played one waltz, accompanying it with the words of a second waltz, then of a third. . . . He did not know the words of the original waltz. He had heard it the first time in Marseilles. Since then he had played it at Dunkirk, Montevideo, and Singapore for his brothers in exile, with the same success. Europe, America, the Far East, days of happiness and hours of distress, lived again in the wild, sad rhythm of his tune, which became so captivating that the couples whirled round and round at breathless speed. Bent over his accordion, he squeezed it convulsively, swaying in time with the imaginary rolling of his old ship as it rode the high seas. . . .

Four o'clock in the morning.

The same feverish atmosphere still reigned in the room, the same thirst for pleasure.

Excitement was growing like a river swollen by torrential rain. The dancers were flinging themselves about more and more.

They were tired of Latin emotionalism, so the orchestra started playing tunes of their own country, *goumbés*. The couples had broken up and everyone was dancing by himself. . . .

'Hi, Papa Charles,
The *goumbé* is the devil !
Old men, come and try it.
The *goumbé* is the devil !'

The accordion led the music, accompanied by the banjo and the mandolin. A jazz tom-tom rhythm was beaten out on tambourines, the *assicots*, while keys were knocked against empty bottles and pebbles rattled in tin cans.

'Oh, what times we live in !
The men are bad today.
They have a wife and children
And a mistress tucked away. . . .'

The women formed an inner circle, standing shoulder to shoulder. They moved in a nimble, jigging round, the men dancing on the outside and answering their satirical song with another :

'O, what times we live in !
The girls are bad today.
They have a man and children
And a lover tucked away. . . .'

The more they jigged about, the more they needed to jig about, each man following his partner's twitching rump.

Then came another satirical song directed by the women against their rivals.

'I don't sell that, I don't,
To buy myself some muslin !
I don't sell that, I don't,
To buy myself some muslin !'

Outside, the atmosphere was electric. It was the moment before
the storm, and flashes of lightning were scarring the dark, heavy
sky.

Inside the tension was rising. A love-song full of promise was
floating in the air :

'However late it is,
However late it is,
Come to my arms !'

Intoxicating scents filled the overheated atmosphere of the room,
perfumes of all sorts mingled with the scent of young flesh :

'Dankalo, dankalo,
Sou ma sopé dankalo,
Come to my arms, come to my arms,
My beloved, come to my arms !'

Translated by Robert Baldick

Joseph Zobel

FLOWERS! LOVELY FLOWERS!

Nobody could remember spring coming so late before. On the first of May the lily of the valley was still not in flower. It was raining and the skies were grey. Everybody was saying that the florists must have made a fortune with their hot-house lily of the valley and that anybody who had found in the woods a few sprigs with two or three little bell-flowers on them must have made thousands and thousands of francs.

As a matter of fact, it was leaves that were being sold everywhere – leaves with, at the very most, a fragile crook studded with a few greenish granules.

That gives some idea how late spring was!

Yet the fact remains that in the forest everything was on the point of bursting out into buds and blossoms; everything was like us, swollen with the longing for spring; and there was no doubt that as soon as the sun broke through, the fine weather would rush on to the scene, all tousled and frisky.

'Because when it's like this, it comes quickly,' the women forecast, on the street corners or in the grocers' shops.

Sure enough, this particular Sunday, the weather was fine. Nobody could have expected it to be such a fine day.

Immediately after lunch the town had spilled out into the forest, where every car which arrived had a great deal of trouble finding a shady spot to park in; just as anybody who had hoped to read or rest by himself could be seen wandering about for a long time. The whole town was there, with its cars, its sweethearts and its newly-married couples; its prams, its crowds of children, and its white-haired inhabitants, always dressed in black, even in warm, sunny weather, whom the Government had just respectfully christened the 'financially underprivileged'; not to mention the Parisians who could be seen everywhere, in whole families – children, parents and grandparents gathered round folding tables, playing cards and arguing while they drank liquids of all colours from plastic bottles.

Others stayed in their cars where the radio poured out the voluble flow of the commentary on some football match at the Parc des Princes.

There were some who were playing ball games, and also a few bald, pot-bellied gentlemen who had already taken off their jackets, feeling younger that way, to run races with their grandsons, to the women's vast amusement.

It was good to be laughing in the sunshine.

There were a great many of those boys in shorts and those young girls in jeans who, with rucksacks on their backs, explored the forest every Sunday and in every season.

For the first time in the year, the ice-cream vendor had re-appeared, in a white linen jacket and a white cap, under the canopy of his little car which had been repainted white and bore a sort of pattern of red letters forming a Spanish-sounding name. The children went towards him like lambs to a drinking trough, and for twenty or thirty centimes he handed them ice-cream cornets in one or two colours – pink, yellow, brown – which at a distance you might have taken for bunches of flowers.

This was in the forest, at a spot where the oaks and the beeches had graciously left a big green space for the grass, and the ladies in their bright coloured skirts bent down there to pick dandelions, daisies, or four-leaf clovers.

The road cut through this big green clearing, a road which you couldn't even cross, because the cars drove by in both directions in two uninterrupted lines; so that you stood there as if you were on the banks of a river, watching the waters flowing past, torn into two contrary currents in the middle.

The speed of the cars produced a violent current of air which everybody treated with caution, because it raised the women's skirts or threatened to fill people's eyes with the fine dust which hemmed the edges of the road.

He was the only person who, on the contrary, remained standing at the roadside, and as each car approached, instead of drawing back, he bent a little further forward, raising his arms. The faster the car was moving, the more he insisted on waving at it, even taking a few steps towards it, as if he were trying to hypnotize it; and now and then, in fact, to everybody's astonishment, a car would slow down, like a bird coming to rest, and draw up a little farther on, while he rushed towards it, brandishing the two bunches of white flowers which had produced the miracle.

The day before, he had probably felt the fine weather coming, beyond any shadow of a doubt, and had thought of all the lily of the valley which had not flowered in time for the first of May and about which people had said: 'A week or so from now . . . as soon as the sun comes out. . . .'

Besides, he had been able to see how far advanced it was already: he had watched it opening, wandering through the forest as he did every day, in all weathers, either to pick mushrooms, daffodils, or dandelions, according to the season, or to gather dead wood.

He knew the whole forest.

He had therefore got up early – not that there was anything unusual about that, for he boasted that he never slept – and he had gone off in the direction of Verneuil, which is the lily of the valley district, just as Recloses is the daffodil district. Everybody knows that, but he was almost certain that nobody would get there before him if he went early in the morning; it is a long way.

And there was plenty of lily of the valley, just as he had suspected. There was so much that, without exaggeration, he could have brought along a scythe instead of bending down to gather it sprig by sprig. He did not stop picking it all morning, either squatting on his haunches and moving forward like a child imitating a duck's walk, or else dragging himself along on his knees. His back and shoulders had hurt, and his thighs and calves had ached as if they had been beaten with a stick. That was what had given him a rather jerky, unsteady walk; but Heaven could be his witness that all the time he had been alone in the forest, his tongue had been stuck to his palate for want of a bottle of red wine. Indeed, he had been so thirsty that he had said to himself:

'At the first pub I come to, even if I haven't sold anything yet, I'm going to give the landlady a bunch of lily of the valley in exchange for a glass of wine.'

The landlady would not have lost on the deal.

It was beautiful lily of the valley, sweet-smelling and – he could be proud of this – prettily arranged.

When he had finished gathering it, he had sat down in the grass, in the sunshine, with the lily of the valley heaped up between his legs; the whole heap of little white flowers next to his boots which looked as if they were made of earth, they were so dirty, and his corduroy trousers which shone like old bark. Then he put them together sprig by sprig in one fist cupped to form a flower-holder, a fist carved and covered with a network of black crevices, which he raised to examine the bunch of lily of the valley. This bunch, with each new sprig, grew and took shape in the sunshine, gradually becoming a big white flower which to all intents and purposes he had made himself, and which he surrounded with a collarette of soft green leaves, carefully chosen. Next, after tying it with a strip of fibre which he held between his teeth, he spun it round with a wink before laying it gently on the grass.

It was like a game, like something that was not really serious, at least for a man of his age who could not be expected to waste his time over flowers.

Yet it was work all the same, and it took a whole morning.

'Anyhow, bunches of lily of the valley as good as this ought to sell well at a franc each,' he thought.

And in fact, business had begun quite well. He had chosen this place specially. Farther down, there was a bend, and a little farther up, a hill. Here, the cars could stop easily and drive off again easily.

True, there were some which drove straight at him at top speed, threatening to wipe him out if he didn't jump back in time on to the side of the road; but now and then the sight of the two bunches of lily of the valley which he held out in both hands reduced the frenzied speed of a handsome car which, gently, obediently, came to him like a good dog being offered a piece of sugar.

'Oh, how lovely they are !'

It was the same exclamation every time. And they seemed to think that the price was very reasonable.

'Oh, they're beautiful!' exclaimed the fine ladies, leaning out of the windows of their cars.

And he would add:

'See how good they smell, Madame.'

Then the lady would stay for a moment with her eyelids – mother-of-pearl eyelids fringed with long black lashes – lowered over the bouquet – offering a prayer – which the dirty, bruised old hand was dedicating to her delicate face.

Sometimes the lady refused the flowers he offered her, making him come closer to the car in order to choose for herself, out of the bag which he carried slung over his shoulder, a bunch which struck her as even bigger or better arranged.

Two bunches, three bunches – and sometimes he was allowed to keep the change.

'Thanks, ladies and gents. My lily of the valley will bring you luck.'

Speed would snatch the car away and carry it off in a roar promptly reduced by distance, and just as promptly increased by the arrival of another car.

Then, passing his hand over his bag, like an animal polishing its fur, he would think to himself with a half-smile:

'If it keeps up like this. . . .'

Quickly he would resume his position at the roadside, his arms in the air, bending forward or stepping forward, or else taking a step back whenever he felt the attraction of his bouquets giving way in the face of the blind speed of the car which had appeared. For the fact of the matter was that it was not at all easy to stop one.

But for some time it had become a sport for him, and he had been keeping a note of the points he scored.

The consequence was that he had failed to notice the van which had drawn up some way behind him; a black van looking like a bumble-bee with all the colours of the forest and the roadside caught in its enamel shell, and its long antenna vibrating nervously, tracing dazzling curves in the air.

Two gendarmes had got out of it, wearing blue uniforms, peaked caps, and boots so tight-fitting and shining that anybody might have thought they were brand-new toys straight out of the window of a big department-store.

He had not seen them.

And what if he had?

So that now, all of a sudden, he heard a voice behind him say:

'What the hell are you up to?'

To tell the truth, he wasn't afraid of the police; he had never killed or stolen, as the saying goes.

All the same, he still thought that it was a bad sign when they came on the scene, especially when they spoke to you like that.

He turned round, holding up his bunches of lily of the valley in both hands.

'Me?' he asked.

'Yes, you!' retorted the other gendarme, coming up behind. 'We asked you what the hell you're up to.'

'But, sergeant . . . I wasn't. . . .'

'Have you an identity card on you?'

'But I wasn't doing anything, sergeant. . . .'

His arms had fallen to his sides like two branches struck by lightning and, immediately, the two bunches of flowers seemed to have lost their brilliance.

'I told you to give me your papers,' the gendarme repeated.

Then, after putting the two bunches of lily of the valley back into his bag, he pulled the lapel of his old jacket away from his chest with one hand, and with the other took out of his inside pocket something like a packet of rotten leaves, which he opened and thumbed through with trembling fingers, under the impatient eyes of the two gendarmes.

'Here you are, sergeant.'

The gendarme turned the card over and, pursing his lips, examined it in an effort to decipher some handwriting half-obliterated with grease. The other gendarme came up and read the identity card over his colleague's shoulder, and then took a thick notebook bound in imitation black leather out of his pocket.

'But I wasn't doing anything wrong, officer.'

'Where do you live?'

'Pardon, officer?'

'I asked you where you live.'

'In the village.'

He pointed to Barbigou, which was out of sight but quite close, barely two kilometres away by road, or else at the end of the little lane leading away from the other side of the road.

'At whose house in the village?'

'Well, to tell the truth, officer, it's with the people I work for now and then.'

'And who are you working for just now?'

'Well, the fact is that, for the moment, people aren't taking on much seasonal labour, because of this never-ending winter. But there are quite a few people who've booked me already. As you can imagine, what with the delay we've had, there'll be lots of new potatoes to pick round here.'

The gendarme, who had taken out of a loop on the cover of his notebook a little pencil with a nickel-plated clip, had started writing, and went on writing, occasionally darting a glance at the card his colleague was holding.

'But I haven't done anything wrong, officer.'

And as the gendarme went on writing imperturbably, he asked:

'What the devil have I done wrong? Don't you think you're being a bit hard on me?'

'You haven't any right to sell lily of the valley from the forest,' one of the gendarmes replied in exasperation. 'You know that perfectly well.'

'What do you mean, I haven't any right? The lily of the valley in the forest belongs to everybody.'

The other gendarme, the one who was writing, lifted his pencil and retorted:

'Exactly: it belongs to everybody, but when you pick it and sell it, it's like robbing the public. Don't you understand that?'

He said this without raising his voice, with a cold look.

Already the children and a few adults who were on the same side of the road had come nearer, and it was turning towards them that he repeated, more and more exasperated:

'What have I done wrong?'

'Not to mention the accidents you risked causing with your antics in the roadway,' the gendarme went on.

The policeman handed his card back to him.

'I swear I didn't know it was against the law, officer, seeing that only last week everybody . . .'

'Yes, but selling lily of the valley is allowed only on the first of May. It's no use acting the innocent.'

From the other side of the road, he could be seen gesticulating, bending over as he spoke and thumping his chest in front of the gendarme, who put his notebook back in his pocket as if to say: 'All right, we'll see.'

Everybody was watching, even those who, sitting on the rocks or stretched out on the grass, were putting on a show of indifference.

The mad flood of cars went on flowing past.

All of a sudden, the onlookers saw him distributing his flowers: one to this gentleman, two to that lady, and then another two at the same time to a little boy who promptly ran off with them. Some children rushed towards him, while others dashed away, shouting:

'Mummy ! Daddy ! Look !'

Those on the other side of the road couldn't manage to cross because of the speed at which the cars were following one another. There were a good four or five who started off, then drew back, until at last, taking advantage of a lull, they all set off together like a pack of hounds, while a panic-stricken lady screamed:

'Jean-Claude ! Jean-Claude ! Oh, Heavens above !'

But it was too late.

The bag containing the lily of the valley was empty.

Now the man was cursing and stamping, throwing his cap into the air, picking it up again, and flinging his arms about in all directions as if he would have liked to explode.

The children drew back in amazement, possibly afraid that he might suddenly turn vicious, but a lady went over to him and said:

'It's really very pretty, your lily of the valley. Thank you for the lovely bunch you gave my grand-daughter.'

She showed him the bunch of lily of the valley which, held

delicately between her fingers, had become a positive adornment. But he wasn't listening to her.

'Can any of you tell me what crime I was committing?' he shouted.

'Here,' said the lady, 'take this.'

Seeing the coin she was holding out to him, he protested :

'Keep your money, Madame. I'm a tramp, a vagrant as they put it. I've no family, I've no right to eat.'

'Oh,' said the lady, 'don't get so upset !'

'I'm not entitled to the workhouse,' he went on. 'There's only prison for me, you understand?'

Braving his wild gesture, the lady succeeded in slipping the coin into the pocket of his jacket and went off, stroking her nose with the bunch of lily of the valley.

Then, grumbling to himself, he walked along the bank with hesitant, unsteady steps, and finally dropped on to the grass and stayed there, curled up, with his face buried in his hands.

He wasn't crying.

He curled up more and more, and now and then let out a groan, like a wounded animal losing all its blood – or a vagrant, a tramp, shamelessly sleeping off his drink.

But nobody was paying attention to him any more.

The clearing had taken on the appearance of a huge country fair in which the sun-topped trees were playing the trumpets and the bagpipes.

Translated by Robert Baldick

Léopold Sédar Senghor

DEATH OF THE PRINCESS

Voice of the tom-tom! Tom-tom of Gandoun, tom-tom of Gambia,
and tom-tom from the opposite bank.
'Peace!' it says, 'and announce your name.' Here is the message,
faithfully recorded:

My sister the Princess of Belborg has gone away.
But the transmission of her reply sealed with her chaste seal
A star gules charged with a crescent or.
'The Princess's compliments! I have understood your message.
'It has refreshed, refreshed my heart! Exquisite drink, favourite
dish!
'My duties hold me within my territories. Clan warfare ate at the
soil,
'Passions overflowed, undermining the foundations of the houses.
'How can I blossom in the pursuits of leisure when I must repair
and rebuild?
'The task was beyond my strength, and your words poisoned my
awakening from drunkenness.
'Ah those short, those too-short nights, when I sat up holding your
epistles in turn to the lamp!
'Outside the wind shivered in the birch trees, and the owls hooted
without end.
'I shall not last till the springtime; if I should last until then
'The fire of the sky would ruin the white men's monuments in a
moment.
'My black Prince, keep this message as I have done yours.
'May it be simple nourishment for you: bread, salt and sky.
'Keep the image of the Princess of Belborg in your mind as the
winter keeps the seed in the death of the earth.'
She has spoken she is silent she no longer exists.

She rests now, tall and very straight
And beautiful; ripe ivory in her robe of snow scented with orange-
blossom.
She rests under the blue fir tree, her tresses laid as neatly as sheaves
of purple corn.
O Princess, my Princess ! For without you what are my orphaned
lands,
My fields without seed, my herds without shelter, my orchards
without water?
What avail my brushwood and my mud-flats, my blackness, my
sunless night?
If only the knowledge of the Mali peasant . . .
– Lost, even to the smile of the Signares !
Shall I keep watch, then, like my father, in loneliness and tears,
While weeds and snakes converse in the women's quarters?
No, no ! Rest, my Belborg, in your peaceful dress, in the blue village
of your dead and my dead.
You will blossom in the garden of my heart.
The mists still laze on the waters of all my rivers
But the light spreads slowly over my eyes of darkness.
Rest, Belborg, rest in your splendid garment.

NEGRO MASK

She rests, she sleeps on the brightness of sand.
Koumba Tam sleeps. A green palm shadows the excitement
of her hair and turns her round forehead to bronze,
And her closed eyelids, double cups, sealed wells.
This slender crescent; this only just darker, heavier lip
– or the smile of the willing woman?
Flat concave of cheek, round convex of chin, sing a silent harmony.
Mask-face closed to the ephemeral, without eyes or content;
Perfect bronze head with its patina of time,
Which neither paint nor flush nor wrinkle marks,
    nor traces of tears nor of kisses;

O face such as God created you, beyond even the memory
 of this age of kisses;
Face of the world's dawn, do not open like a tender mountain pass
 to rouse my flesh.
With my single-purposed eye I adore you O Beauty.

Translated by Oliver Bernard

Guinea

Camara Laye

From The Radiance of the King

Le Regard du Roi, from which the following extract is taken, is a symbolical novel. Its hero, a white man named Clarence, has just arrived in Africa, but has already lost all his money at gambling. As a result he has been thrown out of his hotel; he finds refuge in an African inn. Clarence goes out to find the African king of the country in order to enter his service. The king arrives in great pomp – on one of the rare occasions when he does appear in public – but Clarence cannot get more than a glimpse of him. He is joined by an impudent beggar and subsequently by a pair of boys, Nagoa and Noaga, who are full of bounce. The king leaves for his palace and the beggar follows him to see if Clarence can gain access to him. He comes back to tell the white man that there is no place for him, but advises him to go south where he and the two boys are also going.

The innkeeper insists that Clarence should part with his jacket in payment of his debt. When the innkeeper puts it on it splits in two, and the boys help themselves to a piece each. Clarence, ignorant of this incident, is arrested for stealing back the coat and brought before a mysterious judge. The beggar advises Clarence to run away; he goes through a sinister maze of passages. Finally he, the beggar, and the boys leave Adramé for the south.

During the journey, Clarence is continually assailed by a narcotic odour from the forest around, and he thinks that the three are repeatedly leading him in circles. They eventually reach the south, where the beggar, without the white man knowing it, sells him to the naba – the local ruler. The naba, too old to use his women, instructs Baloum to plant a different member of his harem in Clarence's room to sleep with him each night, while the latter continues to think that he is sleeping with Akissi, his regular mistress. Eventually, Clarence realizes, to his shattering shame, that he has several coloured children.

The king finally arrives, but Clarence feels too ashamed and degenerate to appear before him. However, the king urges him to approach and ask his favour. Camara Laye portrays Clarence as a white man who yearns to identify with Africans, but his Western Christian sensibilities cannot accommodate the African's naturalistic zest for life as an end in itself.

AKISSI

Clarence walked painfully to the threshold of his hut. It was hardly more than six steps – his hut measured barely more than six feet across – but it felt as if it were a hundred. He was filled with an inexplicable heaviness. He was heavy with sleep; he was as it were drunk with sleep. His head and his limbs felt inexpressibly heavy.

He leaned against the wall; he wanted to try to understand why he felt so heavy. But then he realized that he could not think even the simplest thoughts; it seemed almost too much to follow a single thought to its logical conclusion.

The heaviness was now all concentrated in his head; it was partly of course the heaviness inside the hut: the heat, or the smoke, or the fog of breath, or Lord knows what other sultry heaviness. And he just couldn't get his thoughts together; perhaps they were holding out their hands to one another – that is, if they *had* hands – but these hands encountered nothing but the void. Yet as the dewy freshness of the dawn began to bathe his forehead, Clarence began to see that the hands would meet in the end. The heaviness inside him was gradually dwindling away.

At that very moment the sun rose on Aziana. A great rosy flame leapt up the sky and chased away the remains of fog and mist, and everything became of the same rosy colour as the flame: the mists, the public square under the bombax trees, the huts, the low wall of the palace, and the arcade at the back. Then the mists evaporated; and the huts, the wall, the gallery and the earth in the public square turned red; the red earth regained its supremacy; the huts and the gallery took on once again their blood-red tint; the earth was red again, a darker and more velvety red. And the sky turned blue and bluer, and still more blue – gradually turning to that sheerest blue that would soon be unbearable in its azure brilliance.

Then Clarence returned to those thoughts which only a short while before had been holding out their hands to each other in the misted heaviness of his being. The first to meet him told him something about a light, soft object which he had kicked with his foot on rising, and which had almost made him measure his length on the floor. He went back into the hut. At the bedside, he stumbled against a pile of leaves or grasses. But . . . No, they were neither leaves nor grasses ! Now he knew what it was : there was no need to look, no need for any more light than that which feebly lit the interior of the hut, in order to find out what it was; there was no need for him to have gone to the bedside, and to have tripped over something light and soft : all he had to do was to breathe the air as he came back into the hut.

When he went outside again, he found he was holding a great sheaf of flowers. He looked at it for a moment with disgust, then threw it angrily far away from him. It was not the first time he had found these sheaves of flowers in his hut. He had expressly forbidden Akissi to bring any more, but Akissi took no notice of him; she liked the flowers' insidious fragrance.

'Akissi !' he shouted.

A woman came timidly out of the hut.

'Did I not forbid you to put flowers at the bedside?'

The woman made no reply; she stood with her head hanging low, as if she were trying to hide her face.

'Go and throw this rubbish on the square,' said Clarence, pointing to the flowers. 'It stinks the place out.'

The woman picked up the sheaf of flowers and went through the gate of the courtyard. Now she was standing on the square looking from left to right, as if uncertain where she would throw the flowers. Clarence was watching her from behind the low palace wall.

'Throw it down where you are,' he shouted. 'That's quite far enough.'

He took a deep breath of fresh air. He felt as if he were breathing for the first time since he had got up. That heavy odour of flowers and leaf-mould was the odour of the forest – an abominable, unmentionable odour ! The woman came back to the courtyard and started walking at once towards the neighbouring huts.

'Where are you going?' shouted Clarence.

'I'm going for water,' she replied.

He watched her walking away. 'Queer woman !' he thought to himself. 'Never the same for two days on end.' And he began to ponder over that continual change. Was it not strange? It was incomprehensible. He closed his eyes, the better to ponder over it. In Aziana, as in Adramé, everyone closed their eyes when they were thinking. When he opened them again, Akissi was coming back from the fountain; she was bearing a tall earthenware jar on her head.

'Here is water,' she said, putting the great jar down on the ground. The jar had the same red colour as the hut, the same light glaze as the hut's.

'You should not expose your body to the morning air,' she went on. 'The morning air is sharper than the air of night. You will catch cold !'

It was quite true. He was running the risk of catching a bad cold, after the heavy warmth of the hut. In the mornings, the air was particularly keen.

'Put on your *boubou*,' said Akissi.

He donned his *boubou*.

'Where did you get that jar?' he asked.

'I went to get water,' she said.

'That's not what I asked you. You left this hut without a jar and now you come back with a jar on your head.'

'The jar was at the fountain.'

'But I don't like using other people's jars. You don't know where it might have been.'

'This one was very clean.'

Yes, the jar was probably clean. The people of Aziana were very clean. All the same, one shouldn't go borrowing other people's jars. It might cause unpleasantness. What would the woman say when she came to the fountain and found her jar had disappeared?

'But when you left here you didn't have a jar,' he said.

'Naturally I did not have one; this one I borrowed.'

'You do not understand what I mean. I was wondering how, when you had no jar, you could have gone to get water.'

Akissi hesitated a moment, then said: 'I knew that I should find some jar or other at the fountain.'

Lord! what a queer way of thinking Akissi sometimes had! It was impossible to follow her, thought Clarence. She made your head spin! . . . But perhaps she had just as much difficulty in following Clarence, too.

'There are moments when I just don't understand you,' he said.

'No more than I understand the way you change each day. Just now I was watching you going to the fountain and you were a different woman. I sometimes wonder if you are always the same woman.'

'Is a woman ever the same?' she said.

No, a woman isn't always the same; she could not always be the same. He himself . . . But the whole thing was too vexatious to be funny.

'Next time, don't put flowers in the hut,' said Clarence.

He squatted down by the door and began gazing at the sky. 'Another killing day!' he thought. Ah, yes, he had killed a good deal of time already! If his days had left their bones behind them, he could have filled many huts with their remains. But the days left nothing behind. All those days, when one came to think of it, were just a great emptiness; and today would be the same as every day. Yet if Nagoa and Noaga were to come and have a chat, and if Samba Baloum were to come and join them, the day would pass fairly well. It's terrible to have nothing to do!

At first, when he had left the forest behind, it had seemed rather pleasant to be able to sit on one's behind and receive board and lodging in return. But then he had begun to be terribly bored. The beggar had hinted at the small services Clarence might be asked to perform, but there had never been any services to perform, either great or small. Everyone seemed to consider Clarence incapable of doing any work. But he was quite able to work and had proved it. When they had begun to pick cotton, he had watched the women working – for it was women's work – and when they had beaten this felt-like wadding and when the women had spun it, he had still gone on watching, for it was still women's work. But when the cotton had finally been transformed into great hanks of coarse thread, he had begun to work, for at that moment it had become men's work: he had woven the cotton, and had even become expert at it. But could one really go on weaving all day long?

Why was he not given any work? He was becoming frightfully lazy hanging round like this. His woman, Akissi, whom Samba Baloum had brought him on the first day, when he had been showing Clarence the hut which the naba's masons had just finished for him, Akissi relieved him of all material worries. Well, perhaps others could get used to that way of life; perhaps others could allow themselves to depend on their women for everything; but not Clarence. And he yawned at great length. This day did not look like being any less tedious than the others.

Akissi came out of the hut with her mortar and pestle. She sat down on a little stool and began to pound millet. As always, she was the first to beat out the rhythm of the mortar and pestle in Aziana, and this must certainly have disturbed those who were hoping for a long lie in. She lifted her arms very high, and the pestle fell with a heavy thud into the mortar; a fine floury dust began to rise.

'I wonder if I should get washed?' Clarence thought. 'If I don't wash now, when the air is still cool, I shan't have the strength to do so later on.'

'Akissi, where is the jar?' he asked.

He knew perfectly well in which corner of the hut Akissi put it; in fact, the sole aim of the question was to have the jar brought to him, and Akissi took the hint. She came out of the hut with the jar firmly planted on her head. 'I get lazier every day,' thought Clarence. And he slipped off his *boubou*.

'Are you sure the jar was clean?' he asked.

'It could not have been any cleaner than it was,' replied Akissi.

Clarence looked suspiciously at the water. He poured out a little, examined it in the palm of his hand, sniffed it, and then, re-

assured, dashed his face with water and rubbed his fingers with it.
'I wash myself like a cat,' he said to himself. 'I shan't get rid of
the odour like this.'

'Bring the stool,' he told Akissi.

He thought that the only way to rid himself of this odour that
seemed to be sticking to his skin, sticking to it like a second skin,
would be to have a shower. Akissi brought the stool and stepped
on to it. She put the jar on her head again and tipped it towards
Clarence.

'Right!' said Clarence.

The water poured over him like a real shower. It was very
pleasant. Clarence had invented the system and now many people
in Aziana washed themselves in this way. Clarence rubbed himself
down very energetically.

'I don't like you to take jars that don't belong to us,' he said.
'You'd better put this one back where you found it, as soon as
you've finished with it.'

Yes, this invention of his wasn't bad at all, though of course it
didn't need a genius to discover it! The water poured over one
with delicious coolness, and one could get a thorough wash. Moreover, the water seemed to replenish the body with delightful stores
of energy which one could not use in any way; or at least, Clarence could not use them in any way: they were gratuitous stores
of energy, free to all, and yet they were energy all the same – real
energy!

Aziana was now waking up. Clarence could see, beyond the low
wall, people coming and going on the square. They would shout
'Good morning' to one another from opposite sides of the square.
People kept asking Clarence how he was or if he had slept well; a
few came and leaned on the wall and had a little chat with him –
small talk that did not commit anyone. Or they would congratulate
Clarence on looking so well. Yes, that shower taken on his own
doorstep and punctuated by friendly greetings had been a splendid
thing; it had been a real pleasure.

'Here comes Samba Baloum,' said Akissi.

Clarence saw Samba Baloum coming his way. The big lump, as
the two boys called him, was walking as always, with tiny steps

and swaying hips. There was no hurry: he was never in a hurry about anything.

'Slept well?' Samba Baloum inquired.

'Badly,' replied Clarence. 'The odour of the forest stank out the whole hut.'

'It's not an unpleasing odour,' said Samba Baloum.

'It's the sort of odour that drives men mad,' said Clarence.

'Heh! . . . Heh! . . .' said Samba Baloum.

His mouth had split wide open, but it only brought forth a faint, dry cackle. Yet this was supposed to be laughter; but laughter was already too much – it was too fatiguing for words. That is why Samba Baloum's enormous hilarity expressed itself in a little cackle.

'Wash my back, Baloum,' said Clarence. 'I can't reach my back properly. And Akissi cannot pour water and rub my back at one and the same time.'

Samba Baloum washed his back.

'How's that?' he asked.

'That's fine,' said Clarence.

How soft Baloum's hands were! They were soft as sponges. No – as soft as chamois leather. Hands like that ought not really to be used for cleaning things – they were too plump, too soft. One couldn't imagine what Baloum had inside him – lots of fat, certainly, and then lots of flesh probably; and yet – there was still something else: something vaguely spongy; or perhaps it was wind; perhaps he was like those bagpipes made of animal skins that the musicians played on the nights when there was dancing in the square. Akissi, now, had a rather rough hand, a real hand.

'You're looking better than you did when you came,' said Samba Baloum.

'Does that surprise you?' Clarence cried. 'Do you realize that I am doing nothing at all? Abso-lute-ly nothing!'

'It's all right, you're doing quite enough,' said Samba Baloum. 'The naba is pleased with you.'

'The naba! . . . The naba! . . .' cried Clarence.

He couldn't bear the sight of the naba's beard any more. Every-thing hung on that beard – favour and disfavour, grace and disgrace. Who did the naba think he was? He thought he was God Almighty! That old mummy thought he was God Almighty!

'You're getting quite chubby,' said Samba Baloum. 'When the beggar first brought you here, you were like an old hen.'

'Why did Nagoa and Noaga call him an old rogue?' asked Clarence.

'Now if you're going to listen to those two scamps! . . .' protested Samba Baloum.

But the beggar was really a bit of an old rogue. A bit of a rogue and a bit of a knave. He was a lot of rather unpleasant things. 'And yet,' thought Clarence, 'in suggesting that I should take my ease in Aziana, he had the right idea . . . He had an eye for comfort . . .' Was it the same eye in which the suspicious little flame would blaze?

'One can't really call him an old rogue,' he said.

'No, one can't,' said Samba Baloum. He cackled weakly.

'But what *are* you doing, Samba Baloum?' demanded Clarence. 'I can quite well soap my thighs myself.'

'Oh, well, then, I've finished,' said Samba Baloum. And he gave Clarence a hopeful smack on the backside.

'I don't like to be slapped like that,' said Clarence.

'You are a real fighting-cock,' said Samba Baloum. 'The beggar knew what he was talking about.'

Akissi began to dry Clarence. She used a kind of spongy towel. Before Clarence came to Aziana and learnt to weave, this kind of material was quite unknown; people dried themselves with horribly rough cloth which nearly skinned them alive. But Clarence had learnt to weave with yarn which had been deliberately made very soft; now people used these towels all the time.

'Noaga! Nagoa!' Clarence joyfully shouted.

The two boys had just jumped over the wall. Their company would bring a little life into the dullness of the morning.

'Up already?' said Clarence.

'Yes, we are!' cried the boys.

'If they're up early,' remarked Baloum, 'they're up to no good.'

'Clarence, will you tell us if it's altogether unpleasant to be dried like that by Akissi?' said Nagoa.

'What do you know about it?' asked Clarence.

'He has a good idea,' said Noaga. 'Now then, Akissi, don't blush like that.'

'If you're looking for children, you won't find them here,' said Samba Baloum. And he gave Noaga's backside a playful slap.

'I don't know why you go round smacking people's backsides,' said Noaga. 'If you're not smacking Clarence's, you're smacking Nagoa's, or mine. You shouldn't do it.'

'If you do it again,' said Clarence, 'I'll boot your bottom so hard you won't be able to sit on it.'

'May I remind you that, as far as I am concerned, such things have not the slightest importance,' said Baloum.

'You are a queer man,' said Clarence.

'A man, did you say? . . .' said Samba Baloum. And he sighed. 'The king only knows ! . . .' he said.

Clarence put his *boubou* on.

'Akissi, don't forget to take the jar back to where you found it,' he said.

'Isn't it yours?' asked Baloum. 'I'd have sworn it was yours.'

'It's a jar I borrowed,' said Akissi. And she gave Samba Baloum a little wink.

'Yes, this jar is not as beautiful as your own,' said Baloum. 'The material is not so fine.'

'It's not that it is any less beautiful,' said Clarence. 'It's simply that I don't like using other people's jars.'

And now what should he do? He had washed, he had chatted, but the day had hardly begun, and it would be a long one.

'What shall we do?' he asked. It was not one of those days when he would have liked to weave.

'We'll go and see Fatou's presents,' said Noaga.

'Fatou? . . . Who's Fatou?' said Clarence.

'The girl who's just got engaged,' said Nagoa.

'First we'll sit in the shade and smoke a pipe,' said Samba Baloum. 'We'll smoke a pipe and treat ourselves to a calabash of wine . . . Here, you two,' he said, addressing the boys, 'go and get some calabashes from the naba's.'

'And what if the master of ceremonies finds out?' said Nagoa.

'Will *you* take the beating?' asked Noaga.

'If the master of ceremonies shows his face,' said Samba Baloum, 'you can take to your heels.'

And he walked over to the arcade with Clarence.

'Let us sit here,' said Samba Baloum.

They squatted down, and Baloum pulled his usual face; a nasty grimace it was, but which, like everything else to do with him, was not of the slightest importance.

'I shouldn't like the master of ceremonies to find us out,' said Clarence.

'Pah!'

'Don't you know, he's always on the look-out!'

'Don't worry,' said Samba Baloum, 'I'll look after him!'

He took his pipe out of his *boubou*. Akissi had gone back to her pestle and mortar, and the rhythm of the pestle pounding the mortar could be heard. Several other women had joined her, and their pestles were all falling in time.

'Why! here they are back already!' said Samba Baloum. 'The master of ceremonies can't have been so very terrifying.'

The two boys had slung the calabashes on a stick and each bore an end of the stick on his shoulder. They lined up the calabashes in front of Clarence and Baloum, and sat down facing them.

'I drink to the health of the master of ceremonies,' said Samba Baloum.

'That's a bright idea,' said Clarence.

'Here's to him. And the devil take him, if he hasn't done so already!' cried the two boys.

'It's never too late to mend, remember,' said Samba Baloum.

All the time he was drinking, Clarence was watching the sky. The sun was still not very high in the heavens.

'The days are very long,' he remarked, putting down his calabash.

'As long as they're fine . . .' said Samba Baloum.

'They're *too* fine!' thought Clarence. 'Too uniformly fine for my liking. The days follow one another, and they're all alike – deceptively alike; there's not one you could pick out and say it was different from the rest.'

'On the other hand, the nights are short,' said Samba Baloum.
'The nights?' said Clarence. 'I wasn't talking about the nights.'
'Heh, heh! I know what I'm talking about,' cackled Samba
Baloum. 'The nights are always too short.'

'But I *don't* know what you're talking about,' Clarence protested. 'What do you mean? Not all nights are short.'

The night he had just passed, its air rank and foul with the
odour of the forest, was not a short night. That heat, that furious
exacerbation of the senses, that dark state in which one ceased to
be oneself and was transformed into a sort of beast – all that
clashed with the idea of a short night.

'There are nights that are so thick, you can cut them with a
knife,' he said.

'*You* needn't grumble!' said Samba Baloum.

'If we were in your place, *we* wouldn't grumble,' said the boys.

They were eyeing Akissi. Clarence followed their gaze. 'How
stupid they are!' he thought. None the less he went on watching
Akissi, watching her raising the pestle high in the air and pounding it in the mortar ... the thrusting movement of the pestle ...
'I've got a dirty mind,' he told himself. And he blushed violently.
Yet ... Yes, Akissi *did* have her good points. No, he did not mean
that in the sense in which Samba Baloum would have taken it;
Akissi's qualities were not foreign to her nature, but Clarence did
not want to think about them. He knew quite well that he had
become a different man since he had come to live in Aziana. But
he detested this new man, he refused to countenance this new man
who at night so utterly abandoned himself because of the odour of
a bunch of flowers. Akissi had qualities that had nothing to do
with that kind of baseness: she was courageous, she was scrupulously clean, she had learned to cook rather less glutinous dishes
than those which were customary in the South ... She had – yes,
she had very great qualities. And she also had some incredible
faults; one would swear she did things on purpose sometimes –
those sheaves of flowers that she left lying around the hut, or that
borrowed jar which did not belong to them....

'I'm not grumbling,' he said.

Samba Baloum and the two boys laughed heartily.

'Oh, you make me sick,' said Clarence.

'You're a real fighting-cock,' said Baloum.

'First I'm an old hen, then I'm a fighting-cock . . .' cried Clarence. 'I've already told you often enough that I don't care for such comparisons. Besides, you ought to make up your minds: I can't be a cock and a hen at one and the same time.'

'I've made up my mind,' said Samba Baloum. 'At first, I didn't know whether you were a tup or a ewe: you were all skin and bone, and there was no way of telling. But now you're a different person altogether.'

'You have Akissi now,' said the boys.

They laughed, and Samba Baloum laughed too; they were laughing as if the joke they had made were in the very best of taste. . . . 'Yes, I have Akissi . . .' Clarence said to himself. And he turned again to watch her pounding millet. 'I have Akissi, changeable as she is; I have a different Akissi every night.' He puffed fitfully at his pipe. His thoughts began to dwell on his past life. If anyone who had known him in those days could have seen him now, smoking and drinking, crouching in the manner of black men under the arcade, and dressed in a *boubou* like a black man, he would have appeared quite unrecognizable.

And who could tell just what had happened to him? Clarence himself did not know. The odour of the forest had probably had something to do with it; certainly that caressing odour which is the very odour of the South itself – provocative and cruel, lascivious and unmentionable – that had something to do with it all. But Clarence breathed this odour with great distaste, and he always thought about it with disgust. Buttocks and breasts – that's all one saw, and perhaps that's what one breathed, too – the odour of buttocks and breasts. In this respect Akissi was no different from the others; Clarence could not have distinguished her from any of the others in this respect. He could not recognize her face any more than he could recognize the faces of the other women; the only time he could be sure it was her face was when she showed it in the porthole of the hut: Akissi would put her face in the porthole's oval frame, and Clarence would be able to recognize it as hers. But as soon as he saw her whole body, it was as if he could no longer see her face: all he had eyes for were her buttocks and her breasts – the same high, firm buttocks and the same pear-shaped breasts as the other women in Aziana . . . And he found the day too long; he kept waiting for the night, but not in the same way Samba Baloum meant. Good heavens, no! Not in that way! . . . He was afraid of the night; he did not look forward to it. The beast inside him was looking forward to it perhaps, but he feared it, detested it. . . .

He wanted to get up and go, but he found the master of ceremonies standing before him. The man had approached in his own furtive way, appearing unexpectedly and in a manner that was intended to catch people napping. Yet he was only a master of ceremonies, he was not even the naba's right-hand man. Why did he try to give himself such airs?

'Are you drinking?' the master of ceremonies asked.

'I've got to do something to pass the time,' said Samba Baloum. The master of ceremonies looked at each of them in turn.

'I can't help wondering where you got this great pile of calabashes,' he said, when he had finished inspecting them.

'Don't worry your head about that, and have a drink with us,' said Samba Baloum.

'We are inviting you to join us,' said Clarence.

'Do you hear?' said the boys. 'He's inviting you to join us.'

'Don't let's stand on ceremony,' said Samba Baloum. 'It's part of a stock of wine that Clarence keeps in his hut and which he intended us to drink.'

'Your good health!' said Clarence, toasting the master of ceremonies.

'And yours!' replied the master of ceremonies.

He took a sip and kept it for a moment in his mouth.

'It's first-rate, isn't it?' said Samba Baloum.

'It tastes exactly like the naba's wine,' said the master of ceremonies. He looked hard at the two boys.

'If I ever catch you pinching the naba's wine . . .' he began.

'What, us?' cried the boys. 'Us, pinch grandpa's wine? . . . Baloum, you know the sort of boys we are . . . say something!'

'They're no angels,' said Samba Baloum. 'Everybody knows that they're no angels. They're not expected to be; it's not their job. But as for pinching the naba's wine – I can give you my word that they would never do such a thing.'

'But they're no angels,' remarked the master of ceremonies.

'Who wants to be an angel!' asked Samba Baloum. 'Apart from myself – I can't help it . . .'

'Good for you, Samba Baloum!' said the boys.

They all laughed, even the master of ceremonies, who showed all his cruel teeth.

'*He* at any rate,' said the master of ceremonies, pointing to Clarence, '*he* would find it difficult to pass himself off as an angel. Every night . . .'

'That's enough!' said Samba Baloum sharply.

'What do you mean, "every night"?' asked Clarence.

'I know what I'm talking about,' said the master of ceremonies. 'You can play the startled innocent if you like, but you won't take me in. I'm no angel either. I know what *your* little game is!'

'I'm not playing any game!' protested Clarence.

'You're not going to tell me that night after night you . . .'

'Not another word!' broke in Samba Baloum. 'If the naba were to hear what you've been saying, it would cost you dear, master of ceremonies or no. You might find you'd broken your stick across your own back.'

'My stick?' said the master of ceremonies. 'I should like to know where it has got to. I've been looking for it ever since I got up.'

'We're not interested in your stick,' said Clarence. 'I should like to know what you are insinuating when you say . . .'

'Poppycock, that's all it is!' said Samba Baloum.

'If you were referring to the wine . . .' Clarence went on.

'It was nothing to do with the wine!' said the master of ceremonies. 'And if it were a question of the wine – no one knew that you had a private stock of wine.'

'No one enters my hut without my permission, either!' cried Clarence.

'Now that's going a bit too far!' said the master of ceremonies. 'And you have the face to tell me only a moment ago that you weren't up to any kind of game? You must certainly take me for a bigger fool than I thought you did . . . What woman were you with last night?'

Samba Baloum struck the master of ceremonies across the mouth. 'You'll answer to the naba for that impertinent question!' he cried.

'If that's the way you want it,' said the master of ceremonies, 'I'm going. I, too, could if I wished strike you across the mouth, but it would ill behove me to strike a low creature like you. Do you hear me? You're a low creature, not a man. You can take that whichever way you like . . . But as for *him*! . . .' he said, pointing to Clarence. 'As for him! . . .'

He rose proudly to his full height. He was going to leave them when he noticed the stick the boys had used to carry the calabashes.

'My stick!' he cried. 'What's my stick doing here?'

'How were we to know it was your stick?' said the boys.

'It shall be brought to the naba's ear that you have been drinking his wine,' said the master of ceremonies, thrusting the stick under his arm.

'And it shall also be brought to the naba's ear that you drank some of it yourself,' said Samba Baloum. 'And the words you have uttered will be brought to his ear at the same time.'

'I don't give a damn for you and your fighting-cock!' cried the master of ceremonies, striding stiffly away.

'Windbag,' said Samba Baloum under his breath.

'But look here, will you tell me? . . .' began Clarence.

'Drunken drivel,' said Samba Baloum, 'the sheerest drunken drivel!'

'He wasn't drunk,' said Clarence. 'He couldn't have been drunk, when all he had was half a calabash-full of wine.'

'He's never sober,' said Samba Baloum.

'I was with Akissi last night,' said Clarence.

'Of course you were!' said Samba Baloum. 'Who else would you have gone to bed with? You see it *was* just utter drivel, drunken drivel. I can't understand why you seem to attach so much importance to it.'

'Because you do so yourself,' said Clarence. 'Otherwise you would not have threatened to report what he said to the naba.'

'I just said that to frighten him,' said Samba Baloum. 'I just said that to keep him quiet about the wine.'

'I'm beginning to understand,' said Clarence.

'Of course you're beginning to understand,' said Samba Baloum. 'Everything is clear now, and you understand. I had to frighten him off and I seized on the first excuse I could find. But as you could see it did not have much effect: it wasn't, I'm afraid, a terribly good excuse.'

'No, it wasn't very good,' Clarence agreed. 'But he called me a fighting-cock all the same.'

'He only said that because he's ridiculously jealous of his women. He has several women, and a few of them are really pretty, and so he imagines that every man is paying court to them. He must have thought that you, too, were spending nights on the tiles at his expense. He accused you falsely in order to find out the truth. He was pumping you, don't you see? That's the way he is.'

'I've never looked at his women,' said Clarence. 'I don't even know who they are.'

'But he believes everybody is running after them and going into ecstasies at the sight of them.'

'Idiot!' said Clarence.

'That's the word for it,' agreed Samba Baloum . . . 'Come on, let's go and see Fatou's engagement presents.' And he got up, pulling a frightful face. 'She will certainly have received some magnificent presents,' he went on. 'They get engaged, and as long as the engagement lasts everything flows with milk and honey . . . Akissi!' he shouted. 'Stow these calabashes in the hut, there's a good girl. One never knows; some wicked person might come along and steal them.'

'Akissi,' said Clarence, 'where were you last night?'

'Where else would she be, if not in bed beside you?' said Samba Baloum.

'Akissi, this morning when you left the hut you were walking in a way that I had never seen before,' said Clarence. 'It was not the way you usually walk.'

'I was tired,' she said, and she stretched voluptuously. 'I had a good right to be tired, hadn't I?' she said, smiling suggestively.

'Heh! heh! What a fighting-cock you are!' said Samba Baloum, giving Clarence's backside a resounding smack.

'Lay off, Baloum,' said Clarence. 'This is more serious than you might think.'

'They're just cock and bull tales, and more cock than bull, heh! heh!' said Samba Baloum. 'Nobody's asking you what you were doing last night ... Oh, come on,' he said, putting his arm round Clarence's waist and drawing him away, 'oh, you *are* getting chubby, aren't you, and all over, too! Isn't he getting chubby, boys?'

'Chub, chub, chubby!' chanted the boys, and they felt him all over with their lively hands.

'Oh, *you're* not going to start now, are you?' groaned Clarence.

'Oh, they're just a couple of jokers,' said Samba Baloum.

'I suppose you call yourself a joker, too,' said Clarence, trying to avoid the boys' playful hands. 'You all of you keep feeling me all over as if I were a bird ready for market.'

He thought for a moment.

'No, not like a bird,' he went on. 'You keep going over my points, feeling me as if I were a prize stallion!'

'A stallion?' cried Samba Baloum. 'Oh, that's a good one! I've got to laugh. Excuse me, but I've got to laugh.'

He cackled much more loudly than before. As for the boys, they were doubled up with laughter.

'A stallion, a stud-horse, a travelling sire, that's what you take me for!' cried Clarence.

He looked from one to the other and found it rather strange that they should turn their eyes away. Had he said something incongruous? If he had, it wasn't anything more laboured or coarser than what they had said themselves. But it was not at all incongruous: he really *was* a stallion. There were nights, those nights when the odour of the forest filled the hut, when he was simply a foul, filthy stallion ... One day, the king would come and sit under the arcade, he would come and sit in the very place where they were sitting now, fragile and pure, and strong with a strength that was drawn from that purity, so indescribably pure, so rare! ... Clarence heaved a sigh ... Could a stallion approach the king?

. . . He sighed again . . . Oh, how long these days of waiting seemed, waiting for the king's coming! And how heavy! These days were a great void, and a terrible burden; they were . . . One couldn't say what they were . . . They were messy and glutinously filthy . . . Would the king be able to see anything else but this filth? He would see nothing but the filth, the foulness, and he would draw away in disgust, he . . .

'Are you coming?' the boys were saying.

'I'm coming,' said Clarence.

Translated by James Kirkup

Cameroun

Mbella Sonne Dipoko

AUTOBIOGRAPHY

We crawled and cried and laughed
Without hope
Without despair.
We grew up
Fenced in by the forest.
But this world of uncles and fathers and mothers and others –
Our fine world of greenness and grins was blown away
By the terrible storm of growth
And the mind soon flung pebbles at the cranes of the off-shore
    island.
But today
Floods flee the rising sun
And owls hoot from the edge of the dark song.
Like cripples blinded by sandy winds
Dreams drift under the low sky of our sleep
And our hearts listen to the voice of days in flight
Our thoughts dusting the past.

LOVE

1
Let's go and learn by the candles of fire-flies
The difficult lesson on radio signalling
Which others older than us have felt
On the blackboard of the long night
So that tomorrow when we are apart
We may transmit on the frequency of our love
Those intimate messages we can never post.

2

And the voice became silent.
The night passed
Six times at eight o'clock
Twelve times the postman
Without a word for me.
Still from dawn I watched for the mail
I watched for the message dusk might bring.
Like a maimed dove the wind arrived with the perfume of time
Pining in the grottoes of our dreams
And the elected in the Night's Kingdom prayed:
Eulogies to the initiated one!
And the tongues of the temple candles trembled
Lighting up the dream pages of love.

3

Wipe your tears in the distance
I do not want to live any longer
For days have grown beards
And nights have become lonesome.
Letters cannot comfort me.
They remind me of the past which you know is dead.
And so you send a ghost to me when you write those letters
Letting my lips kiss a face so far behind.

Ferdinand Oyono

From The Old Negro and the Medal

Le Vieux Nègre et la Medaille is a tragi-comedy about Meka, an elderly
man who has been summoned by the local white administrator to receive a medal from the High Commissioner. This is for his service to the
French Government as a father of two soldiers who died fighting for
France in the war, for his services to the local administration and to his
church. His community goes hysterical about this 'honour', and gather
in great numbers in the open air to witness the ceremony. A circle has
been drawn with lime within which Meka has to stand, in the blazing
sun, waiting for the Commissioner to arrive. All the white officials and
church dignitaries are sitting in the shade, including a Greek who is to
be honoured in the same manner. After several exhausting hours the
ceremony is performed. A reception is held in a hall. Meka is left sleeping in it when the crowd is made to disperse by the police in some confusion, just when a political meeting is in the making. Meka wakes up
to find that the roof of the hall is collapsing in the wake of a violent
tornado. He has just found his way out of a pool of water when French
police arrest him because he has no papers and is in a white quarter. He
is humiliated at the police station before he is thrown in a cell. 'Bird's
Gullet', as the police officer is nicknamed, recognizes him as the award
winner. He releases Meka, displaying the attitude that he is doing the
old man a favour. Meka is disillusioned in the white man's brotherhood
talk. Below is an account of old Meka's ordeal in the sun.

WAITING FOR A MEDAL

Meka stood bareheaded and quite still, his arms to his sides, inside
the circle painted with whitewash where he had been placed to
wait for the arrival of the White Chief. The guards were having
difficulty keeping back the crowd of his fellow-Africans massed
behind him. In front under the shade of M. Fouconi's veranda

were the whitemen but Father Vandermayer with his black cassock and his black beard was the only one Meka could recognize. For him, whitemen were like antelopes, their faces all looked the same.

Meka peered around him cautiously like an animal that feels watched. He had to control an urge to pass his hand over his face and wipe off the sweat which had gathered in a bead at the end of his nose. He became aware that the situation he found himself in was foreign to him. Neither his grandfather nor his father nor any member of his huge family had ever been placed as he was inside a whitewash circle, between two worlds, his own world and the world of those others who had been called ghosts when they first came into the land. He was not with his own people, and he was not with the others. He wondered what he was doing out there. He could just as well have waited with Kelara, who was somewhere, he knew, in the crowd screaming behind him, and been called out for the medal when the great Chief of the whitemen had arrived. What was this absurd idea of the Chief of the Doum whitemen to have him inside a whitewash circle? He had been there an hour already, perhaps longer. Still the great Chief of the whites had not come.

It was hot. Meka began to wonder if his heart was beating in his feet. He had put his shoes on at the top of the hill where M. Fouconi's office first comes into sight. He could hardly feel he had them on as he went to report to the Commandant. Meka had marched to his position underneath the flag as if he had been the King of Doum. He had not even given a glance aside at the tribal chiefs whom he recognized by their red shoulder bands.

'More of them bursting with envy!' he said to himself. 'I despise them! I despise them!'

Then he had brought his heels together in the way he had seen soldiers do when a whiteman went by. A whiteman went by him, gave him a smile, then went over and joined the other whitemen, pointing back at Meka with his finger. Then Meka heard confused voices raised among the Europeans. But he stood rigidly to attention. He felt he was as hard as a plank of wood.

His tiredness had started first in his stiff neck. Meka again began to look around him. Now that he could feel his heart was beating in his feet, he started to worry about whether he would be able to stay in his circle until the great Chief of the whitemen arrived. He looked down at his shoes. They looked as if they had swollen since the morning when he had emptied out the sand he had filled them up with for the night. He tried to move one of his feet; he clasped his fists and stopped breathing. For a few seconds he felt a great sense of peace. Then he tried to put all his weight on his right foot which was hurting less than the other. His left foot grew easier but now he could not tell what was going on in his right foot. It felt as if the needle Ela had given him was going through his little toe, then up through his ankle, right up to his thigh and sticking into his backbone. The needle multiplied into a million needles swarming and pricking in every part of his body. Meka was bathed in sweat.

'It's a good job I didn't put socks on,' he said to himself.

He tried to call up to his imagination a more excruciating pain than the one he was feeling.

'But what about it?' he said to himself. 'I am a man, just as my ancestors made me and left me. They are watching me now, in this situation . . . I must not let them be ashamed of me. I was circumcised with the knife and the doctor spat out pimento on to the wound. I did not cry out . . .'

He clenched his teeth a little harder.

'I did not cry,' he thought. 'In all my life I have never cried. A man, a real man, never cries . . .'

That is what Meka was, a man and a real man. Was he not the son of the great Meka who held out for so long against the first whitemen? Well then, was he going to cry now in front of them and in front of his own people who knew his father or had heard the stories of him?

Transfigured, Meka looked over to the whites. He stretched out one foot and moved the other to the side. Then he did it the other way round, and brought his heels together again. He turned around and smiled at the Africans, as if he wanted to reassure them. He could not feel his shoes any more. He looked up at the flag waving above his head, he looked at the whites and at the soldiers. Then he braced his neck.

'Even if he doesn't come till the night, I will wait,' he said. 'Even if he doesn't come until tomorrow, or for a year or till the end of the world . . .'

Suddenly his forehead wrinkled and an ominous expression crossed his face. There seemed to be a heavy weight at the bottom of his belly. From far far away he could feel approaching the urge to satisfy a need.

M. Fouconi was in the first row of the Doum Europeans, sitting between Gullet and his assistant, a young man with a plump figure. He had a profusion of dark hair and a wide pelvis. The Africans called him 'Next-to-nearly-woman'.

M. Fouconi came forward, down the steps and into the court-yard. His assistant joined him. They chatted for a moment a few feet away from Meka. M. Fouconi looked over to him and smiled. Meka returned the widest smile he could manage. Then the two whitemen went over to discuss with the Chief of the soldiers. M. Fouconi with his assistant still following went back to the group of whitemen.

'What if I just went away,' thought Meka. His feet were broil-ing. 'What if I just went away?'

He put the question to himself several times and shrugged his shoulders. Then, taking his courage in both hands, he wiped his hand across his sweating face. He looked around as if to see if there was anyone who had noticed.

He swayed and made a vague movement. He wanted to whistle. He took a hold on himself and wiped his hand across his lips. He wondered what he ought to think about to help him forget the urge he could feel becoming more and more pressing, and the heat of the fire that was consuming his feet. He would have given the whole world to be behind his hut under the magnolia tree where he crouched down every morning after his prayers. He closed his eyes.

'Almighty God,' he prayed to himself. 'Thou alone seest all that passeth in the hearts of men, Thou seest that my dearest wish at this moment as I wait for the medal and for the White Chief, alone in this circle, between two worlds' – he opened his eyes, looked in front of him and behind, then shut them again – 'between two worlds, O God, which Thou hast made utterly different from each other, that my dear wish and great longing is to take off these shoes and to have a piss . . . Yes, a piss . . . I am only a poor sinner and not worthy that Thou shouldest hear me . . . but I beseech Thee to aid me in this position which I have never been in before in all my life. In the name of Jesus Christ our Lord. So be it. I make the sign of the cross inwardly.'

He opened his eyes and passed his tongue over his lips. He felt easier.

It was half past ten. M. Fouconi was beginning to grow restless for the High Commissioner was now an hour late. They were waiting for him to take the salute. M. Fouconi went over to the group of native officials, then to the group of chiefs. He crossed over in front of Meka.

'Hot, isn't it?' he said to him.

'Yes, yes,' said Meka.

That was the limit of what he could say in French. M. Fouconi was joined by Gullet and his assistant. The whitemen began to cross back and forth in front of Meka.

'They are lucky not to suffer with their shoes,' thought Meka bitterly. 'They are wearing sun-helmets and they are young . . . I am a poor old man but I have to leave my head basking in the sun like a lizard.'

The Europeans passed across in front of him again. Their clothes were so white they hurt his eyes. He closed them, and his ears were tortured by the grating of the pebbles crushed by the whitemen's heavy feet.

Meka could not tell what hurt the most, his feet, his belly, the heat or his teeth. If he had been asked at that moment what was wrong he would not have been lying, as he usually was, when he gave his reply that the pain was everywhere at once. He was sorry he had not called at Mammy Titi's.

'At least there I could have taken something to stop me feeling the pain,' he told himself.

He looked over towards the Commercial Centre. At the same

moment the bugle sounded, and excitement stirred everywhere. Meka saw a huge black car flying a small tricolour approaching smartly towards the courtyard where he was standing. The car came to a stop in front of M. Fouconi and his assistant. The Commandant of Doum opened one of the doors. The enormous whitemen climbed out. Meka wondered which of them could be the great Chief they were all waiting for.

The two whites followed by M. Fouconi and his assistant moved up and down in front of the soldiers. Then M. Fouconi led them to the veranda of his office where the Europeans of Doum were awaiting them.

A few moments later M. Fouconi presented the party of African officials to them. Then the party of tribal chiefs. Here they shook a few hands. When Meka saw them coming towards him, he felt a knife blade going through his bowels. He clenched his teeth and braced his muscles as he did when he had to face danger. M. Fouconi indicated Meka with the point of his chin and then turned round to his chiefs, talking all the time. Meka wondered if they hadn't guessed about his urgent need. He blinked and clenched his fists. When M. Fouconi had finished what he had to say, the two whitemen, one after the other, each offered him a soft hand. He squeezed them like a damp rag. Then they went back to their own people.

Meka was at the end of his strength. It was so hot that he looked up into the sky to make sure the sun was still up there and not resting on his back.

'Why didn't they give him the medal? How could they leave a man of his age standing there for an hour? Had they lost the medal he was to have or forgotten to bring it?' The thought of this terrified him. What would he tell his friends, especially those who had watched him assume a kind of importance over the presentation. Ah, these whites. Nothing was straightforward with them. They ran when they walked and they were tortoises when they had made you a promise. They were taking their time over there, on the other side of the courtyard, dragging out their presentations and their salutations. He shook his head and looked down at his feet. He managed to hold himself from jumping in the air. 'I've got the feet of Nti! I've got the feet of Paul Nti,' he said in panic. He crossed his hands over the lower part of his belly. It made him feel much better.

He quickly put his heels together when he saw the two white strangers, with M. Fouconi, his assistant and M. Pipiniakis coming towards him. He thrust his arms as far as he could down the sides of his thighs, held his head high and stood absolutely still. He saw M. Pipiniakis stand by his side. M. Fouconi and the others remained a few steps in front of them.

The bugle sounded and there was a roll of drums. One of the enormous white men came towards M. Pipiniakis.

'It is him, the great white Chief!' thought Meka. He had never seen anything or anybody like him. All that he noticed were the voluminous folds of skin under his chin that almost concealed the knot of his tie.

The great Chief was speaking to M. Pipiniakis, as if he were speaking to someone who was deaf. M. Pipiniakis stood as still as a statue. When he had finished the Chief took a medal from a small case which M. Fouconi's assistant held out for him and pinned it on to M. Pipiniakis's breast. Then Meka saw the great Chief grasp his shoulders and put his cheeks one after the other against the cheeks of the Greek. At each movement the folds of skin under his chin trembled like a withered dun-coloured breast.

Then it was Meka's turn. The white Chief stood in front of him and began to shout. As he opened and shut his mouth his lower jaw went down and came up, puffing up and then deflating the skin under his chin. He took another medal from the case and came towards Meka, still talking. Meka had time to notice that it was not the same as the Greek's medal.

The white Chief was now at his shoulder. Meka looked down at him just at the moment when he was pinning the medal on to his breast. He could feel the hot breath through his khaki jacket. The Chief was sweating like a wrestler. It looked as if it had been raining over his back. A large damp patch stretched from his shoulders down to his buttocks.

Meka wondered anxiously if he was going to push his damp turkey-crop against each shoulder as he had done with M.

Pipiniakis. He breathed again when the white Chief, after he had pinned on the medal, took a few steps backward and shook his hand. Meka's hand swallowed up the hand of the Chief like a scrap of damp cotton rag.

Meka squinted down at his chest. The medal was certainly there, pinned on to his khaki jacket. He smiled and lifted up his head. Then he noticed that he was singing under his breath and that the whole of his face was beating time. His body was swaying in spite of himself and his knees bending and stretching like a spring. He no longer felt any pain. He could not even hear his bones cracking. The heat, his need, the pain in his feet – as if by magic they had all disappeared. He looked down again at the medal. He could feel his neck growing. Yes, his head was climbing up and up, up to heaven like the Tower of Babel. His forehead reached the clouds. His long arms gradually rose like the wings of a bird poised for flight . . .

Translated by John Reed

Ivory Coast

Aké Loba

From Kocoumbo, the Black Student

This extract is from Aké Loba's first novel. Kocoumbo, after having lived the first twenty years of his life in a bush village, leaves for France for higher studies. His father has been encouraged by the local French administrator, M. Gabe, to send him to France. Kocoumbo suffers the effects of uprooting – the solitude, the large gap in age between himself and his classmates – in a provincial *lycée*. He leaves and makes for Paris, mingling with the thousands of other uprooted African students. Here the clever Durandeau helps Kocoumbo, and he meets, among the numerous characters of the Latin Quarter, Joseph Mou, who loses faith and takes to hard drinking. As a result of the death of his father, Kocoumbo is forced to abandon his studies and take up a factory job, Here he becomes a close acquaintance of a militant white Communist who tries to convert him to Marxism. Kocoumbo loses himself in the dark world of the Pigalle, but M. Gabe, his father's friend, rescues him and makes it possible for him to complete his studies. When the hero is ready to return to Africa to work as a magistrate, Durandeau, now a politician, denounces him and threatens to continue to do so back in Africa, because he believes that Kocoumbo has caused the arrest of one of Durandeau's intimate friends. The following extract is a scene in which Kocoumbo is being accused by Durandeau.

A JUSTICE OF THE PEACE!

The north wind was sharp and piercing. In front of the Palais de Justice, Durandeau, Douk, and Mou were stamping their feet tirelessly. The uninterrupted stream of buses and cars going by added gusts of air to the icy blast; the sound of the engines was deadened by the bitter wind.

Douk glanced at his two companions, put up his collar, and said to Durandeau:

'I don't know why we don't go to see him instead of making him come here. In this cold weather . . .'

'What! Me go to see him!' exclaimed Durandeau. 'What do you take me for?'

'But you rang him up, didn't you?'

'Yes.'

'Well, well! I thought you'd sworn that you'd never speak to him again. How did you manage on the phone, then?'

Uninterested in Durandeau's reply, Douk gave a huge yawn, looked at the time by the gilt clock of the Palais de Justice, and yawned again, stretching his arms.

'I didn't sleep a wink last night. When I was leaving the Latin Quarter, about half-past one, I met a Spanish girl . . .' He yawned again and wiped his eyes.

'When I yawn like that, it makes my eyes water.'

Then, furrowing his brow, he suddenly exclaimed incredulously:

'Tell us, Durandeau, did you really ring up Kocoumbo?'

'Oh, you make me tired! Go away and leave us alone.'

Durandeau's forehead was lightly etched with wrinkles now. His cheeks had become fleshier. His new raglan overcoat contrasted with the clothes of the other two, who were dressed, one like a poor man, the other like a tramp.

Douk turned to Mou, who had not opened his mouth yet, to seek his approval.

'I ask for nothing better than to go away too,' said Mou. 'What are we doing here?'

His back was bent, his eyes were even duller than before, and the unstitched hem of his old gabardine hung down in places towards his shoes.

'I organized this meeting,' said Durandeau, 'to call Kocoumbo to account for the arrest of Nadan.'

'You think he had something to do with it?' asked Mou.

'I'm sure he had,' said Durandeau in a peremptory tone of voice. 'It was he who denounced Nadan. We are going to protest here at such a shameful deed, and we shall protest again in Africa! This is a matter of considerable importance: it must be used to show everybody that Kocoumbo is a coward, and that nobody can trust him, in spite of all his diplomas. From now on, he must be shut out of political life. He will never be anything but a pen-pusher any more.'

'No, Durandeau! Kocoumbo doesn't like politics,' protested Douk. 'I know him better than you do.'

'Can you give me the name of a single educated African who doesn't want to go into politics? Doesn't Kocoumbo sleep and eat and complain about life? Doesn't he bear grudges against other people? Well that's politics! But I'll break him, in Africa!'

'Why waste your breath when you've nothing to say?' said Mou. 'You see politics everywhere! I'm cold and I want to go.'

'Who's forcing you to stay? Get along with you!' said Durandeau in an irritated voice.

'What a bastard!' exclaimed Douk. 'Look, did you come here to settle a personal score, or to reveal the truth about Nadan?'

Durandeau could have throttled him. How could Douk, like Mou, dare to talk to him like that?

Ever since his dreams of becoming a doctor had collapsed, Durandeau had set his heart on a political career; he was absolutely determined to obtain an important post in Africa. He plotted, bribed, pulled strings. It was even said – and what wasn't said in this hotbed of diffuse, effervescent ambitions? – that after a meal, when he had eaten and drunk his fill, he went so far as to see himself as Prime Minister! His present aim was to make a reputation for himself: he wanted people to say that he had supported his fellow countrymen in France, that he had protected and defended them. Nadan's imprisonment was just what he wanted, for everybody would talk about it at home: if, in the midst of the scandal, Durandeau could appear as a man of honour and loyalty – while at the same time damning Kocoumbo! – then the election campaign which he planned to undertake on his return to Africa could be a triumph.

'Ah, at last!' said Douk. 'Here comes Kocoumbo!'

Kocoumbo had seen Douk's signals; a smile promptly softened his sullen face. Durandeau watched him coming with a mixture of curiosity and hatred.

'You know why I came here today,' he said to Kocoumbo with-

out offering him a hand which the other would not have taken.
'Why did you denounce Nadan? Why did you have him slung into
jail?'

'You don't believe a single word of what you're saying,' retorted
Kocoumbo in a slow voice. 'You know perfectly well why Nadan
has been arrested, and that I had nothing to do with it.'

Kocoumbo turned his back on Durandeau and explained to
Douk and Mou:

'Nadan is a close friend of mine; he comes from the same village
as I do. When I found out what he was doing, I was more ashamed
than any of you; I felt ashamed of what you said about him. I've
often offered to help him so that he could give up his filthy job and
go on with his studies. Now that that same Nadan, whom you all
spurned, is in prison, you have the nerve to come and blame me for
it! All I can tell you is that he's going to find out that a life of
crime is punished sometimes. I'm sorry about that for his sake, and
I pity him. But others might learn from what's happened to him.'

'So you're preaching at us now, are you? Because you've "done
France" you've got the urge to educate other Africans. In other
words, you think you're superior to your fellow countrymen. Did
you get the meaning behind his words, you two?'

Durandeau wanted to impress Kocoumbo's 'declarations' on the
memory of his two 'witnesses' so that he could quote them to the
students of the Cité Universitaire.

'You can read what you like into my words,' said Kocoumbo,
shrugging his shoulders. 'In any case, you can rest assured that I
prefer Nadan to you.'

'Hey, boys,' Douk broke in, his eyes sparkling with inaccount-
able mischief, 'you may want to go on arguing, but I warn you
that I'm frozen. Fancy talking about things like that outside, with
people looking at us! Come on, let's be serious! Let's go and
carry on the argument in a café!'

They crossed the bridge and hurried into the café adjoining the
Théâtre Sarah-Bernhardt, where they sat down in an empty corner.

'Where was I?' asked Durandeau. 'Oh, yes, I remember . . . In
spite of the position you occupy – perhaps you deserve it, I can't
tell – you haven't any right to accuse Nadan.'

'First of all, tell me straight out what's behind all this,' replied Kocoumbo. 'Ever since I've known you, you've done nothing but tell lies.'

'Now you're insulting me! Me, your patron! Me, who used to stint myself for you! Me, who gave you a taste for study! In return for all I did for you, you betrayed me; in return for all Nadan did for you, you had him sent to prison: you are an ingrate and you'll pay for your ingratitude!'

Kocoumbo stood up with a threatening air.

'That's enough!' exclaimed Douk. 'You're keeping the waiter hanging about for nothing. He's got a job to do! He hasn't any time to waste. And as for us, we need something hot. All right, all right!' he called out to the waiter, who was balancing his tray on a patient hand. 'Give me a good hot coffee, please, with a small glass of rum and a croissant. No – no rum: that doesn't go with a good hot croissant. Give me a good white coffee instead with a couple of croissants. This morning, I feel capable of eating anything up to five croissants. Now I come to think of it, give me five croissants just for me. I'm hungry, I am!'

Distracted from their quarrel by this shrill, staccato voice, the other two each ordered a coffee.

'A small bottle of rum for me,' said Mou.

As the waiter hesitated, he explained:

'A small flat bottle; not absolutely small, just medium small . . . And above all, no coffee – it wakes me up!'

'A whole bottle!' exclaimed Douk. 'You're as much of a toper as ever, and no mistake! . . . Well, what now?'

'You know, Douk, the distress Nadan's suffering causes me calls for nothing less than a bottle of rum. The idea that he's all alone in a cold damp cell makes me thirsty.'

'Take it easy, Mou!' said Douk, grinning all over his face. 'Are you tasting rum or oysters? You're going to kill yourself!'

Durandeau broke in:

'We aren't in this café to drink. We are here to discuss a matter which is very important to us. I say that . . .'

Mou raised his voice to interrupt him:

'Let me drink, you lot. Let me drink to forget everything: our poverty, our suffering, and Nadan's imprisonment. When I see that we have nobody we can rely on, when I see jealousy and pettiness on all sides, then I want to forget everything!'

He stopped and fixed his tearful eyes on Kocoumbo as if the latter were responsible for his torments.

'You are soft, that's all,' said Douk. 'You aren't the only one here who's suffered. I've suffered too, and so has Kocoumbo, but you won't see us drinking.'

'Oh, you can't understand, Douk. Lengthy meditation on collective suffering is something you will never know. And now, shut up!'

He pressed his lips together to show what he meant.

Douk sat down again and tossed croissant crumbs into his mouth.

'Speaking for myself . . .'

'Shut up, for God's sake!' shouted Durandeau.

'No, I won't shut up! Nobody gives orders here! I want to have my say too!'

Mou's eyes had become feverish.

'You laugh at me because I drink,' he said, 'but you, Durandeau, are a crook. You, Kocoumbo, haven't an ounce of pity in you. And you, Douk, do nothing but preach at me. You think I'm drunk, don't you? Well, I'm not! I'm perfectly clear-headed, as transparent as a piece of glass. You lot haven't any heart, soul, or mind left. Poverty and self-interest have eaten you away. Today when I have a chance to . . .'

Mou began expounding his drunken arguments.

'Oh, my friends,' he lamented, 'what it is to have no moral support, to have no hope left! What can a man do except drink in order to forget?'

'All that's just an excuse for drinking rum,' said Douk, who was beginning to feel happy.

The action of stroking the radiator gave him a certain sense of well-being, and Mou's troubles consoled him.

'Lend me a twenty-franc piece,' Douk said suddenly to Kocoumbo.

As the latter started putting his hand into his pocket without protesting, Douk promptly corrected himself.

'No, I mean a hundred francs, old chap. Life is so dear for us!'

He took the hundred francs, went over to the cash-desk, obtained some change and planted himself in front of the pin-ball machine. Dic, dinc, drinc . . . in . . . dindin, toc, totoc . . . The motor was hard at work, like Douk. The metal ball rolled, bounced, bounced again, shot upwards, rolled down again, slipped between the big buttons, and then rushed down the slope to be swallowed up by the hole at the bottom. Douk got it out again by rattling the trip-lever. A third zero evoked a vehement protest from the player:

'Your machine is robbing me, *patron*! What the devil are you doing, keeping an old tin can like this in your café?'

Mou, in his corner, dozed off. Everything around him struck him as blurred and shapeless.

'So you say that you had nothing to do with Nadan's arrest?' asked Durandeau.

'That's what I've been explaining to you for the past hour. One fine day, the examining magistrate summoned me as a witness, at the request of a black who said he was a cousin of mine. This was Nadan; it seems that the investigation has brought to light some pretty serious facts.'

'And according to you, how did he come to be arrested?'

'It was a woman arrested before he was who brought his name into it.'

'That's what you say . . .'

A peroxide blonde came into the café. She took off her coat and came to sit not far from Durandeau and Kocoumbo. She sat down carefully so as not to spoil the pleats in her skirt, and called the waiter. Douk turned round, left his game, darted a conspiratorial glance at Durandeau and, beaming suddenly, sat down again beside his companions. The next moment he brought out a packet of gauloises and asked:

'Have you got a light, Mademoiselle?'

He always spoke to a girl straight out like that.

'No, Monsieur,' she replied.

And she turned towards the bar, pouting like Brigitte Bardot.

'You don't mind if I keep you company, do you? I can't bear to see a beauty in isolation !'

Without waiting for permission, he sat down at her table.

'Whoever loves me follows me : whoever follows you loves you !'

Proud of the phrase he had coined, which brought a condescending smile to the painted lips, he maintained a satisfied silence for a moment.

Durandeau, who was following the scene with considerable interest, had lost his train of thought. He continued in a loud voice, talking not so much for Kocoumbo's sake as for the benefit of the next table.

'You see, my dear fellow, I've been around; I know what life is like. I've helped you all. Mind you, I consider it quite natural to help you.' (His eyes were fixed on the girl.) 'If you haven't any money, that isn't your fault, but I can't allow you to ... We have to face up to our country's problems; our country is waiting for our help ...'

'Have you finished?' Kocoumbo broke in impatiently.

The young girl, having swallowed her coffee, went out. Douk followed her.

The two of them stopped at the bus stop. The others could see them arguing through the window. Durandeau did not take his eyes off them. In a hurry to have done with Kocoumbo, he assumed a dignified air to say :

'All right, the incident is closed ... In any case, I have to go ...'

'Oh, no !' said Kocoumbo, seizing him by the lapel of his jacket. 'The incident isn't closed ! You've accused me of denouncing Nadan and called me an informer in front of my pals ! No, the incident isn't closed : you're going to apologize to me !'

Cold and grave-faced, Kocoumbo seemed to have grown taller before his eyes.

'How dare you speak to me like that?' retorted Durandeau, stung to the quick. 'I suppose it's because you're a Justice of the Peace? Me apologize to you? Ha ! You may be an ingrate, a cynic, and a Justice of the Peace, but as far as I'm concerned you're just a peasant and you make me sick ! Me, Durandeau, apologize to a peasant? Go to hell, you dirty coward !'

Kocoumbo's fury came to a climax. His gaze lit up with a feverish gleam which dilated his pupils. Calmly and unhurriedly he slapped Durandeau as his father had taught him to slap scoundrels: across the eyes. Durandeau slumped to the ground.

When Kocoumbo was outside in the street he heaved a deep sigh. Douk, carried away by his enthusiasm, abandoned the girl and rushed over to him.

'Bravo!' he cried. 'I saw you through the window! I was expecting anything but that! You are a real Justice of the Peace! Now he'll have to show us all a little respect!'

Kocoumbo shrugged his shoulders and disappeared into the crowd. Douk went back into the café, watched Durandeau pick himself up, and shouted at him:

'Well, I'm damned! That fellow Kocoumbo! He's become absolutely impossible!'

Translated by Robert Baldick

Dahomey

Paulin Joachim

BURIAL

Because time subdues sharp angles and closes wounds
I want to forget the bare and baneful time of the first ages
the time of silver nitrate corrosive and bone-destroying
the time of our breakdown between the navel and history
with the needle flickering crazily at zero hour
the time of the inarticulate prayer
of simulated life and of the shame of being stretched out to the
    point of stupefaction
the time when we were affiliated to poverty
as one is connected to the gas or electricity supply
the time when eternity was turned inside out and the spectre of
    death no longer even gnawed at our minds
the time when I was aggressively healthy under the solar inflation
the time of tears and impatience
the time of the sleepwalker
the time when we were forced to invent
a third ear with which to listen
to what is not said by the rod of time
by the baleful power suspended over our heads
to which has been given a mandate from all eternity to break our
    backs

But because time heals those wounds and softens angles
I wish to rear up a monolith to time
I ejected by time and exiled by former ages
now reintegrate time
and become its sacred aorta
see how my territory widens
my land of shadows awakening hollowing itself out
like a limitless reservoir for the ages to come.

                           Translated by Oliver Bernard

Jean Pliya

THE FETISH TREE

In the history of African-Negro civilization, the name of Abomey, the historical capital of Dahomey, occupies a special place. To explain its past importance, writers often refer to its artistic wealth and the remarkable political and military organization of the kings, but they forget the occult forces of ancestral customs and fetishes. Colonization introduced into Dahomeyan society a division which is developing more and more at the expense of tradition.

The tarred Bohicon Road is like a real backbone along which the essential contributions of the new order are arranged: the schools, the hospital, the post office, the water tower, the police station, and finally the cemetery, where about a hundred white tombstones blaze in the sun. In the old days, the dead were buried in their houses, because they belonged body and soul to their families. Loyalty to their memory had become a cult. Their present isolation is a sign of a slow but painful break-up.

Running from west to east, the road suddenly comes to a stop. It then broadens out into a splendid square, in the centre of which the war memorial stands like an obelisk. All around are grouped the administrative buildings, in either the colonial or the modern style: the Prefecture, the Law Courts, the Council Chambers.

The Houndjro Market, right in the centre of the town, forms a rather dismal ensemble. Halls with corrugated iron roofs stand there next to ramshackle straw huts.

On both sides of the main street, old Abomey, the Abomey of the craftsmen and the princes, vegetates, clinging to the remains of a once brilliant civilization. The royal palace, converted into a historical museum, now offers its treasures only to anonymous crowds of tourists. At the very most, a few dances are organized outside the tiered house of Ghézo, on the occasion of the traditional festivals, which the kings' descendants faithfully commemorate.

The life which animates the city along the main street seems to set the tone of the place. However, in the secrecy of the fetishist covens, and in the old men's heads weighed down with wisdom, the mysterious force which sustained the fervour of the kings lives on. If you go for a walk in the districts scattered in the scrub, you will notice that the dusty alleys take curious turns. They seem to take care to avoid certain tumbledown huts or isolated trees. And if, in your perplexity, you ask one of the countless children with intelligent eyes whom you meet everywhere for an explanation of these abrupt bends, he is sure to reply that the sordid hut shelters a fetish and that the sacred tree symbolizes an ancestor.

The making of a modern nation may call for the destruction of certain relics of the past. But the young men in authority are sometimes faced with insoluble dilemmas, especially as they know nothing of the local civilization except those of its antiquated vestiges which have survived.

Paul Lanta is one of these young men in authority. Cotonou, his native town, the biggest and busiest in Dahomey, is a town without a past. He lived there until he obtained his school-leaving certificate. After a rapid course in the topographical service, he was engaged as a government clerk and put in charge of certain town-planning operations. But Lanta liked to regard himself as a civil engineer. Modern to the fingertips, he thought that present-day youth should not be deterred by any obstacle. His professional diligence had earned him rapid promotion. He was posted to Abomey to help with the execution of the plan prepared by the town council.

He always dressed with studied elegance: terylene trousers with knife-edge creases, a nylon shirt with a red silk tie, and shoes with horse-shoe buckles. A short man, he walked with a firm step, his head held high, and seemed to be full of his own importance. He mixed only with young men of education, lived in the residential district, and scorned the company of his elders. What could anybody learn from those old people, he used to ask himself.

When he came into his office at the town hall that morning,

Monsieur Lanta carefully dusted his desk and sat down. As a methodical man, he consulted his block-calendar and saw that the team whose work he was supervising was due to start that very day on the opening up of a new street. He picked up a little brass bell from his desk and shook it vigorously. A few moments later, an old orderly as gaunt as a syphilitic, dressed in a crumpled, tight-fitting jacket which was fraying at the elbows, knocked at the office door, came in almost at once, and stiffened in a military salute.

'Go straight away to the camp of the Republican Guard,' said Monsieur Lanta, 'and ask for Anatole, the warder in charge of the prisoners detailed for opening up new streets.'

'Yes, sir,' replied the orderly.

'I want him to come along at once with his men.'

'Yes, sir.'

The orderly went out. The door, caught by a draught, shut with a bang behind him. After tidying up his desk, Monsieur Lanta stood up and went out in his turn. In the huge courtyard of the town hall with its neatly mown lawns, a dozen prisoners of all ages and all heights, dressed in blue shorts and sleeveless shirts without collars or buttons, were lined up in two columns. The scarred soles of their bare feet showed that they never wore shoes. Some of them were holding hoes or matchets, others rakes or wooden forks.

'We shall be working today on the Sinhoué Road,' Monsieur Lanta explained to the warder Anatole, who had just finished straightening his cap with its gilt buttons and its silver-grey peak. 'We are going to open up a street as quickly as possible at right-angles to the one that runs west of the Houndjro Market. Off you go!'

At a word of command from Anatole, the prisoners set off at a walking pace along the tarred road whose edges had been furrowed by the torrential rains. Although it was early in the morning, the sun was already warming the smooth black asphalt. But as yet there was no need to seek the refreshing shade of the acacias planted along both sides of the road. A certain sultriness in the air indicated the approach of stormy weather, which is very common in March, at the end of the dry season, especially in this region of the Central Plateau.

They reached the market and turned right, following a track of rust-coloured laterite reinforced after a fashion with quartz gravel. A quarter of a mile farther on, a path branched off from this track: this was the Sinhoué Road. By taking short cuts, Monsieur Lanta had reached the crossroads first, and he was waiting.

The prisoners looked all the way along the winding path which had to be widened to the proportions of a street. They realized straight away that this was not going to be an easy day's work. For on the left, just after the first bend, there was a magnificent iroko, still known as a 'loko': what the botanists call *chlorophora excelsa*. The foot of the tree, invisible from a distance, was surrounded by a tangle of bushes and shrubs from which there rose a bole as straight and powerful as a cathedral column, topped with dark green foliage. Creepers as thick as cables criss-crossed to weave a net which hung from the top of the tree to the undergrowth. Huge branches formed a leafy vault above the path, casting an unbroken shadow over the ground.

·At the sight of this tree, one was filled in spite of oneself with a sense of awe.

A serious question immediately preoccupied the prisoners: were they going to be forced to cut down this tree? In the meantime, without a word, they calmly began their work. With the help of a ten-metre measuring tape, and starting from the market road, two men measured out the width of the future street. A little farther on towards the tree, they planted marking-stakes to which they tied lengths of string. Once the working area had been fixed in this way, they started clearing it. When the weeds were not too tough, the hoe dug them up and the rakes swept them away. But soon the prisoners could not put off any longer the problem which was worrying them. The warder Anatole, who was a native of Abomey and well aware of the situation, shared his men's fears. He did not look forward to ordering them to cut down the iroko. He therefore agreed to let them send a delegation to Monsieur Lanta, who was sitting on a rock a little way off.

'Boss, please don't be astonished at this question,' said the spokesman. 'My workmates and I want to know what we are to do with that tree.'

'Why do you ask?' said the civil servant in surprise. 'Have you ever heard of a tree being left right in the middle of the roadway? Our job, as part of the town-planning scheme, is to open up beautiful, clean, straight streets, and to do that we have to clear, cut and uproot everything in our way so that asphalt can be laid down later.'

'But our tools aren't up to the job! We haven't any saws or axes, but just matchets.'

'Oh, get along with you!' cried Monsieur Lanta. 'Is this the first time you've been told to cut down a tree?'

'No, Boss; but the other times they were just little trees, or at the very most shrubs. We've never had to cut down a tree as big as this. Our workmates have sent us to tell you that that tree over there is an iroko, a fetish tree, and that it would be very dangerous to try to fell it.'

'Now, I don't want any nonsense of that sort, you bunch of idlers! Get on with your work, and stop worrying. Seeing that you say you haven't got the necessary tools, just clear the ground all around. Tomorrow we'll provide you with axes and hand-saws so that you can cut down that iroko.'

When the disappointed delegation returned and delivered this reply, there was consternation among the prisoners. Their shining, sweating faces, to which blades of green grass and tiny seeds were stuck, assumed scowling expressions. Muttering to themselves, they reluctantly resumed their work. Their progress slowed down, the nearer they got to the tree. Monsieur Lanta, who had not taken his eyes off them since their unexpected move, was puzzled. He got to his feet, went over to the working-party, and questioned the warder Anatole. The latter seemed scarcely any easier in his mind than the prisoners. When his superior asked him to explain their attitude, he prudently shifted the responsibility on to their ringleader, a man who seemed to possess a certain authority over the team.

'That man,' he said, pointing to an old prisoner, 'claims that the tree over there is sacred and that it is forbidden to cut off even the smallest branch. He must have got his mates all worked up.'

Sure enough, all the prisoners now seemed determined not to go any further. Reprimands and threats of punishment were of no avail. Monsieur Lanta decided to use persuasion to try to solve this problem. He took aside the man Anatole had accused, an old man called Mehou whose kapok-grey hair curled oddly into the shape of little balls. His face was remarkable for the breadth of his forehead and the sharpness of his eyes.

While the others continued their work unenthusiastically, Monsieur Lanta and Mehou walked about a stone's-throw away.

'Well,' began the civil servant, 'what's this cock-and-bull story you've been telling to discourage your workmates? We can't allow any rebels or saboteurs. The regulations are particularly strict about that sort of thing. What have you got to say to that?'

'Boss,' replied Mehou, standing at a respectful distance, his head bowed and his fingers twined together behind his back, to keep himself in countenance, 'it isn't a cock-and-bull story. I was born in Abomey, before King Béhanzin was taken prisoner and deported to the white men's country. My father was a great fetishist chieftain, and I pride myself on knowing the history of the sacred woods which in the old days used to shelter the covens. In the time of the kings, this part of the country was covered with forests of irokos. Nobody had the right to touch those fetish trees, under pain of severe punishment. But some time ago, people began cutting them down to make chairs, tables and doors. Now there are very few left. The trees which have escaped the woodcutter's axe have become more precious as a result. Our sorcerers choose them as the centre for their nocturnal celebrations. Any offering made to a god is placed at the foot of an iroko or at a crossroads, so that the effects can be spread to the four winds. It's dangerous to make fun of the sorcerers. To live in peace, to enjoy good health, and to have no trouble in our work, we have to seek their protection.

'The iroko you are ordering us to cut down has a history you must know. King Tégbessou is said to have been saved several times by a bird which lived in that tree and which warned him in wartime of the tricks of his enemies from Zâ. In memory of these great services given to the kingdom of Dan, it has always been respected. That is why we ought to spare it. If you go up to it, you'll see that the lower part of the trunk is hollow. That is supposed to be the lair of a serpent which watches over the tree and to which any man threatened by an evil spell can offer up a sacrifice in order to be cured. Even without the serpent's presence, that iroko is a redoubtable fetish. Forgive us if we are unwilling to incur its vengeance.'

Somewhat irritated by the lengthiness of the old man's explanations, Monsieur Lanta looked sceptical. He smiled sarcastically as he listened to these tales from another age. This was not the first time that well-meaning people had advised him to respect some fetish or to guard against the sorcerers. In his heart of hearts, he wondered how anybody could be alarmed by such unconvincing stories.

'That's all very fine,' he said, 'but hard to verify. In the second half of the twentieth century, we can't believe in fetishes any more. Otherwise, in spite of being independent, we should never succeed in building a modern civilized nation. We have to fell that tree for public purposes, and nothing is going to stop us. The old town of Abomey has to be given a new, up-to-date look.'

Just then, another prisoner joined them and offered to find a woodcutter who would be sure to agree to fell the iroko. This providential individual was called Dossou.

Monsieur Lanta, being a realist, decided to call a halt to the day's work and to employ Dossou's services. The men returned to camp, their work half done.

At nightfall, Anatole got the prisoner who knew Dossou to take him to see the woodcutter. Dossou's house, which was in the district of the Houtondji blacksmiths, on the outskirts of the town, was a round hut without any windows. The mud walls were rough-cast and whitewashed, and covered with a thatched roof. Through the solitary rectangular opening, which was closed by a lattice-work rattan curtain, rays of dull yellow light were filtering. A little distance away, an apatam of wooden planks covered with palm-leaves leant against the enclosing wall. This was the kitchen.

A wood fire was glowing in a crude hearth made of three blocks of dried clay. The smell of sauces floated in the air. Earthenware cooking-pots stood here and there. Clucking hens were looking for a roost for the night. The prisoner clapped his hands.

'Who's there?' asked a man's voice which was deep and very calm. Without waiting for a reply, it called out:

'Cossi! Go and see who's at the door.'

The young man who answered to this name had a cotton pagne knotted round his neck. He opened the rattan curtain a little way, smiling broadly; but he took fright at the sight of Anatole's new peaked cap. Wiping the smile off his face, he said politely:

'Good evening, sir.'

'Good evening,' replied the warder, conscious of the effect his uniform had produced. 'I want to speak to your master.'

'Right. I'll call him straight away.'

When Dossou learnt that a Republican Guard wanted to see him, he hurriedly searched his conscience, for he thought that his caller was a gendarme bearing a warrant. Trusting in his reputation as an honest workman, and sure that he was innocent of any crime, he stood up without a word and asked his visitors indoors. Shaking hands with him, the warder noticed the exceptional strength of Dossou's grip.

The hut was divided in two by a wall. One half served as the bedroom, the other as the living-room. The visitors were invited to sit down on low, three-legged stools, in crudely carved wood. On the wall there hung axes, hand-saws, matchets and thick coils of rope.

Dossou was a real athlete with a bull neck and long arms with knotty biceps. His eyes squinted and seemed to be perpetually laughing. He was dressed only in a coarse loin-cloth. He walked towards his stool. Anatole noticed that he limped with his right leg, which was less developed than the other. His strength had, as it were, been concentrated in his muscular arms.

Cossi squatted on his haunches near the door, determined to know the reason for such an impressive visit. Without standing on ceremony, and puffing himself up slightly, Anatole informed Dossou in a few words of what was wanted of him. He did not fail to emphasize the eventual danger he would be running by agreeing. He then asked him if he was willing to collaborate with the government. A relieved Dossou relaxed with a sudden laugh. Would he agree? Of course, and enthusiastically! Flattered that the 'Governor', the Prefect himself, should appeal to him in his capacity as a feller of trees, Dossou could not contain himself for vanity and joy. Who could tell if he would not be appointed a civil servant one day? Besides, deep down, he had never doubted in his own destiny. He was a native of Allada. At the age of fourteen, accompanying his woodcutter father in the forest, he had fallen from a tree and broken his right leg. Since then, he had sworn never to ply any other trade than that of a woodcutter.

Henceforth felling trees meant wreaking a personal revenge for him, settling scores with the instrument which fate had used to disable him. His hands could not wield anything but the axe. A free-thinker who was afraid of nobody, he was hugely amused at the idea that a dozen able-bodied men had been unable to perform a task as easy as the one which was being asked of him.

'There hasn't been a single tree in living memory,' he said, 'that I've been unable to master. Do you remember the baobab at Cové which nobody but I could cut down? You don't? But you can't have failed to hear about that exploit of mine. It was five years ago, in the days of the white commanders. They congratulated me in public and promised me a medal.'

Sensing a movement of impatience on the part of his distinguished visitor, Dossou pulled himself together.

'What day is it tomorrow?'

'It's market day, and Thursday,' the prisoner replied.

'That's perfect! A good day for my job. Everything's fine. Do we meet on the Sinhoué Road?'

'Yes. Don't be late. In the civil service, time is important,' Anatole concluded sententiously.

'You can count on me.'

It was completely dark when the two men came out of the hut. As they had just left the smoky light of a palm-oil lamp, the night struck them as darker by contrast. They groped about before finding their way. The sky had the cruel purity of those skies during the dry season when, for four or five months, the farmer dreams of the cool rains. The air was fresh. In the grass along both sides of the path, swarms of fireflies were intermittently lighting up their greenish phosphorus. Anatole was pleased with the success of his mission. As soon as he had taken the prisoner back to camp, he went to see Monsieur Lanta and gave him a full report.

The next day, early in the morning, Dossou informed his assistant Cossi that they were going to do a job which would stand out in his life and bring him a great deal of prestige and money: namely, felling the iroko on the Sinhoué Road for the 'Governor'. Cossi, who had known all about it since the warder's visit, had been thinking and worrying about the problem for part of the night. He ventured to reply timidly:

'Master, can't we refuse this deadly job?'

'Shut up, you little fool: you're talking nonsense! Who do you take me for? You've lived such a long time with me . . . What fresh exploits have I got to perform to prove to you that I'm invulnerable?'

'Forgive me, Master, I'm not casting any doubts on your powers, but people say that that iroko is a magic tree which can work evil. It seems that . . .'

'That's enough! Don't you know that, as far as magic is concerned, I've taken precautions long ago? I wasn't born yesterday! In any case, I'm not in the habit of arguing with cowards. Take my best axes and go and sharpen them as usual.'

Cossi unhooked the two heavy axes from the wall and made for the kitchen. First of all he poured some palm-oil on to a big millstone made of Dassa-Zoumé granite, balanced on an oil-drum filled with sand to keep it steady. With a regular, rasping motion, he carefully sharpened the steel until it could cut like a razor. Then, with a glum expression on his face, he took the tools and set off in front of his master.

As for Dossou, proudly draped in a brightly coloured calico pagne, he walked along calmly. But he had scarcely left his house before he met one of his former neighbours coming the opposite way. He scowled in irritation. 'I don't like that at all,' he said to himself. He looked annoyed, for he regarded this as an evil omen. Dossou did not believe in the host of fetishes which the old people worshipped, and consequently he did not observe their prohibitions. For him, the only laws which counted were those of Dada Segbo, the Supreme Being, the unique creator of day and night, of inanimate objects and living creatures, who in the event of danger warned men by means of signs intelligible only to the initiated. Thus, for fear of offending him, he was careful to choose only working days, and avoided touching a tool or any metal on the days dedicated to Gou, the guardian divinity of blacksmiths, warriors and all workers who handle sharp instruments. Similarly, according to whether the first person he met after leaving home in the morning was a woman or a man, he considered that he was going to have a good or a bad day. Apart from that, Dossou was convinced that worshipping a serpent, a stone or a tree was a superstition unworthy of him. In any case, the piece of luck which had come his way today was so exceptional that he had no doubt that the outstanding task which had been entrusted to him was a gift from Dada Segbo.

The morning sky had the same purity as that of the previous night, with the sole difference that the golden stars had disappeared, giving place to a sun of dull silver.

Soon Dossou and Cossi passed the Houndjro Market, which was already coming to life. They met merchants on bicycles, each carrying his wife on the luggage-grid, a baby on her back and full baskets on her head. The pedestrians hugged the walls to avoid the vehicles filling the roadway. As a lorry heavily laden with Indian potatoes went by, clouds of yellow dust enveloped Dossou and Cossi. To avoid breathing it in, they stopped, pinched their noses between their left thumbs and forefingers, and then continued on their way. Cossi said nothing. In his opinion, there had been far too many evil omens already. No more were required to make him feel pessimistic.

As soon as the woodcutter reached the working-site, he made for the iroko. For a long time he eyed his powerful adversary supported by broad buttresses like ships' hulls. The ash-grey trunk, smooth in places, was peeling in others, or cracked like crocodile skin. Straight away, Dossou took charge of operations, and, like a real foreman, gave detailed orders to the prisoners who were to help him to clear the ground round the iroko. In a matter of moments the bushes and the weeds were cut down. They had to tug at the net of tangled creepers in order to strip certain branches. Some of the men piled up the brushwood, which would be burnt later on when it had dried up.

Right against the tree there was a straw hut sheltering a crude dummy made of two balls of clay, the smaller representing the head and the other the body. At the bottom of the huge paunch a wooden phallus stood erect. This fetish, the Tolegba, a familiar feature of the Dahomeyan landscape, is very popular. It is sprinkled with palm-oil when people bring it offerings. They had to smash it to smithereens.

When the base of the trunk was completely accessible, Dossou took off the pagne which he was wearing draped over his shoulders like a Roman toga, keeping on nothing but his loin-cloth. He stroked his thick biceps, spat into his horny hands, rubbed them together to obtain a better hold, and then seized one of the skilfully hafted axes in his wrestler's grip. Removing the bark with a series of little blows, he first of all girdled the trunk at a convenient height, ringing it with a notch into which the sacrilegious tool would bite. Refusing to send somebody up the tree to fasten a rope which would make it fall in a given direction, he calculated the angle of felling with a practised eye.

Then the axe began to dance. As the first blows cut into the buttresses, some weaver-birds which were building their nests in a near by palm-tree flew off in a twittering cloud. Red ants settled on the prisoners, who prudently withdrew. The entire frame of the giant shuddered under the rape of the axe. The brick-red flesh was opened. Chips of wood flew in every direction and littered the ground. The tempered steel described bluish circles in the air, with gleams of silver. Sweat streamed down Dossou's face, ran down his back, spread out and drenched his loin-cloth. In the west, the sky was gradually covered with slate-grey clouds. The stormy atmosphere charged with electricity heightened the general tension.

The man panted for breath as he threw himself into his task. Once, the axe sank so deep into the wooden flesh that the bevelled edge was caught as if by a powerful vice. Dossou arched his body backwards on his good leg and tugged vainly at the handle. He had to have help in order to free the tool.

'Never mind,' swore Dossou. 'I'll get the better of you yet!'

It was only grudgingly that he agreed to a break for the midday meal. When the prisoners and their leaders came back at the beginning of the afternoon, the tree was three-quarters cut. By examining the gash, an expert could have told that the iroko was nearly three hundred years old.

The woodcutter's movements, which had been strong and calm at first, now became feverish. His eyes turned bloodshot. He was fighting the tree, as if the two of them were locked in single combat. As the support grew narrower, he seemed to be seized by a murderous frenzy and to feel that he was engaged in a pitiless struggle. He refused all offers of help and looked irritated when Monsieur Lanta urged him to take a rest. 'Leave me alone,' he muttered. And the blows went on striking the iroko at a breathtaking rate.

The others, now wonder-struck spectators, applauded the infectious self-assurance shown by the woodcutter, whose victory seemed certain. An improvised choir spontaneously sang Dossou's praises after the fashion of strolling minstrels. With a song accompanied by their hands beating time against their chests, they sustained the woodcutter's ardour.

When only a thin strip of wood still joined the trunk to its base, and a few feeble blows would have been enough to fell the tree, Dossou broke off his onslaught at last and straightened his pure ebony body with its perfect muscles.

'You can finish the job now,' he said triumphantly to the prisoners.

Cossi and one of the prisoners began almost playfully to bring Dossou's task to completion. The woodcutter, with a certainty which was usually almost miraculous, had calculated that the iroko would fall in the opposite direction from the path on which the men were standing. Its trajectory, he had declared, did not involve the slightest risk. All the same, for safety's sake, Monsieur Lanta, Anatole and the prisoners, who were divided into two groups on either side of the iroko, had left the immediate vicinity.

With his right forefinger hooked like a claw, Dossou cleaned his moist forehead and started walking about with the confident step of a victor. It never occurred to him that he might be threatened by any sort of danger. Convinced of his own powers and certain that the tree would fall in the direction he had imposed on it, he strutted about from one group to another, amused by the general consternation and apparently flattered by the admiring gaze of the prisoners. Some merchants on their way home to Sinhoué quickened their pace when they reached the iroko. They hurried away, calling upon the ancestral shades and crying: 'Hélou!' – 'Death to him who commits sacrilege!'

At last the iroko was cut in two. The foliage started swaying like a boat's mast in a storm. Spasms shook the giant in every limb. A dull creaking sound like a death-rattle indicated that the support had just given way. Dossou was standing on the path, just opposite the tree. The trunk suddenly started falling. The greenish-black parasol swayed unexpectedly in the direction of the path. Panic rooted the onlookers to the spot. At the anguished cry which came from their throats, Dossou swung round. He scarcely had time to realize the imminence of the danger threatening him. Dumbfounded by his adversary's deceit, he made a frantic effort to flee, but his crippled leg could not follow the impulse of his whole being as he tried to avoid the fatal blow. Before starting on his limping run, instead of looking to see which way the tree was going to fall, he turned his back on it. The force of impact being multiplied tenfold at the level of the branches, a terrible blow flattened him on the ground. The noise made by the fall of the tree and the crash of the branches drowned the inhuman cry he was about to utter. Torn leaves and frightened insects flew about in a mad whirlwind. Then, very suddenly, silence fell: a silence so absolute that the cackling of a toucan could be heard in the distance. Everybody seemed to be waiting in a daze for Dossou to emerge from under the branches. When it became obvious that nobody was going to hear even the slightest groan, the men all moved at once, like panic-stricken ants.

It was then that the storm which had been brewing all day finally burst, adding to the solemnity of the scene with explosions of thunder and blinding flashes of lightning. The thunder god Heviosso showed his anger by spitting fire. Under rain rattling down like hail, the rescuers, armed with axes and hand-saws, had to cut dozens of thick branches to reach Dossou's unrecognizable body. They then grasped the full horror of the iroko's shattering riposte. A knot in one branch, swollen until it looked like the head of a gigantic club, had struck the woodcutter in the back. The bowels had spurted out of the belly. The blood had turned black as it flowed away on all sides, as if the crumpled leaves had soaked in it. The skull had become an indescribable pulp, a mixture of whitish brain, dark hair and crushed bone. Nobody dared to take charge of the remains of the foolhardy Dossou, not even Cossi, who was crying his heart out. The prisoners covered up the body again with branches and went off, silent and horror-stricken. Monsieur Lanta, dumbfounded by what had happened, did not understand. He could not understand.

At nightfall, the fetishists who worshipped the iroko came along in a procession to take possession of the human remains. They laid them on a bamboo hurdle and carried them through every district in the town, to the sound of twin gongs and by the light of hurriedly devised torches. Inquisitive crowds gathered in the doorways, astonished by this nocturnal procession; but as soon as they saw the body they understood the purpose of the ceremony. Within a few hours, the whole town was fully informed.

The funereal gongs rang out like a warning to anybody who might try to commit another sacrilegious act of this sort. Finally Dossou's corpse was thrown to the jackals and the vultures.

For the fetishists, death itself is not sufficient punishment for the crime of deicide.

Translated by Robert Baldick

Gambia

Lenrie Peters

After they put down their overalls
And turn off the lathes
They do not return to the women
After they have bathed
Instead, with Hyena's thirst
They turn to the open-air bar
To swallow the hook of imported liquor
As they sit reckless across the log
Hypnotized by the bees.

They belch the arrogance of doubt
As they lie in refined stupor
Waiting for the sharp sun
To show them the way out.
Less sure than when they took the potion
They lumber back to the clever tools
They do not love and do not understand
Hoping the sun's anger would cool
So they can carry their dark glasses in their hand.

South Africa

Ezekiel Mphahlele

REMARKS ON NÉGRITUDE

Made at the Conference on African Literature in French and the University Curriculum held at the Faculté des Lettres, University of Dakar, 26–29 March, 1963.

Yesterday I was personally attacked by someone who, because of my views against *négritude*, associated me with 'colonialism, neo-colonialism and imperialism'. He charged me, in effect, with hindering or frustrating the protest literature of *négritude*, its mission. If I had not exiled myself from South Africa five years ago, after having lived for thirty-seven years in the South African nightmare, I should either have shrivelled up in my bitterness or have been imprisoned for treason. My books have been banned in South Africa under a law that forbids the circulation of literature that is regarded as 'objectionable, undesirable or obscene'. So, you see what things I have been called in my life; my body itches from the number of labels that have been stuck on me! As for what I really am, and my place in the African revolution, I shall let my writings speak for me.

We in South Africa have for the last 300 years of oppression been engaged in a bloody struggle against white supremacy – to assert our *human* and not African dignity. This latter we have always taken for granted. During these three centuries, we the Africans have been creating an urban culture out of the very conditions of insecurity, exile and agony. We have done this by integrating Africa and the West. Listen to our music, see our dancing and read our literature both in the indigenous and English languages. The bits of what the white ruling class calls 'Bantu culture' that we are being told to 'return to' are being used by that class to oppress us, to justify the Transkei and other Bantustans. And yet there still survive the toughest elements of African humanism which keep us together and supply the moral force which we need in a life that rejects us.

If you notice the two segregated sections of a town like Brazzaville, Congo, you cannot fail to see the sterile and purposeless life of the whites in their self-imposed ghetto as distinct from the vibrant and vigorous life of the black community. The blacks have reconciled the Western and African in them, while the whites refuse to surrender to their influence. This is symbolic of the South African situation. The only cultural vitality there is is to be seen among the Africans: they have not been *uplifted* by a Western culture but rather they have reconciled the two in themselves. This is the sense in which I feel superior to the white man who refuses to be liberated by me as an African. So, anyone who imagines that we in South Africa are just helpless, grovelling and down-trodden creatures of two worlds who have been waiting for the 'messiah' of *négritude,* does not know a thing about what is going on in our country. My detractor, an American Negro who would like to teach us how to feel African, cites the entry of James Meredith into Indiana University as symbolic of the triumph of the Negro's *négritude* in Mississippi (sic). Are we really to believe that the U.S. Federal Army went to Indiana to make it possible for Meredith to sing the blues or gospel songs? Surely his entry is to be seen as part of the Negro's campaign to be integrated socially and politically in the American population, even while emancipating white America in the process; to assert his human dignity. Of course, I am quite aware of certain – and luckily they are few – non-African blacks and whites who come crawling on their bellies into this continent as it were, prepared to be messengers or lackeys of some of us, prepared to eat the dust under our feet in self-abasement in an attempt to identify with Africa. Such people are prompted to do this out of a guilt complex whereby they seek to bear the sins of past colonizers whom, they imagine, we associate with them. Elsewhere I have warned against this ugly self-abasement because it prevents the 'patient' from criticizing adversely anything the African says or writes, ripe, raw and rotten. I fully agree with James Baldwin when he says in a brilliant and most moving essay in a recent issue of The *New Yorker* (17 November

1962), that the Negro must solve his problem inside America, not by a romantic identification with Africa. I appreciate also his remark that the Negro refuses to be integrated 'into a burning house', i.e. the American social and political life that is sadly misguided, in which whites do not believe in death. And yet he also says that white and black in the U.S. need each other badly, that the white American needs to be liberated from himself but can only do this when he has liberated the Negro. After this, integration must come. Although he appreciates the Black Muslims, he foresees that one day he may have to fight them because they are such a menace.

Now to *négritude* itself. Who is so stupid as to deny the historical fact of *négritude* as both a protest and a positive assertion of African cultural values? All this is valid. What I do not accept is the way in which too much of the poetry inspired by it romanticizes Africa – as a symbol of innocence, purity and artless primitiveness. I feel insulted when some people imply that Africa is not also a violent continent. I am a violent person, and proud of it because it is often a healthy human state of mind; some day I'm going to plunder, rape, set things on fire; I'm going to cut somebody's throat; I'm going to subvert a government; I'm going to organize a coup d'état; yes, I'm going to oppress my own people; I'm going to hunt the rich fat black men who bully the small weak black men and destroy them; I'm going to become a capitalist, and woe to all who cross my path or who want to be my servants or chauffeurs and so on; I'm going to lead a breakaway church – there is money in it; I'm going to attack the black bourgeoisie while I cultivate a garden, rear dogs and parrots; listen to jazz and classics, read 'culture', and so on. Yes, I'm going to organize a strike. Don't you know that sometimes I kill to the rhythm of drums and cut the sinews of a baby to cure it of paralysis? . . . This is only a dramatization of what Africa can do and is doing. The image of Africa consists of all these and others. And *négritude* poetry pretends that they do not constitute the image and leaves them out. So we are told only half – often even a falsified half – of the story of Africa. Sheer romanticism that fails to see the large landscape of the personality of the African makes bad poetry. Facile protest also makes bad poetry. The omission of these elements of a continent in turmoil reflects a defective poetic vision. The greatest poetry of Léopold Sédar Senghor is that which portrays in himself the meeting point of Europe and Africa. This is realistic and honest and most meaningful symbol of Africa, an ambivalent continent searching for equilibrium. This synthesis of Europe and Africa does not necessarily reject the negro-ness of the African.

What have we to say about 'benevolent dictatorship'; chauvinists, peasants who find that they have to change a way of life they have cherished for centuries and have to live in the twentieth century? Let me italicize again: an image of Africa that glosses over or dismisses these things is not a faithfully-conceived one; it restricts our emotional and intellectual response. An image of Africa that only glorifies our ancestors and celebrates our 'purity' and 'innocence' is an image of a continent lying in state. When I asked the question, at the Accra Congress of Africanists last December, how long our poets are going to continue to bleat like a goat in the act of giving birth, I was suggesting that Ghanaian poets should start looking inwards into themselves. Now I am being accused of encouraging 'artistic purity' by asking writers to cease protesting against a colonial boss that has left their country. What is 'artistic purity'? Am I being asked to lay the ghost of *l'art pour l'art*? Surely meaningful art has social significance or relevance and this very fact implies social criticism – protest in the broadest form of the word. Gorky, Dostoyevsky, Tolstoy, Dickens and so on did this, but they were no less Russian or English; certainly they were much more committed than *négritude* poets. They took in the whole man. Camara Laye's *Le Regard du Roi*, Ferdinand Oyono's *Le Vieux Nègre et la Medaille* and Mongo Beti's *Le pauvre Christ de Bomba* are not bullied by *négritude*. They are concerned in portraying the black–white encounter, and they do this, notwithstanding, with a devastating poetic sense of irony unmatched by any that one sees in the English novel by Africans (there are fascinating works in the three main Bantu languages in South Africa which are of the same standard). I am suggesting here that we as writers need to be emancipated from ourselves. *Négritude*, while a valuable slogan politically, can, because its apostles have set it up as a principle of art, amount to self-enslavement – *autocoloniza-tion*, to quote a French writer speaking of African politics and economics. We should not allow ourselves to be bullied at gun-point into producing literature that is supposed to contain a *négri-tude* theme and style. For now we are told, also, that there is *un style négro-africain*, and that therefore we have to sloganize and write to a march. We are told that *négritude* is less a matter of theme than style. We must strive to visualize the whole man, not merely the things that are meant to flatter the Negro's ego. Let it not be forgotten, too, that *négritude* has an overlap of 19th cen-tury European protest against machines and cannons. In the place of the cuckoo, the nightingale, the daffodil, Africa has been dragged to the altar of Europe. *Négritude* men should not pretend that this is an entirely African concept.

Notice also that while *négritude* poetry evokes images of ritual, animals letting out blood for the sacrifice, naked feet and breasts, these are only outward trappings: the poet still does not, and per-haps cannot as an uprooted person, penetrate the essence of tradition.

Several of us, as a result of the physical and mental agony we have been going through in South Africa, have rejected Christi-anity or any other religion as a cure for human ills. But if I wrote a poem or novel expressly to preach against religion without my seeing the irony of the good and bad in things done in the name of religion; if I omitted the irony of Christians and educated Africans who still revere ancestral spirits, and several other ironies and paradoxes, then it would not be a lasting work of art. I think that a writer who is too sure about his rejection of the use of a god can be as overbearing as the one who is too sure about his need of an existence of a god, like Browning. I say, then, that *négritude* can go on as a socio-political slogan, but that it has no right to set itself up as a standard of literary performance; there I refuse to go along. I refuse to be put in a Negro file – for sociologists to come and examine me. Art unifies even while it distinguishes men; and I regard it as an insult to the African for anyone to suggest that because we write independently on different themes in divers modes and styles all over Africa, therefore we are ripe victims of balkanization. But then I speak as a simple practising writer, not as a politician or a philosopher, or a non-African Africanist who is looking for categories and theories for a doctorate thesis. I refuse to be put in a dossier. And yet I am no less committed to the African revolution, to the South African freedom fight. Let *négritude* make the theme of literature if people want to use it. But we must remember that literature springs from an individual's experience, and in its effort to take in the whole man, it also tries to see far ahead, to project a prophetic vision, such as the writer is capable of, based on contemporary experience. It must at least set in motion vibrations in us that will continue even after we have read it, prompting us to continue inquiring into its meaning. If African culture is worth anything at all, it should not require myths to prop it up. These thoughts are not new at all. I have come to them after physical and mental agony. And this, of course, is not my monopoly either. It is the price Africa has to pay. And if you thought that the end of colonization was the end of the agony, then it is time to wake up.

The fear that university teachers who distrust *négritude* or reject it as a principle of art may exclude from the syllabus literature inspired by this school does not do justice to them. And the suggestion that they have a grave responsibility when they decide which African authors have to be taught is insulting to their intelligence. Why should they feel more responsible than they have been in the teaching of French? Is African writing in French not French literature? I am sure university teachers can be trusted to distinguish literature from a sociological or anthropological document that masquerades as literature! They can examine actual texts, can't they? Why should *la litterature engagée* be so spoiled as to want to be judged by different standards from those that have been tested by tradition? Why should it be afraid of being judged against the social context that gives rise to it and run for cover behind the black mask?

We acknowledge that *négritude* as a socio-political concept defines the mind of the assimilated African in French-speaking territories. The British never set out to assimilate their colonial subjects. They hate to see people come out of their culture to emulate them (the British). They like the exotic African, not the one who tries to speak, walk and eat like them. They love Africans in museum cases, so they left much of African culture intact. But literature and art are too big for *négritude*, and it had better be left as a historical phase.

From An African Autobiography

ON THE LONG ROAD

Lagos, 14 August 1957

Dear Mr M —,

I am sure that by now you have received your air ticket money. We are looking forward to seeing you early next month when the school re-opens. It will be the first time for me and all the other teachers here to see a South African Negro. You are bound to like Nigeria and our people. We are all brothers, we black people of Africa, whether you are from the east, west, or south. . . .

Just before I boarded the plane at Jan Smuts airport, my friend, Bloke, said to me: 'If you ever feel you want to come back, Zeke, take lots and lots of booze to work the urge out of your system.'

Thinking back on that day now, 6 September, 1957, I remember how numb I felt; numb from an overwhelming sense of inevitability that often fills one when the moment has come towards which one's efforts have within a short space of time been desperately gravitating. I had not given much thought to the question whether or not I was going to a better political and social climate. What mattered was the mere chance of escape.

Eighteen months, and I had not yet joined battle with my conscience or a desire to return. I had moments of deep thought, naturally. If I went back, what could I do outside the classroom from which I had been banned? Nothing. I had tried several times before my escape to rationalize on the problem of adaptation to a job – literally a job. I had tried to tell myself then that if I went about with as detached a mind as when one is urinating, spiritually uninvolved, I should conserve enough energy to write at night. But time after time I had come to realize that the effort of trying to detach oneself sapped one's energy. One soon found oneself shouting back at the boss and returning home with an inflated spleen. So it was no use trying out the same argument once I had got to Nigeria. I also asked myself if returning would alleviate the miseries of my people. I couldn't see it happening. Yes, there was always 'the arts' and once back, I could be re-absorbed. But twenty years of this continuous patching up against a background of hunger and insecurity had given me a touch of cynicism.

Thirty-seven years of age in a country of tensions is too long for one suddenly to develop a sense of guilt over escape. Yet it is too long for one to forget, to be lost in the new-found freedom. One develops a habit of thinking about oppression, and I was still wiping off the sweat in which I woke up when I jumped physically out of the *apartheid* nightmare.

I was too baffled by this freedom to continue writing fiction, and the impact of the new life on me was so violent that certain of my standards of judgement were being severely tested. During the first fifteen months I taught in a boys' grammar school. The complacency of the boys struck me forcibly, and I became progressively annoyed by it. If only I could bring a bunch of African boys and girls from South Africa to Nigeria for their schooling, I thought wistfully. Boys and girls whose future is bleak in spite of all their keenness, vitality, and drive – boys and girls who are being challenged at every turn by the environment, by labels like *Europeans Only* at public places and entrances, the machinery of the white man's law, the white man's domineering attitude. . . . I was teaching mostly Yoruba students in Lagos. The small number of Ibo boys in the school were a source of inspiration : critical, self-confident, restless, challenging (even if sometimes obstructionist). Ibos are generally pushful; they have the guts to challenge authority. They seldom beg for favours, and I admire the man who does not beg for favours.

Complacency? Yes, coupled with the expert ability to take in all a teacher says like a sponge; and an indifferent sense of urgency.

Later on I excused the complacency and the uncritical outlook; the social and political life of this country, unlike the harassing life of *apartheid*, must tend to induce self-satisfaction rather than insecurity. The restless and critical attitude of the Southern African student is often a subconscious revolt against his environment; it often falsifies human conduct and relationships.

I shared this experience with most of the fellow South Africans teaching in Nigeria – then about twenty. They told me that their standards of discipline were very often misunderstood by their headmasters and Nigerian colleagues. They were said to exact too much from the pupils and to exercise too strict a code. This seemed to suggest the difference between the West African and the South African. The Nigerian in the classroom, in public service or business was, I found, apt to respect the textbook slavishly and to ignore happily the discipline that makes one start and finish to time, analyse results, assess a system of values and get to know the whole world that is related to his special job. The South African, teacher or no teacher, has been pushed and kicked about all his life until he has come to walk with his body leaning forward. He has to keep moving and doing something with that sense of urgency. Or else he trips and falls. The South African teacher keeps in school from 8 a.m. to 4.30 p.m. I suddenly realized how fastidious I had become in this 'go-slow' machinery. So many Nigerians had been to British universities where I presumed competition was very high; the Nigerian student, even locally, had such unique opportunities and practically no political and economic tensions to worry about.

Was I never going to outgrow the habit of being on my guard when face to face with a European? I enter a department store and find all the assistants are Africans. A thing inside me thaws. Then I have to meet the manager – a white man. Immediately I tune my defence-mechanism. I rehearse my vocabulary in the South African idiom where words never seem to keep their referential meaning. And then what do I find? – a polite white man, exasperatingly neutral. I feel hollow because there is no need to exchange words or to assert myself.

Before my family arrived I lived in a school-house in Lagos. I asked a washerman who took the European schoolmistresses' washing to do my laundry. The ladies agreed to this. But they did not want him to wash my laundry on the same day as theirs. Lest they mixed. The washerman told me about this and I flared up. I was prepared to tell them, if they should mention it to me, that they needn't be put out, because I was used to such treatment in the south, but they never said anything about it to me, which deflated me somewhat.

I go to a bank and give a cash cheque to the teller. 'Cheque for reference!' he bawls out as he pushes it into a hole in the wire net. I wait, prepared for quite a spell. I know, as everybody else does, how slow and easy life is in West Africa. A European comes and pushes a cash cheque towards the teller. Immediately he is given his money without reference formalities. (Now why should that be? I ask myself.) Yet another European comes and I am waiting, this time together with a lot of other Africans. His cheque does not need a reference. He gets his money without waiting. (If the teller knows the bank balances of these fellows, I muse, then bank clerks must have a most retentive memory. No, I say to myself, I've come here to relax and think. To convalesce. I shouldn't allow myself to be upset. But I still wonder. . . .)

Later, when I was in an adult education programme, I had occasion to go to a town called Ilorin in the Northern Region. It is still a very colonial region, with 'Residences' and 'D.O.s'. Sir Ahmadu Bello, the Premier of the Region, was being knighted in London, and I was sitting in the catering rest-house in Ilorin, waiting to be served. Waiting in good old South African style (apart from the fact that black and white do mix in Nigerian public places). I called for something on the menu and waited. A bunch of Europeans entered and took a table. Two of them called for the same item I had asked for. The next thing I saw was food being carried to them. The same waiter served me, afterwards. It happened again and again. The fault of the Europeans? Hardly. They were not sheltered by a barricade of *apartheid* laws which protect their counterparts in South Africa. I put it down to that cardiac trouble which inflicts the whole of the Nigerian North: subservience to white people 'who led us very gently and successfully to self-government', and a domineering attitude towards the peoples of the Eastern and Western Regions – 'southerners', they are called in the North, and almost equivalent to untouchables. The waiters were very nice to any Negro who came and talked their language (Hausa or Fulani). There was a register where we wrote our names and origins. It was easy for them to know what sort of customer they were dealing with – outsider or insider.

Once I arrived at the Ilorin rest-house and found two letters pinned on the notice-board, addressed to me and to a Nigerian. My letter asked me to vacate on the following night the châlet I had been assigned. Dr Azikiwe (then Premier of the Eastern Region) and his parliamentary group were coming. I was sent to a drab-looking châlet. It had a sagged ceiling and a mud floor.

At once the letter pressed a buzzer; a message was vibrating through the sensitized fibre of my being. I scanned the list of occupants for the day. All Europeans – except the two of us who had been written to by the white supervisor. So! I thought – it's the darky who must be made to give way to another darky – cunning! Did the supervisor think a black man would feel proud where a European might feel humiliated? Could it be that some of the European occupants had received their own letters before we had arrived? Maybe there were other Negroes – with European names? . . . How could I be sure? The uncertainty annoyed me all the more. The Nigerian, according to the entry in the register, was from Lagos, and I had come from Ibadan – southerners? When I asked tactfully what his letter was about, he gave me a smile as broad as the Niger and said with an obvious exuberant pride: 'Yes, I've also been asked to move. Dr Zik's coming today!' Yes, I said, but I barely managed to put on a grin. Later I felt I had cheated myself out of some fun. I should have abandoned myself. I should have tried to enter into the same emotional state. . . .

But that is the pain of it. I am a product of *apartheid*. Having tasted the joys of freedom in Nigeria – freedom to move, to associate, to speak – and broken through some of the British-inspired conservatism among Nigerians, I always wonder how I managed to survive. For *apartheid* conditioned me to patterns of response which have with the passage of time become set and prescribed. Each day I've been keyed up to meet a new situation. I suspected I was in for victimization as a black man. I was proved wrong, and how awkward I felt. It was like lifting a foot to go up or down a step which is not there. My momentum had already been committed, and the landing of the foot was jolting.

The challenge has continued to grin at me. There was one thing which I could not appreciate although I knew my view of it might very well be distorted. Some spectacles condition a man to an upside-down or grotesque world as if it were normal. For there are fears in Nigeria, fears on the part of minorities, and these are only exacerbated by the politicians. In the beginning the national constitution ensured that ethnic minorities within the regions be grouped together in separate states according to their cultural affinities. I thought of our battle against ethnic grouping in South Africa which the government has been enforcing in both school and home. I felt that so much of the work that had been done by African leaders to break down tribal barriers was being undermined. I seemed to hear Dr Verwoerd's voice somewhere in the tangle of phrases the powerful Action Group was using to support the creation of 'more ethnic states' in Nigeria. How could I consider the aspirations of the politicians, no doubt intensely sincere, with a mind unclouded by years of struggle against *apartheid* in all its forms? I was so sure about meanings in South Africa – could I know what was evil in another African context? Maybe there are those who *want* to be 'grouped ethnically'. . . .

In a year my suspicions, hate, anger, and bitterness were consolidated. The sediment of it all was down there in the pit of my stomach, waiting for time's purgative. I came to know that the absence of any enemy – in this case, the White Man who had turned my years in this world against me – made the heart beat more furiously.

You are a product of *apartheid* and all the forces of oppression that go with it. Your personality has a set of windows, and they open and shut as often as outside stimuli demand a response from you. But the stimuli move within a very narrow range of relationships: in terms of black *versus* white, master *versus* servant, privileged *versus* unprivileged. You come to a different situation such as that in Nigeria, where master–servant and rich–poor relationships are not vitiated by colour conflict. You need to have new windows which do not open out on mine dumps and skyscrapers darkening African shanty towns; out on suburban white society and blacks in location camps; out on police armed with sten guns, tear-gas, and batons, charging on men, women, and children. But alas, the windows you need to open here have been shut so long, oh, so long. You don't even know that some of them exist. You continue to open those shutters which have been swinging back and forth under the pressure of *apartheid*. And you realize that your responses were askew. When you eventually open other windows, they make a rusty creaking sound. How ecstatic I could suddenly become at the sight of the decency of the police in Nigeria – and how vitriolic against 'Western standards' under very slight provocation. . . !

I have no romantic ideas about Africans or Nigerians, only a vague feeling that where race conflicts are negligible, Africans can treat one another decently. I have no illusions about the fact that the problem of haves and have-nots is a universal one (and that in Southern Africa it is only magnified by colour prejudice). But I was not prepared for the rude shock that assailed me. I saw times without number the manner in which Nigerians treated their domestic servants, chauffeurs, and other workers. A man who considers his social or economic status to be high, whether he is literate or not, treats his domestics in a way I have come to associate only with the white man in the south. As in the rest of Africa, the monied African is seldom literate.

'What I go do with books?' he says. 'Na me want to see Governor General, I go see hum. Degree don't tok, mawny tok.'

The educated Nigerian's position, as one of a class, has been elevated in the same exaggerated degree in which the educated man in Southern Africa has been beaten and trampled down and humiliated by whites. I was once at a meeting and the presiding officer had brought his chauffeur along. The driver sat in a distant corner of the room, holding his employer's briefcase. Every time the chairman wanted a document from his case, he gave a signal and the chauffeur rushed to give him the bag. The document was taken out and the briefcase carried back to the corner to wait for another signal a few minutes later. I used to be outraged by the sight of domestic servants walking miles and miles to and from the market with loads on their heads – in spite of the fact that their masters had cars. I was told: 'They don't mind it. . . .' Some of them 'are relatives', cousins, brothers.

A benign-looking neighbour of ours from a house opposite came to see how we were settling down, just after our arrival in Ibadan. We told him our refrigerator wasn't working. Couldn't we keep our meat in theirs for the week-end? He agreed. I took out the meat, put it in a bowl, and held it out for him. He looked me up from toe to head with visible disgust. 'My boy will come for it !' he said brusquely. I was literally stupefied. Should I have given the fellow a 'demonstration lesson' by carrying the meat across the road myself?

A fellow South African teaches in a town forty miles from Ibadan. His headmaster wanted to carry a large piece of mutton to his house about five hundred yards away. There was nobody (but himself) to put the meat into his car. So he drove to his house, ordered his servant to follow him on foot and put the meat into the car. At the house he waited for the servant to arrive and take the meat out. And South African blacks? – might they do the same if they could afford the luxury of a chauffeur or a domestic? They might.

It was difficult for my wife to strike up any real friendship among the women. She soon realized that it was not a common thing for them to return a visit; and yet they were most hospitable when they were around. Often they were not around, because a woman in Yoruba society has a different social programme from her husband's, and when a man invites you to 'pop in', he does not necessarily mean his wife will be there when you come. Only the most sophisticated arrange it that way. Ibos and mid-Westerners opened up more readily. Perhaps being themselves isolated in Yorubaland, the Ibo women were happy to get allies.

We were all accepted by the men, Yoruba or not, without any visible reservation. Sometimes we sensed a similarity between our behaviour patterns. At other times the vaunted 'African personality' crumbled. But the fact that we belonged to no West African ethnic or tribal or language group made it easy for us to travel light among Yoruba, Ibo, Hausa, who are highly suspicious of one another. On some occasions I even sensed an attempt on the part of Nigerians to use me as a buffer or shock absorber in the strong conflicts of tribal arrogance.

A fellow South African teaching in the Eastern Region once wrote to me: 'Nigerians, who otherwise could be very sporting chaps, have this great weakness – the way they take themselves so seriously. No sense of humour except when it is at someone else's expense. Their mistake is in aping the British. They are only copying what the British were two generations back – descendants of the Victorian age of false modesty and pretentious decorum. They are as rigid as plaster and they practise a social caste system undreamt of in South Africa. . . .' I do not think the analogy with the British is really as simple as this, but there is truth here, although Nigerians dislike the imputation of fissures in their 'Africanism'.

I remember suggesting to South Africans teaching in Ghana (I was there in December, 1958) that 'it would be a great pity if we grouped ourselves into a colony in order to resist assimilation. . . .' Some agreed with me, others did not. But it was not easy to sink our identity; as a group we felt so strongly about the oppression of the millions we had left behind. We were probably as unassimilable as a pebble in a mouthful of rice.

Some South Africans in the West have come out to seek adventure, and they do not care to speculate on their social position in the host country. I worried so long about the problems of 'roots' and 'identity' and 'integration' until I didn't know whether I wanted to be integrated into Nigerian society or not. Perhaps it was just as well we had not come to the West out of a sense of mission but for sanctuary. We had to be taken for what we were worth.

The Europeans in Nigeria – how do they fit in? The teachers seemed to be the hardest-working of the lot (even considering their privileges). The others, in government and business, looked like soldiers of fortune. In a rest-house bar the opening conversational gambit, like weather in England, is 'What department are you in?' Here are the traders, merchants, commercial representatives, and civil servants. A man from the Public Works Department comes in, looking desperately wan, shuffling along with a prehistoric gait. He sits and begins to complain about his African workers : 'lazy . . . no sense of urgency . . . shamming illness . . . they can never do without us whites. . . .' And he belches importantly at intervals for emphasis. Or nowadays there is gossip about their 'African superiors' (*nomen et omen*). . . .

A European friend put it like this to me one day : 'Of course, you as a South African are, like us British expatriates, not involved in this set-up. But we're in a better position. We represent a source of authority, a power of some obvious sort. We can be badly mistaken and still be listened to with respect. But you couldn't venture an opinion here because you don't represent anything the Nigerians recognize as an existing force. . . .' This was several years ago. Since then, the defence pact Nigeria made with Britain when she became independent in 1960 has been vehemently challenged and has now been revoked. In 1959 Nigerian students for the first time had demonstrated their protest against the imprisonment of Dr Hastings Banda. Demonstrations were held after Sharpeville and the death of Lumumba. A general mood has been building up against the West in talking of Nigeria as a republic. Chief Awolowo (former Premier of Western Nigeria and once leader of the Opposition in the Federal House of Assembly) used to be regarded as the last bastion of all the political institutions Nigeria had inherited from Britain. But now even he has suggested that Nigeria join the Ghana–Guinea–Mali Union (and, anyway, is at present in jail).

Colour-conscious Europeans in West Africa do not (and cannot) make their presence felt (even if they were stupid enough to try).

They tend to be forgotten. The academic lot in Ibadan keep to themselves, either because they are bogged down in the mire of pseudo-Oxbridge academic snobbery from which they dare not save themselves or because they are products of a culture of formal invitations, over-privileged exclusiveness, and stock labels.

Oh, how easily I talk about the difficulties of adjustment. But it is not at all easy to describe the kingdom of freedom I moved in and what it did to me. You have to feel it yourself to know it, to know that the immigrant's journey is on a long, long road. As he goes on he is somehow at the same time making a spiritual journey back through a tunnel. The thudding footsteps of nearly forty years' torment beat down on him, threatening to deafen and confuse him. Things around him dance and dart out of perspective. Is that why freedom tastes sweeter and is a better tonic?

Richard Rive

DAGGA-SMOKER'S DREAM[1]

Of course there were times when he must have it. This wasn't
one of them. There were times when the craving gnawed inside
him like his longing for Honey, when his world spun round,
dragging him down into a whirlpool, spinning and longing, and
longing and spinning, and holding on tightly although there was
no grip. There were times when the longing grew to a passion, a
thirst that left his throat burning and that no amount of cheap
wine could assuage; so that there remained only the desire to sink
away into nothingness, forgetfulness, muddled oblivion – sharpening the appetite, not reducing it.

Karel wanted to forget, but not merely for the sake of forgetting.
He wanted to forget that he had kicked Honey, that he had kicked
her insensible, that he did not use fists but feet, that he had
kicked until the sole of his shoe had glowed with blood – a fascinating red that had made him wish to paint it even redder with sheer
brutality. He had to forget, because he did not know why he had
kicked her. She had sat on the pavement sipping a 'Bunny' and
twirling her shoe on the end of a bare toe. And he had called her
in, and he had kicked her and kicked her.

Grimy steps and dirty bow-legged, pot-bellied children. Neon
lights apologizing over District Six. The children fascinated Karel.
Dirty children with runny noses and spindly legs, and there, leaning against the wall, the dagga pedlar who recognized him.

Forgetfulness. To forget that he had kicked Honey. Sixpence-
worth of forgetfulness that brought oblivion. Oblivion for sixpence.
Sixpence, and one became a man. Sixpence, and one was so strong
that one could draw a breath through the teeth and defy the whole
damn world. All for sixpence and neatly wrapped in brown paper.

The notice board on the train became difficult to read. S . . . L . . .

1. *Dagga*: opium or hemp.

E . . . and where there should be a letter there was nothing. Peals of hysterical laughter because he had the right to kick Honey if she showed her body in the street. Not jealousy but respectability. Respectability even if she wasn't his wife. Well, maybe a little jealousy. Bodies on exhibition and a blur where G should come to spell out, 'SLEGS BLANKES', which meant whites only; which meant running on rubbery legs to the Second Class compartment.

A crowded train going God knows where. But then he was going God knows where. And why should he sit even if there were seats? Standing against the door people could see him, could laugh with him, and maybe at him. Maybe see Honey's bleeding face through him. They were his friends at the back of the train, that was why they laughed with him. Laughed at Honey. He was popular at the back of the train, and everyone getting up and grinning at him. Salt River . . . Plumstead . . . Retreat . . . Plumstead . . . Salt River. What the hell did he care? Everyone staring at him. Everybody but the white man reading a book. What the hell did he mean by reading a book in a Second Class compartment? Reading a book while Karel was entertaining the people. And the train jolting. What the hell did he think he was? A white man? And he, Karel, a dagga-smoker. A dagga-smoker who had kicked Honey. Others are looking at me and a white man ignoring me. Reading a book and ignoring me. He and that girl in front of him.

'Hullo, darling?'

Peals of laughter from the back as he sidles next to the girl.

'Leave me alone.'

'I'm only saying hullo, sweetheart!'

More laughter.

'Leave me alone!'

'Ag, I on'y want to touch you. *Jy's nie kwaad 'ie* – not angry?'

'Leave me alone!'

A long pause broken by the tittering at the back.

'I'm not one of those girls you pick up at Minnie's.'

'Leave 'e girls at Minnie's alone, bokkie. What kin' offa girl are you den?'

'I said leave me alone!'

'Why, honey?' The name erupted and retreated dizzily.

'I said leave me alone!'

'I'm a coloured man en' you're a coloured girl, so it's O.K.'

Then with a leer at the reading man, 'Or do you on'y want white men?'

The man skipped a line and then went on reading.

'If you smoke dagga, smoke it for yourself. Now let me go!'

'You pertickler, hey, on'y want white men, hey?'

Karel looked around him for his friends and met the eyes of the white man staring coldly at him. Karel stared back defiantly and then saw the pleading eyes of Honey. He dropped his eyes in a haze of shame, self-consciousness and pseudo-bravado.

'I say, gi' us a kiss, bokkie?'

'Mind – let me get out!'

He would not let her pass. He felt humiliated by her attitude. Crushed. He did not know how. He had a right to kick Honey. He must do something, say something to put her in her place. His friends must not stop laughing. He must hear them click their tongues and say what a devil he was when he had dagga in him. To behave like someone who was a devil when he had dagga in him. Even though his heart was sore with humiliation and the longing to forget.

'Kiss me first, bokkie, then you can go.'

'Let me go.'

'*Net een soentjie* – just one kiss!'

'Leave me alone, I'm warning you!'

'What a silly bokkie. Won't even gi' me one kiss,' he said, grinning slyly at the white man. No response. Why the hell didn't he open his mouth?

'Ag, I don't want you for a girl any more.'

'I'm not your girlfriend. Let me pass!' She appealed to the white ticket examiner.

'It's all right. It's on'y my girlfriend, guardjie!'

'I don't know him. Let me pass, I'm telling you!'

'*Komaan, laat haar verby jou dronk skepsel!*'

'Awright, guardjie! All forgotten. Solong, sweetheart.'

She gathered up her bag and made for the next compartment. Karel shook his head and focused his eyes. She had left. He felt that Honey had again walked out on him. Sipping a blooming 'Bunny'. He felt the white man's eyes on him. Now swells of humiliation and self-pity. He must do something to redeem his ego. Show that white man that he is Karel. Keep those at the back laughing with him.

'To hell with ev'ryone on the train !'

No response other than the peals of laughter.

'I'm born in District Six, in 'e Mokkies Buildings, and I'm prepared to knock hell outta ev'ryone here.'

(A pathetically thin figure with pupils hanging low in the eyes. Karel, drunk, drunk with power because his oaths go unchallenged.)

'These blerry whites that can't afford to set First Class. I'm a coloured man an' I can't sit "slegs blankes". But dey can sit anywhere 'ey bloomingwell like.'

'These white bastards mast clear out !'

Spume fluttered.

'I'm not afraid of anyone ! Black or white ! I'm born in District Six !'

Plumstead . . . Retreat. The white man shut his book and opened the door.

'To hell with you all !' Karel almost wept. 'To hell with you all. Open the bloody window ! Why do kaffers ride Second Class? The bloody place stinks !'

He clambered over a passenger, and amid raucous laughter proceeded to open all the windows.

Alex La Guma

BLANKETS

Choker woke up. The woman's wiry hair got into his mouth and tasted of stale brilliantine. The old double-bed sagged and wobbled when he shifted his weight, and there were dark stains made by heads on the crumpled grey-white pillows, and a rubbed smear of lipstick like a half-healed wound. His mouth felt parched from the drinking of the night before, and he had a headache.

The woman was saying, half-asleep, 'No, man. No, man.' Her body was moist and sweaty under the blanket, and the bed smelled of a mixture of cheap perfume, spilled powder and human bodies mixed with infant urine. The faded curtain over the room window beckoned to him in the hot breeze. In the early, slum-coloured light, a torn under-garment hanging from a brass knob was a spectre in the room.

Choker felt ill and angry. The unwashed, worn blanket brushed his face and he smelled it with the other smells, and thought vaguely that he had slept under such blankets all his life. He wished he could sleep in a bed in some posh hotel, under fresh-laundered bedding. Then this thought was displaced by desire for a drink of cold beer, even water. He felt irritable, and thrust the bedding from him.

The woman turned beside him under the blanket, protesting in her half-sleep, and Choker sat up, cursing. The agonized sounds of the bed-spring woke up the baby who lay in a bath-tub on the floor, and it began to cry, its toothless voice rising in a high-pitched wail.

Choker sat on the edge of the bed and cursed the baby and the woman in his mind. He wondered why the hell he had crept in with somebody else's woman in the first place. And she with a bloody baby, too. The child in the tin tub kept on wailing.

'Ah —,' he snapped angrily at the infant.

The woman woke up and looked at him, dishevelled, from the soiled pillow. 'You made such a noise. You woke the child,' she chided.

'Ah, hold your mouth,' Choker told her angrily. 'Get up and see to your damn kid.'

He stood up and walked around the bed to find his shirt and trousers. The woman asked, 'You going?'

'Of course, yes. You reckon I want to listen to this blerry noise?'

'Well,' the woman said crossly, 'Can I help it? You knew *mos* I had the child.'

The baby kept on wailing. Choker looked at it as he pulled on his trousers and buttoned his shirt. 'Babies, dammit.'

She asked, in a humbler tone, 'You coming back?'

'Maybe. Maybe not. I don't know.'

'Listen,' she said. 'Careful when you come, hey? I don't want my man to see you come here. He got an idea you been coming here. He'll maybe do something to you.'

Choker sneered: 'Him? Jesus, I'll break him in two with my bare hands.'

He laughed, standing hugely in the room. He was a big man, with muscles like bulges of steel wire, and great hands. He was brutal and vicious, and used the thick, ropy, grimed hands for hurting rather than for working.

She said, 'Awright, man. But even though he left me, he don't like 'nother man coming here. He may be watching out for you.'

'The hell with him,' Choker growled. 'His mother.'

The woman said nothing, and climbed out of the jangling bed to attend to the baby. She sat on the edge of the bed in her limp petticoat and suckled it.

She said, 'If you wait a little I'll make a little tea.'

'Forget it.'

Choker looked at her, sneered and shook his head, and then went out.

He walked along the corridor of the house, past the other rooms, frowning irritably against the nagging ache in his head, and the brittle feeling in his mouth and throat. There were holes in the boards of the floor, and he walked as carefully as his heavy body allowed.

In the morning sunlight, outside the smelly house, he headed for the tap in the dry, hollowed-out area which had once been a garden. He drank thirstily for a few moments, and then splashed his face, drying it on the sleeve of his shirt. He thought, To hell with her, I'll be boggered if I go back to that lot.

Around him were the rows of old, crammed houses and tumbledown box-board-and-tin shanties of the suburban slum. Chickens and dogs picked their way around among the weeds. He made his way idly through the broken streets and pathways. People avoided him, or gave him a casual greeting and passed on quickly, knowing his reputation. He was a drifting hulk, an accursed ship moving through a rotting sargasso.

Choker was passing a walled-in yard when the three men stepped quickly from a gateway behind him. One of them cried, 'That's him,' and then, before he could turn, pain speared him with red-hot blades. He felt the pain in his head and the pain in his body almost simultaneously, and he fell, cursing. They didn't even wait to examine him, or to try again, but fled swiftly from the reach of the grappling-iron hands, leaving him to bleed in the roadway.

Choker lay in the road and felt the pain and the trickling of blood against his skin. He wanted to get up, but his legs were suddenly useless, and his arms would not lift his body. He lay there, his throbbing mind stubbornly cursing his attackers, while a crowd gathered, everybody talking excitedly.

Somebody said, 'Better carry him off the road.'

'I don't want nothing to do with it, hey.'

'Well, he can't *mos* just lie about there.'

'Better go over to the shop and phone for the am'ulance.'

'Okay. Did you see them?'

'Look, pally, I didn't see nothing, man.'

'Well, pick him up. Look, Freddy, you take his feet. Sampie, you he'p him. Me and Points can take his arms.'

Lying there, bleeding and feeling ill, Choker thought, — you all, and then he felt himself being lifted roughly. He thought it was a hell of a thing to be so weak all of a sudden. They were bundling him about and he cursed them, and one of them laughed, 'Jesus, he's a real tough guy'.

Choker lay on the floor of the lean-to in the backyard where they had carried him. It was cooler under the sagging roof, with the pile of assorted junk in one corner: an ancient motor tyre, sundry split and warped boxes, and an old enamel display sign with patches like maps of continents on another planet, where the paintwork had worn away, and the dusty footboard of a bed. There was also the smell of dust and chicken droppings in the lean-to.

From outside, beyond a chrome-coloured rhomboid of sun, came a clatter of voices. In the yard they were discussing him. Choker opened his eyes, and peering down the length of his body, past the bare, grimy toes, he could see several pairs of legs, male and female, in tattered trousers and laddered stockings.

A man was saying, '. . . that was coward . . . from behind, *mos*.'

'*Ja*. But look what he done to others, don't I say?'

Choker thought, To hell with those baskets. To hell with them all.

Somebody had thrown an old blanket over him. It smelled of sweat and dust and having-been-slept-in-unwashed, and it was torn and threadbare and stained. He touched the exhausted blanket with thick, grubby fingers. The texture was rough in parts and shiny thin where it had worn away. He was used to blankets like this.

Choker had been stabbed three times, each from behind. Once in the head, then between the shoulder-blades, and again in the right side. The bleeding had stopped and there was not much pain. He had been knifed before, admittedly not as badly as this, and he thought, through the faraway pain, The baskets couldn't even do a decent job. He lay there and waited for the ambulance. Blood was drying slowly on the side of his hammered-copper face, and he also had a bad headache.

The voices, now and then raised in laughter, crackled outside, somewhere far away. Feet moved on the rough floor of the yard and a face not unlike that of a brown dog wearing an expired cloth cap, peered in.

'You still awright, Choker? Am'ulance is coming just now, hey.'

'— off,' Choker said. His voice croaked.

The voice withdrew, laughing : 'Ou Choker. Ou Choker.'

Another voice said : 'That burg was waiting for him a long time awready.'

'Ja. But Choker wasn't no good with a knife. Always used his hands, man.'

'That was bad enough, I reckon.'

The hell with them, Choker thought. He was feeling tired now. The hard grubby fingers, like corroded iron clamps, strayed over the parched field of the blanket. . . . He was being taken down a wet, tarred yard with tough wire netting over the barred windows looking into it. The place smelled of carbolic disinfectant, and the bunch of heavy keys clink-clinked as it swung from the hooked finger of the guard.

They reached a room fitted with shelving which was stacked here and there with piled blankets. 'Take two, jong,' the guard said, and Choker began to rummage through the piles, searching for the thickest and warmest. But the guard, who somehow had a doggish face and wore a disintegrating cloth cap, laughed and jerked him aside, and seizing the nearest blankets, found two at random and flung them at Choker. They were filthy and smelly, and within their folds vermin waited like irregular troops in ambush.

'Come on. Come on. You think I got time to waste?'

'Is cold *mos*, man,' Choker said.

But it was not the guard to whom he was talking. He was six years old and his brother, Willie, a year his senior, twisted and turned in the narrow, cramped, sagging bedstead which they shared, dragging the thin cotton blanket from Choker's body. Outside, the rain slapped against the cardboard-patched window, and the wind wheezed through the cracks and corners like an asthmatic old man.

'No, man, Willie, man. You got all the blanket, *jong*.'

'Well, I can't he'p it, *mos*, man. Is cold.'

'What about me?' Choker whined. 'What about me? I'm also cold, *mos*.'

Huddled under the blanket, fitted against each other like two pieces of a jigsaw puzzle. . . . The woman's wiry hair got into his mouth and smelled of stale hair-oil. There were dark stains made by heads on the grey-white pillow, and a rubbed smear of lipstick like a half-healed wound.

The woman was saying, half-asleep, 'You see? You see? What did I tell you?' Her body was moist and sweaty under the blanket; and the blanket and bed smelled of cheap perfume, spilled powder, urine and chicken droppings. The faded curtain beckoned to him in the hot breeze. The woman turned from him under the blanket, muttering, and Choker sat up. The agonized sounds of the bed-spring woke the baby in the tin bath-tub on the floor, and it began to cry in a high-pitched metallic wail that grew louder and louder. . . .

Choker woke up as the wail grew to a crescendo and then faded quickly as the siren was switched off. Voices still excitedly shattered the sunlight in the yard. Choker saw the skirts of white coats and then the ambulance men were in the lean-to. His head was aching badly, and his wounds were throbbing. His face perspired like a squeezed-out wash-cloth.

Hands searched his body. One of the ambulance attendants asked: 'Do you feel any pain?'

Choker looked at the pink-white face above him, scowling. 'No, sir.'

The layer of old newspapers on which he was lying was soaked with his blood. 'Knife wounds,' one of the attendants said. 'He isn't bleeding much outside,' the other said. 'Put on a couple of pressure pads.'

He was in mid-air, carried on a stretcher flanked by a procession of onlookers. Rubber sheeting was cool against his back. The stretcher rumbled into the ambulance and the doors slammed shut, sealing off the spectators. Then the siren whined and rose, clearing a path through the crowd.

Choker felt the vibration of the ambulance through his body as it sped away. His murderous fingers touched the folded edge of the bedding. The sheet over him was white as cocaine, and the blanket was thick and new and warm. He lay still, listening to the siren.

Can Themba

The following story was one of the eight prize-winning stories in a contest organized by the South African Centre of the International Pen Club and open to writers of all races in South Africa.

THE URCHIN

One sling of the braces would not keep up on the shoulder, just like one worm of pale-green mucus kept crawling down the chestnut lip and would suddenly dart back like a timid creature. But Macala wore his long pants (surely someone's – someone older's – castaway three-quarter jeans) with a defiant pride just ready to assault the rest of the known world. Other boys his ten-year age only had short pants.

He looked up and down from Mafuta's Chinaman store along Victoria Road, Sophiatown, and he thought of how his day ought to begin. Mafuta's was no good: he kept two too-ferocious dogs in his shop, and fairly authenticated rumour had it that he also kept a gun that made a terrible noise. But the vistas up and down Victoria Road offered infinite possibilities for a man. To the left, there were queues on queues of half-frightened, half-foolish people who simply asked to be teased. Then Moosa's store with all those fruity, sweety things in the window: but they said Moosa trained at night with irons. Opposite, across Millar Street, there was a Chink butcher, but his counter was fenced off with wire, and Ooh ! those cruel knives and hatchets. There must be a lot of money there for it to be protected so formidably. And, next to the butcher, the Bicycle Shop with its blaring juke-box: *Too roo roo roo tu! Too roo roo roo tu-tu!* Where a passer-by girl would suddenly break into a dance step, seductive beyond her years.

All like that, up to Chang's, and from there just the denuded places the Demolition Squad had left in Sophiatown.

To the right, Macala stared at Benghali House. The only double-storey building in the whole of Sophiatown. In front of it all sorts of pedlars met: sweet-potato sellers, maize sellers, and sweet-reed sellers, African pimpled squash sellers, shoe-lace sellers – all be-damned whether or not the shopkeeper alone held a licence to sell anything.

Macala's eyes glittered as he saw the Ma-Ndebele women squatting in their timeless patience behind their huge dishes of maize-cobs, dried morogo peanut cubes, wild fruits like marula, mahlatswa – things the urban African never sees on trees these days.

To Macala, these women with their quaint and beaded necks and legs that made them look like colourful pythons, were the fairest game.

He stepped off the veranda of Mafuta's shop, off the pavement, and sauntered swaggeringly towards those placid women in front of Benghali House. He was well aware that the street-corner loungers, enormous liars all of them, were watching him, thinking that the slightest move of Macala promised excitement and trouble.

He stopped in front of a Ndebele woman transfixed to her white dish, as if one with it, as if trade meant just being there at the strategic place and time: no bawling, no bartering, no bargaining.

'Dis – how much?' and that to Macala was English with a vengeance. She looked up at him with large baffled eyes, but before she spoke, Macala lifted his foot and trod on the edge of the dish, sending its contents churning out of it into the dust of Victoria Road's pavement. He shrieked with delight as he ran off.

What she hurled at him in virulent Ndebele may have been curses, prayers, lamentations. But to Macala it was reward enough, the kind of thing that proves the superiority of the townsman to these odd creatures from the country. And the passing generation's men and women shook their heads and muttered gloomily: 'The children of today, the children of today . . .'

His momentum took him to the vegetable vendor just opposite Mafuta's. In fluid career, he seized the handle of the cart and whirled it round and up for the devil of it. Potatoes, onions, pumpkins, cabbages went swirling into the air and plump tomatoes squashed on the macadam. The khaki-coated vendor stood aghast a second before he broke into imprecations that shuddered even the sordid Sophiatown atmosphere. But Macala was away on his mischievous way.

He had passed the 'Fish and Chips' too fast for another tilt, and met his pals on the corner of Tucker and Victoria: Dipapang, Jungle and Boy-Boy. Together, they should have been 'Our Gang' but their organization was not tight enough for that.

Boy-Boy's was the brain that germinated most of the junior devilry of the team, but he did not quite have Macala's impetuous courage of execution. He looked like a social worker's explanation of 'conditions in the slums': thin to malnourished, delinquent, undisciplined, dedicated to a future gallows. Yet his father was an important man and his mother a teacher. Jungle qualified by the ease with which he could talk of using a knife. In real big-tsotsi fashion. Dipapang initiated nothing, thought nothing, was nothing, but always so willing to join in, try and finish anything the others cared to start.

'Heit, Macacix!' called Boy-Boy. 'It's how there?'

Macala suddenly felt in the mood for the jargon of the townships. The near-animal, amorphous, quick-shifting lingo that alarms farm-boys and drives cops to all branches of suspicion. But it marks the city slicker who can cope with all its vagaries.

'It's couvert under the corzet,' Macala replied, bobbing his head this way and that to the rhythm.

'Hai, man, bigshot, you must be the reely-reely outlaw in this town,' Boy-Boy parried and lunged.

'Naw,' Macala feinted, 'dis town, Softtown's too small for me. I'll take Western and Corrie and Maclera and London, and smash them into a mashed potato.'

Boy-Boy fell for it. 'Whew!' he whistled, 'don't say you'll crowd me out!'

Macala took him by the throat and went in for the kill. 'Didn't I tell you, buster, to keep out of my country, or else...'

He proceeded to carry out the menacing 'or else' by choking Boy-Boy and slowly tripping him over a leg he had slipped behind him until they rolled over as Boy-Boy fell, and tumbled into the gutter.

Boy-Boy gasped: 'Ah give up, boss, da country's yours.'

The mock battle was over and everybody laughed . . . except Jungle. He was reputed to be 'serious' and that meant of the homicidal type. He sat there on the pavement drain with his mournful face, sharpening gratingly on the concrete his 3-Star jack-knife which from some hazy movie memory he called his 'gurkha'. As the laughter trailed off, he suddenly drawled: 'Have you guys heard that Mpedi was arrested yesterday?'

They stared at him in genuine stupefaction. Then Boy-Boy said: 'Yerrrr! How'd it happen, Jungle?'

But Jungle was not one for elaborating a story. Very unsatisfactorily, he said: 'Waal, he was drinking at de English Lady's joint . . . and . . . and dey got him.'

'You mean he didn't shoot it out? You mean dey took him just like dat? But I bet ya dey couldn't put handcuffs on Mpedi!' But Macala was very unhappy about the tame way the idol of the township was arrested.

Boy-Boy it was who made a story of it. 'Yerrr! But there is an outee.'[1] He rose from the pavement and stood before the fascinated gaze of his pals. He stuck his thumbs into his belt and swayed his hips as he strutted up and down before them. Then he mimicked the bull-brained fearlessness of Mpedi, the mirror and form of almost all young Sophiatown, the clattering terror of men, and the perennial exasperation of the police station across the road.

'Ya! Da room was full – full to da door. Clevers, bigshots, boozers, bamboos, coat-hangers, hole-diggers, and bullets, blondes, figure 8's and capital I's, wash-planks and two-ton trucks. Da boys were in de stack and da dames were game. . . .

'Then Bura Mpedi stepped in, his eyes blood-red. The house went dead-still. Ag, man, Bura Mpedi, man. He stood there and looked left . . . and looked right. . . . His man was not there. He stepped in some more. The house was dead. He grabbed a beer from the nearest table and slugged it from the bottle. Who would talk?' Boy-Boy's upper lip curled up on one side in utter contempt, 'Heh, who would talk!'

Macala and his pals were caught in Boy-Boy's electric pause.

1. Outlaw, used with a sense of pride.

Even Jungle was aroused by this dramatic display of township bullycraft.

Boy-Boy's histrionics continued: 'Yerrrre! a drunk girl came from under a table, and tried Mpedi for a drink. "Au, Bura Mpedi, give me a beer." Bura Mpedi put a boot on her shoulder and pushed her back under da table. Hai, man, hai man, dat outee is coward-cool, man. And he hates cherry coat-hangers. But dat night his eyes were going all over looking for Mahlalela. Yeffies! If he'd caught Mahlalela dat night . . . !'

Lifted by the wide-eyed admiration of his pals, Boy-Boy went on to surpass himself. He flung out his right arm recklessly, and declared: 'But dat's nutting yet! You should have seen Bura Mpedi when dey sent four lean cops to come and take him. Payroll robbery, Booysens . . . one thousand pound! Assault with G.B.H.,[1] Newlands . . . three men down and out! Housebreakin' 'n *Thatha*[2] . . . Lower Houghton!

'Dey came, man dey came. Four cops, two had guns, two had small inches.[3] Dey surrounded da joint in Gibson Street, and dey called out to him to give up. Dey didn't know Mpedi with moon-wash in his brains and a human intestine round his waist. He drew his point-three-five and his forty-five, and he came out shooting: Twah! Rwah! Rwah! Da two cops with small inches ducked into a shebeen near by and ordered themselves a ha' nip brandy. One with da gun ran down Gibson Street for reinforces. Da last cop took a corner and decided to shoot it out with Mpedi. But da bullets came so fast he never got a chance to poke out a shot.

'Hee-e-e, I tell you Mpedi was da outee.' Then, still carried forward by the vibrance of his enthusiasm, Boy-Boy rounded off his dramatization by backing away slowly as he fired off imaginary guns, and barked: 'Twah! Twah! Twah!'

But the elation that had swelled up in Macala was now shot through with envy. 'How come,' he grumbled, 'da cops got him so easy now?' Yet what really worried him was that he knew how far he was beneath the fabulous Mpedi; that even in his own weight division, he could not make such an awe-inspiring impression. He was not even as good an actor as Boy-Boy to recount and

1. 'Grievous Bodily Harm.'   2. Taking away, theft.   3. Batons.

represent the exploits of the almighties. He looked at Boy-Boy bitterly and told himself: I'll beat his brains out if he gets smart with me.

It was Jungle who wrenched him out of his sour reverie. 'Boys, I think we should go finish off da Berliners,' Jungle said, prosaically.

A flash of fear leapt into Boy-Boy's eyes, for he knew this meant war. Macala was himself a bit scared, but seeing the fear in Boy-Boy, he screwed his heart through a hole too small for it.

And Jungle's 'gurkha' went on scraping the pavement concrete, *screech-screech! screech-screech!*

'Come ahn, let's go,' Macala suddenly decided.

They swaggered along Victoria Road, filling it from pavement to pavement as if they were a posse. Silent. Full of purpose. Deliberately grim. Boys and girls scampered for cover. Grown-ups stepped discreetly out of their way. Only the bigger tsotsis watched them with pride, and shouted encouragements like: *Da men who rule da town! Tomorrow's outees!*

On the corner of Meyer Street, they broke up a ring of young dicers and forced them to join up. Along the way they collected non-schoolgoing loafers who lounged against shop walls; blue-jeaned youngsters who twisted the arms of school-girls in rough love; odd-job boys who ran errands for shopkeepers; truants, pickpockets, little thugs, within their age limit – the lot.

By the time they turned into Edith Street, they were a miniature army of hell-bent ruffians. Macala led them and felt the strange thrill of the force behind him. He chose Edith Street because it rose into a rocky hill with plenty of stones for ammunition, and dropped suddenly into that part of Sophiatown they called *Berlin*, where the walls were smeared with crude swastikas.

Macala split his men into two groups. Those with thick, bronze buckle belts were to go under Jungle through a cut in the row of houses precariously perched on huge boulders.

The excitement chopped Macala's breath into collops as he gave out his instructions. 'You boys get dem from de back. You start de war. When dey come running up Edward Road, dey'll meet us. Use dat butcher of yours Uncle Jungle.'

Jungle gave one of his rare smiles, and his men took position.

Macala and his group, first placing a sentinel on the hill-top, slowly clambered down the rocks and waited for Jungle to get around.

Though going into the den of the enemy, Jungle did not find it difficult to rout them. There was a biggish group of them playing dice in the usual ring, and when he swooped upon them, they instinctively thought it was the police and dashed up Edward Road, sticks and buckle belts raining on their heads.

Jungle himself had chosen a heftily-built fellow and was stabbing at him as he ran. Boy-Boy was later to describe it graphically: 'Yerre! Dat guy just wouldn't fall. Jungle had him – zip! But he ran on. Jungle caught him again in the neck – zip! He stumbled and trotted on his hands and feet. Jungle got him in the buttock – zip! But, yerrr! He just wouldn't fall!'

Before the Berliners could rally and make a stand, they had run into Macala's stone-throwing division. Though very one-sided, the fight became fierce. The Berliners were now fighting, and because they were trapped and because they had to fight with their bare hands most of the time, they became young devils from the playgrounds of Hell.

Stones and all sorts of other missiles were hurled in all directions. Knives were brandished and plunged, big-buckled belts were swung in whistling arcs, arms were flailed in the centre of the imbroglio with desperate savagery. Women screamed, shops closed, traffic diverted itself. Now and then, a blood-bespattered boy would stagger off the street to a side wall just to sit down and watch. Too done in to flee.

Then suddenly came the shrill warning cry, 'Arrara! Arrarayii!' The action stopped almost as abruptly as those ancient films which froze in mid-motion and transfixed the movement into a photograph. And just as suddenly after, they scattered all pell-mell. When the police van came round the corner, it was impossible to decide which flee-ers to pursue. For, now, everybody was running up and down and off the streets. The scores of small boys, ordinary pedestrians who had just alighted upon the scene, Fah-fee runners with full-blown cheeks a-chumping the incriminating tickets of their illicit lottery; everybody was running. In Sophiatown, you do not stop to explain to the police that you had nothing to do with it; or that you knew some of the culprits and could help the police.

The mobile squad were satisfied with merely clearing the street.

Breathless and bruised, Macala found himself at the open commonage called Maccauvlei, adjacent to Waterval Hospital, which served as the waste dumps to the city, and 'golf course' to those Africans who went in for the sport of leisure. Macala knew that most of his gang would sooner or later find their way there. He sat on a mound of ash, gasping heavily.

By the time Boy-Boy had arrived there, he had regained his breath, and was pitching chalky, burnt-out pebbles rather pointlessly. Jungle came, for once, apparently, in his seventh heaven. Dipapang, too, grinned happily though his shirt had been torn down and hung like a hula. A few other stragglers from the Black Caps joined them, and then came the News. News that oddly took the shape of 'They say'.

'Dey say,' announced one urchin, 'dat one of de Berliners is dead.'

Stultifying fright seized them all. Some small boy simply broke out crying. Macala had trouble with a choking clod in his throat.

'Dey say,' came in another boy, 'de Berliners are going to call in de Big Berliners.'

'Agh,' grunted Macala in contempt, 'we'll go'n tell Bura Shark.'

'Dey say de cops're going to round us all up tonight.'

Despite all their bravado, all their big-shot stances and their blistering contempt for cops and the law, there is one thing that this knighthood really fears, and it was expressed by a crackling of interjections from each according to his own lights:

'Six lashes and reformatory!'

'De cane and off to a farm!'

'Cuts with a light cane and no fine!'

Someone elaborated the procedure by filling in the gory details: 'Dey say, two huge cops hold you down over a big bench an' you got nothin' on. You can't move. Now, maybe de magistrate he said: "Six cuts." Dat's nothin'. If you cry, for every one you get two. An' dose cops who give de lashes, dey train for you, dey pick up weightlifting for you, dey grip a grip all day for you. Den when de other cops got you on de bench, an' you can't move, an' you don't want to cry, de lashing cop he takes de cane, he swishes it over his head, one-two-three, whish! De tattoo jumps up on your buttocks.

'Dey say, he den goes to sit down, light a sigareete, and talks with de other cops. Den he comes again. One of de cops holding you turns your head so you can see de lashing cop coming. He swishes de cane, one-two-three, whish! 'Nother tattoo comes up, dis time with blood. Red blood from your buttocks. He goes for 'nother puff at his cigarette, or maybe he looks for his tea dis time.

'He comes again. Dis time he sneezes his nose on your buttocks, and makes jokes how black buttocks is tough. He swishes the cane, one-two-three, whish! If you don't cry, maybe you get your six lashes straight. But if you cry, only just *Maye Babo* – oh-ho-ho! ...

'An' dey say, sometimes after you get lashes, six days, two weeks you can't sit in de bus, you give your seat to de aunties. Hai, dat cane dey keep in de salt water when nobody get lashes!'

By that time the horror of the prospect had seeped through every delinquent soul. It was Macala who spoke first.

He said determinedly: 'Me, I'm not going home tonight.'

But Boy-Boy did not like the idea. He knew that his mother would not rest until she had found out where he was. Worse still, she might even go ask the police to help her find him. 'Naw, Macacix, I'm going home. I don't like cops catching me when my ma is not there. I'm going home.'

As he walked away, the whole little gang suddenly broke up and walked home their different ways. As they scattered, Macala went frantic with panic. With consternation twisted in his face and his arms floating like a blind man's in front of him, he looked half-comic as he stood on that mount of ash.

'Hey, hey, you guys won't leave me alone. We're de boys . . .'

He heard a sound of impatience behind him: 'Aargh! Let them go, Macala.' He turned round and reeled unsteadily a little as he saw Jungle standing there, not looking frightened at all.

'Wh-what you going to do, Jungle?'

Jungle took out his 'gurkha' and scraped it across his palm from left to right, right to left. Then he said: 'I'm going home, Macala,' and that mournful expression crept across his countenance. 'And when de cops come to get me tonight . . .' He made an ugly motion with his knife under his chin. He walked away with the slow, lanky movement of that gawky body of his.

By the time Macala decided to leave Maccauvlei, it was getting dark. But he knew where he was going. Rather unnecessarily, he skulked along the fences of the street, looking this way and that. Now and then, he would petrify at the zoom of a passing car or duck into an alley when headlights bore goldenly through the dark of the street. But ultimately he reached the open space where Gerty, Bertha, and Toby Streets used to be. He saw the dark building for which he was headed. He ran forward and stopped in front of it, but this side of the street. Slowly now. Somewhere here there is a night-watchman, a Zulu with a thick black beard and barbel moustache, black uniform and black face that rubbed him out of sight in the dark, and a gnarled knobkerrie known to have split skulls.

But Macala knew where the corrugated-iron fence had snarled out a lip of entrance for him. He went on his hands and knees, and crawled away from the immense double gate towards this entrance. He found it and coiled himself inside. He knew there were stacks of corrugated iron in this timber yard, and if he touched them, the racket would alert the night-watchman. So he did not go far, just nestled himself near his exit.

A little breeze was playing outside, hasting a piece of paper down the street, and now and then a bus or lorry would thunder by. But Macala slept, occasionally twitching in the hidden mechanics of sleep. Far from where he could hear, a woman's voice was calling stridently: 'Mac-a-a-ala ! Mac-a-a-a-la ! Hai, that child will one day bring me trouble.'

Dennis Brutus

Let not this plunder be misconstrued
This is the body's expression of need –
Poor wordless body in its fumbling way
Exposing heart's-hunger by raiding and hurt;

      Secret recesses of lonely desire
      Gnaw at the vitals of spirit and mind
      When shards of existence display eager blades
      To menace and savage the pilgriming self :

Bruised though your flesh and all-aching my arms
Believe me, my lovely, I too reel from our pain –
Plucking from you these agonized gifts
Bares only my tenderness-hungering need.

Todd Matshikiza

From Chocolates for My Wife

THE PARTY

Eric Hopland was one of those inquisitive, bewildering, rather flurried attachments that one collects along the way. He was honest and unpredictable. Newly arrived in South Africa from Britain he did what all knowledgeable tourists did. Look up the Black staff newspapermen for a 'knowledgeable' how-do-you-do. The Black staff had big chuckles in the newspaper office where I worked. We bumped frequently into the tourists in the passage leading through the maze of editorial departments. They would be exchanging black names and black addresses.

'I'm from the *Toronto News*.'

'I'm from the *Manchester Post*.'

'Yes, I thought you looked rather overseasy. Ha, ha, ha.'

'You seeing Dan Choco? I hear he's the big noise around.'

'Not jus' now. Had a helluva fling with him last night some bloody place.' 'Naw, not Back-o'-the-Moon? Sophiatown? Gawd! An' did you meet Fats?'

'Shucks, you wouldn't say those big, fat, black dimpled buttocks could jive like that, hey!'

'Hell, I mus' go there again. Freddie Maponya's taking me to see Mabel.'

'He's the Sports Department guy? He's taking me to meet the Congress blokes but I b'lieve you got to take some brandy along, coupla bottles to make them open up.'

'Yes, meantime they plug you cockful of Shimiyana. Some randy home brew mixed with brandy, you all get thoroughly pissed an' you get nothing from them, only great big chunks of laughter.'

'I must see this guy, maybe I can cable something back home if I nip in before he gets into a drinking mood.'

We moved up and down the passage with proofs and copy from chief reporter to news editor.

Once I passed through in time to catch a dainty that got me a bonus that week. I was delivering copy on the jazz artiste Margaret Maseko. The couple in the passage were saying, 'What a greedy maw!'

Eric Hopland, unlike the others who wafted in and out, anchored himself somewhat permanently on Joe Jojo who wrote in impetuous philosophical irritability, his talk daring, bold with mustard and bubble-gum and his life a simple day-to-day occurrence of miracles.

This easy-going intellectual, Joe, bristling with English literature, vermouth and sleep was right for Eric, the songwriter. Eric was also easy, unbothered yet anxious. He pegged himself at Joe's desk punctually at five each day, but not securely. He hopped anxiously, rocking like a fishing-boat on a tremendous puzzled sea. His big, flat head shone down his enormous forehead into his blank face. He hopped madly, nervously at each new disturbance or old one such as the junior editor rushing in shouting for copy in a profane manner. We named Eric 'Hopping Hopland'.

The staff would ask, 'Where does that white guy Hopping Hopland, where does he stay?'

'Ehe, but he's okay. He gets the booze if you ask him. He's okay.' His name passed around popularly but his hop drove me mad and out of the office each time he called. Joe said to me, 'That guy is keen to make friends with you. He's a lyric writer and you're a musician an' he's dying to chat but you're always ducking him. He says you seem a severe type, but I told him you're helluva boozy, so he's going to ask to meet you some time.'

Hopping Hopland sure did ask me to come over let's have a chat 'bout a musical he's got in mind. The lyrics are half-way through but he doesn't want to take a chance on Africa, a subject he hasn't really quite dug.

'Joe, I can't stand the man's philanthropic hop.'

'You don't dig Eric, boy. He is dolly,' (okay, un-White).

'Who's coming to this evening besides you an' me?'

'I'll bring Ernest Kolisang, the "Nkunzana".'

'Ehe, the "Nkunzana" will be there? Hell!'

Telephone, where are you?

'Tri-i-i-ing.'

Female, caustic, impersonal voice: 'Hello.'

Me: 'Coloured Welfare Section, please.'

Caustic: 'Who d'you want there?'

Me, very meek: 'Mrs Matshikiza, please.'

Acid scream: 'Wh-a-a-at, wh-o-o-o?' Do I capitulate?

'Mrs Ma. . . .' No chance to finish here. The line is hot and hurried.

'What's her firs' nime?' The voice is easy now, simmering like a stew with the lid on tight.

'Esmé.' I am anxious to get through, and I must pay for it.

'Why don't you say so at firs' 'cause we dunno their naytiff nimes 'ere.'

'Excuse me, it's her surname. Not her native name.'

'Well dunno the naytiff surnames or naytiff what nots. An' is it business or private?'

My heart said speak bold and stand on your rights. Answer strong. They can't hurt you on the telephone like when you're physically face to face and if you answer back they bang your head against the wall to drum a lesson into it. Tell her who you are. The whole hell of who you are. The receiver was perspiring in my hand. My ear was hot and incensed. Suddenly my heart became strong as a double brandy and I changed my legs and said, 'Listen, if I can't speak to the person I want I'll make trouble for you.'

She said, 'Listen' (Afrikaans equivalent for who-the-hell-are-you), 'listen, I got instructions on this here switchboard, you hear?'

'Then, put me and your instructions through to the manager. Now!' I braved, adding, 'Listen, if you don' do that I'll call him personally through his private number.'

Brief cursing, threatening mumble.

Exit switchboard.

Enter Esmé.

'Is that you Chummy? Look I'll be late for supper. Going to see this chap Eric Hopland who's asked me and Joe along. Shall I bring the car round and you drive home?'

'No, I'll go home by train. You might be so late that you'll just get into trouble walking through town. You know your papers are not right,' she reminded me.

So Joe sat next to me to show the way. The 'Nkunzana' sprawled his limp, lazy limbs all over the back seat, sickening about his father's death, the legacy of property and vast lands, the tenants who won't pay up-to-date, and the Congress Youth League. He babbled, 'Ya, that's what I think this bloke wants to know. I'll tell him we'll blow up the bridge on Freedom Day and he can tell the papers in England, that'll be damn good publicity, hey Joe !'

Hopping Hopland's luxury flat is on Boogie Woogie Avenue which carries the large African pedestrian, cycle and bus traffic to Alexandra Township.

The road hums, buzzes all day with hurrying black faces, alert for gangsters, pimps, preachers and politicians. We entered Highbury Court by the side entrance, the one for hawkers and traders. Tiptoed cautiously almost as though we carried our shoes in our hands. Ah, he's on the fifth floor. Press the button quietly, gently. Dammit. The lift *had* to come down with a loud buzz, producing the Zulu night-watchman out of the eight o'clock shadows.

His big stick, pierced ears and police whistle wagged at us.

'What the hell do you Tsotsis do here this time of night? Nobody goes up there to the top now ! Only me, Gumede, that's me, or the Flying Squad. Go away ! The girls are sleeping up there. No visitors for servants. Go !' He was emphatic and precise, but his eyes told more. So we acted fast.

'Au, Gumede we are your children. Even this pound is chicken feed. You are bigger than the moon over there. This pound is nothing. Money is nothing to Gumede, lion of lions. But Gumede will please accept this humble pound as we go away.'

'Give that pound here. I let you in only this time. Hurry, quick, quick, quick. God help you if the Squad catch you on top of them !'

We shot to the fifth, saluting Gumede as we pushed up. The

long, dark porch took ages to get us to Eric's door. The neighbours might come out any moment now. The flat would be on snarling Boogie Woogie Avenue. Even during the bus boycott this avenue snapped black and white fangs at each other. White liberals gave the walking blacks lifts up an' down the twelve miles to work and home to Alexandra township. One morning the car halts abruptly and hurls the black woman bang against the front seat, hard. Hard. Little boys shouting, 'Come back, Africa,' see the incident and they shout even louder at the black woman, 'Come out and walk with the people. What you doin' in a white man's car. White man bang you in there all alone, all on your lonesome.'

Always Boogie Woogie Avenue snarls like that.

At last the long porch arrived at Eric's door, thank heavens, he left it open so's we can slide in fast. Then he locked the door and hopped uneasy welcomes from handshake to handshake.

He led the way into the sitting-room and watched us frown or smile as he uttered, 'You all know Fay, don't you!' Shucks! We all knew Fay, didn't we. And there she was, perked on the divan and waving us seats around the room, smiling pearly white teeth, darting rapid, pernicious wit out of her ebony black face, this African beauty.

She curled up on the couch like a trained pet, purring at us.

'Kunjani Bafana, how is it boys?'

'Kunjalo Ntwana, it is like tha-a-at, Fay man,' we shrugged.

Joe added famously, 'C'est la vie!'

A gallon of red wine on the table. Glasses, some thirsty, others half-full. Some food, chaps. Some excellent opera on the turntable. When I heard this magnificently done at Covent Garden shortly before I left England . . . is there any opera here . . . we're short of one fork . . . the orange squash is in there, Fay. . . .

We ate quietly wondering secretly who had prepared this junket. Maybe all sorts of things. Then there was a loud, loud crash, smash in the street. An explosion of glass. Voices yelling, 'Afrika-a-a'. Always when there is a crash, a death, a wedding, an arrest, a release, Africa yells 'Afrika-a-a'. What was it this time? Instinctively we flung the curtains wide, and peered into the electric-lit street below. Hundreds of Africans milled around the tram that had crashed into a motor-car. 'That sure was a loud bang, hey!' And we went back to lounge.

'If you guys were sweet, one of you would tuck me up and nice an' cosy. I can't find a nice position on this damn thing, can I now?' She shuffles distractingly all over the improvised couch and puffs, 'Eric deah, w'en ar'you goin' to buy decent furniture?'

'Have you got another fag for me, Fay?'

'Turn the lights down a bit, dear. We can hardly hear the music for the lights.'

Joe thumbed through a bookshelf. The 'Nkunzana' sank deeper and deeper into a cross-eyed, cock-eyed, after-dinner liqueur.

'Ah'll have that many times over.'

I stood near the music, keeping time with my increasingly loud heart-beat. Something hoppingly fishy about tonight.

Joe stood over there engrossed. Not quite upright as the arrow. Not quite bent as the bow. Freshly scarred each morning either mentally, politically or plain physically. He turned round briskly, his index finger between the pages of a book, waving the book like an auctioneer's hammer about to ram the bitter truth home. 'Aha! This is what I like. This chap says, "persecution is a test of truth" aha, aha, that's why I've always called my digs in Sophia-town the House of Truth. Nothing happens there but the truth.' Joe the ex-teacher spoke, 'Truth is when you stand and don' run, even when you can. Truth happens,' he clicked his fingers, 'jus' like that!'

The cross-eyed, cock-eyed 'Nkunzana' flashed a momentarily brilliant comment, before he sank again. 'Truth is like a little child saying "My Mummy said I mus' tell you she's not in".'

Fay wasn't going to be left out. 'Ehe, when I was a child playing hide-an'-seek I hid my eyes an' said to the others, "Where am I?" '

Eric also, 'Funny, that! We played the same games in England. Tell me, do your children play hop-scotch?'

The street below had gone all quiet again. The occasional bus to the townships roared by and we were settling down to a topic to break Eric's reluctance to warm up. Then there was a light tap, half-knock at the door! Eric swept glances inquiringly at each one of us as if to ask if we were expecting any friends to join us. Then he said, 'Maybe it's the girl upstairs.' He went to open the door and let in two husky men. They lingered at the door, with Eric hopping worse from one leg to the other and demanding an explanation somewhat hesitatingly. They stared past him across the porch and saw . . . me. I had been standing in full view of the front door. Ah well, they'd seen me so they wouldn't rush in at me. There was only one exit after all. They went into the kitchen. Eric made a gesture with his hand, like signalling us to shut up, scram, do something. Joe whispered, 'This is shit street, boys!' His wiry frame disappeared into the lavatory behind the kitchen.

The 'Nkunzana', all graces gone and now sober, shoved in fast behind Joe. Fay changed instantly from the purring, cuddling couch kitten and moving swiftly, silently, deftly like a man-eating jungle cat, she dashed into the built-in wardrobe. Lucky the flat was compact with convenient hiding-places very handy. Then the 'Nkunzana' remembered the jar of wine. He dashed out of the lavatory and back again with the jar as fast as a lynx, just as the men reappeared from the kitchen. Eric was protesting mildly, like weak tea, insipid and lukewarm. 'I can't understand how anyone can just enter premises and begin searching without introducing themselves properly.'

'Under the new laws we don't have to have a search warrant.'

'But you're not in uniform, how would I know you are police?'

They ignored him, and moved towards me. They stopped half-way across the room and stared at me without uttering a word. The last time I had felt cornered like this was the night six burly African policemen stormed into my house in Orlando when Esmé and I had Anthony Sampson and a beautiful Portuguese woman journalist for dinner. She had an enchantingly iridescent complexion that played in the dancing candle-glow, between ruby-red lips, damask cheeks, flame-blue eyes and my special Spanish wine. The African police noticed that too. Their eyes never left Miranda. They confiscated the wine and while I stood before the station commander waiting to be charged for being in illegal possession of wine, Esmé overheard the others saying, 'Man, we were damn fools tonight. We should have hit these chaps unconscious over the head, and raped that beautiful girl.'

Rape the girl? I saw you sipping at my wine as you marched me to the station. *That* was rape.

That night in Orlando with the six burly African policemen was a picnic. Easy. When Diliza said, 'Do you know why it is easy with the Black one?' I said, 'Yes, because they feel strong, with much power behind them.' Diliza said, 'No, it is because you and I are ordinary men, and they are policemen. Ordinary men pay for their drinks. Policemen don't.'

The two white men closed in on me like the walls of an inquisition. The one on the left wore a suit of clothes bulging with boerewors. He had frying-pans for hands. He said, 'If you move I'll clap you dead with these.' And he raised the frying-pans in my face, then I knew he would. He moved hipfully, slowly forward and bent his big bulk over the table to smell the contents of the glasses. His nose twitched as though the wine made him sick. His banana fingers clawed around one glass, wrinkling and unwrinkling at the knuckles like a baby elephant's trunk.

'We have to search your place I'm afraid.'

'Don' be afraid, there's nothing here,' jittered Hopping Hopland.

'In case you have anything to ask later Sergeant van de Walt is my rank. Tha's Constable Koekemoer.'

Koekemoer, dark enough to pass for black. He had a bony frame, so like reeds on a broken raft that I wished he hadn't a double-breasted suit. And he wore windows, or spectacles, beneath his huge, cowboy-brimmed brown hat that wore the signs of a disused road signpost in the Kalahari. He's the one that moved in my direction, crippling along to make me realize the hunch on his back under his coat was a revolver. The ones they mercy-kill horses with.

Mazisi Kunene

UNIVERSAL LOVE

And feed you my hand
Until you grow high into the stars
And wait there for the coming of the sun
To break the dawn fire
For me, where the lips are cold.
Forced to love beyond the crown of the horizon
Swallowing the power of thunder
And make the eternal feast on the rock
Not letting me nor my kinsman
Forget the drunkenness in the clouds
Who alone is real in the fall of fantasy
A visible long round embrace of the earth.

Lewis Nkosi

THE PRISONER

1

Like their jailers all prisoners are the same basically. It doesn't matter what colour their skin is. When they are talked to they tend to whine ignobly; there is something in the timbre of their voices which disturbs me profoundly. It's not easy to lay one's finger on it. If I were pressed for an answer I would say it is a mixture of offended surprise, a mingling of protest and pleading which is most unmanly. It is as if the prisoner both loved and hated his role, as though he both revered and despised his jailer; altogether I am surprised that fate should thrust a human being into such a role.

I look at George here – shabby, ill-washed, ill-fed, and the skin a little sallow because of lack of sunshine – and I am reduced to tears. After all George was once my master and jailer, though you wouldn't know it now. A white man entrusted with the destiny of twelve million blacks, and out of that number George had the misfortune of having me as his special ward. This, as George used to tell visiting statesmen, was the 'unkindest cut of all'. Still I recognized the pride in his voice when he said it; he enjoyed having me as prisoner. To some extent I believe that George would have felt limited without a prisoner to whom to show his special brand of kindness; so when he rebuked fate for having appointed him lord over me I knew what to think of it.

He was tall then, broad and tanned like all *ware* South Africans. I used to think then that a peculiar strength emanated from George. He had, to say the least, the air of one born to command. His gestures were easy, his voice was contemptuous, and there was a glint of mockery in his eye which was most fetching. I used to lurk in the kitchen plotting some of the nicest dishes and confectionery to cook and bake for George, so persuasive was his personality, so compelling were his gestures; it was truly a pleasure to obey his command. Now you see only the empty husk of what used to be a man imbued with a stern spirit of command. Those blue eyes are now turned into a dusty colour, his hands and legs are emaciated beyond recognition. Well, that's what Fate does with men of destiny. For that's the kind of man I used to believe George was.

I see, you grimace. I suppose you don't believe that Fate has anything to do with this. Perhaps you don't believe in Fate at all. Suit yourself, no one has to believe in anything. Nevertheless, sometimes you think : there, but for the grace of God, because any moment the roles could be switched, you could easily find yourself in chains, denied bread, wine and the body of a beautiful woman. Like George there !

You should have seen George's wife when they first got married. Even now it still hots up my blood to see her walk in here. My God, what a prize cow. At forty she is still firm and rounded out, with a pink vivid skin. In the nude her stomach is a goblet of gold. Don't ask me how I know these things, I may be black but women are women and they love men with power. To be fair, though, sometimes I have a feeling that she comes less to see George than to see me. We have a room at the back there with bare whitewashed walls and knitted bed-spreads. I can tell you of many nights when Francisca and I have lain down there worrying about George's position in the world.

Francisca who has a voice like a reed in the wind always ends up by shedding tears : 'How can fate be so cruel to him, Mulela?' she asks, nestling very close. It is strange to sleep next to George's wife while he lies in the cell covered with rags and lice, writhing in the agony of a desire unfulfilled these past twelve years. Sometimes it breaks my heart just to think about it. There have been occasions when I have ended up weeping myself. The misery of another human being, whether white, black, or yellow, is not a very nice thing to see, least of all by one who used to be his servant, his slave and prisoner. Even Francisca's goblet of honey is not enough to assuage one's sense of sorrow. I tell you it is not enough (though it helps) to stem the great tide of pity. Yet there is no need to feel superior, no need to pity George at all; for who can be so brave as to stand up here and declare for all the world to know that he doesn't need pity? Well, I ask you. No one; we all need pity – even Francisca there, warm, smooth-limbed, a veritable prize cow, she needs salvation.

Do you know these days we love without feeling loved? We experience Grace without feeling saved. We experience even occasional joy without knowing true happiness. In abundance we have all the flesh we need but always we are left unsatisfied and yearning for more. Is it any wonder daughter sleeps with father and mother sleeps with son? As a matter of fact, I think we are in a worse prison than George here. By comparison George's prison is a minor heaven. With a body already withered, his sexual desire is at an ebb. Sometimes I have a feeling that to George, exhausted as he is by his particular kind of anguish, an exposed, succulent breast is no longer his problem. No incandescent flash of thigh disturbs his sleep or smashes the dykes of his body open for the flood of lust which is always threatening us with ruin.

I'll tell you something. I used to think of Africa as a better place to live in. I used to think that here it was possible just to sit in the sun, eat mangoes and take a woman when the need arose – a kind of Garden of Eden, you understand. But that is no longer satisfactory. What we want now is more than a body: it is the tinselled wrapper that we seek. A nipple wrapped up in silk and supported by elastic wires and gauze, proves more desirable than the exposed sweating paw-paw breast of a market woman. From Cape to Cairo, from Madagascar to Moçambique, we have all been crippled, we are helplessly depraved and we lack true spiritual plenitude. So you can tell me, my friend: who are we to pity George, the prisoner? Though I am now George's jailer I am equally a prisoner of circumstance, I rage in the cell of my body, but who will free me?

I know, you must be impatient to see him at close range. You want to examine his physical condition with a thoroughness which is his proper due. That I appreciate. Also the Social Welfare Department, as you say, is anxious about his condition, what with all the ugly rumours about torture and other unmentionable brutalities, though I must say, I'm surprised that people in your Department(people of your background and training)can be so completely misled by false and unjustified reports in the newspapers. We all know what newspapers are like – garbage cans of rumour and scandal, that have an insatiable love of tragedy and of the slightly unsavoury. To read their columns you would think they employ men so depraved in morals that a mere whiff of a woman's arse is enough to send them into ecstasy!

At any rate, I think I can reveal to you quite frankly that apart from an occasional whipping with a leather thong which is permitted by the Prison Code, George has never been tortured. It is true that once or twice I have been compelled to put his thumb in a screw when he failed to address me properly as 'master'. Nothing very serious, as I say; besides, in the modern world we have learned to live with such unpleasantness as a kind of necessity. George emitted a few horrible screams, but then George has always been something of a physical coward. While he was boss and jailer, protected by a white skin, you wouldn't know it. I also feel it is necessary to mention the fact that while George was master here it was foolhardy in the extreme to forget to address him as 'bwana', 'baas', or some such tedious nomenclature. Where titles were concerned, whatever sense of humour George possessed deserted him altogether. He took these social conventions most seriously. So we wouldn't let him get away with anything, we had to insist that he observe the same social obligations. There were times when I felt it necessary to apply electric shocks in order to revive him from what seemed a fatal lapse of memory.

Of course, such things happen in jail; I wouldn't like to deny that. As a matter of fact, if I remember correctly, something as unpleasant as that occurred last Christmas. In order to commemorate the birth of his Lord and Saviour we had kept George well stoked with alcohol, but to our amazement he got terribly sozzled; in no time he was reduced to a raving maniac. He was, as you might say, in the clutches of a disgusting nostalgia for old days when he was master and lord over the place. Completely beside himself with excitement, he marched up and down the place, shouting and foaming at the mouth; his whole face was beaded with sweat, the eyes bulged horribly, and his emaciated legs clattered like sticks on the floorboards. Never have I seen such an exhibition. The man had quite forgotten the humble station to which he had been reduced by Fate in the latter years : he wielded a whip, issued commands (in a cracked voice at that) and generally made a nuisance of himself.

As you well can understand the whole thing was in shocking bad taste. I'm afraid I had to act very promptly to remind George of his changed status. A few electric shocks were sufficient to restore his memory. Apart from these minor incidents George has never been ill-treated. In fact, it is my personal pride that I have always treated George with considerable gentleness – especially considering the fact that he was once my jailer.

2

Ah, I knew it ! Of course, I knew you would come to that. I knew you would want to know how George and I came to exchange our roles. An interesting question. Very interesting, I could write volumes on that question. However, I believe no single answer is possible.

There are those who believe that the time had simply come for a change to take place, which seems to me an untenable argument on all possible accounts since there are no facts to support such a conclusion. Others believe again that success – wealth, power and prestige – entails an erosion of spirit. I am inclined to discount such sentimental nonsense. In any case such an admission by me would imply a confession that I visualize a time when I myself would be relieved of my duties as jailer – something I can only regard as idle speculation.

Nevertheless, I believe the seeds of George's destruction were contained in his very nature, in the very system he fought to uphold, in the very metaphysical assumptions he so steadfastly held. The whole edifice was bound to come crashing down sooner or later. You see, at the core of George's civilization was a well-conceived madness.

It is a matter of common knowledge that we Africans have never devised a metaphysical system which divided Matter from Spirit, therefore we have never believed the Body to be inferior to the Soul, we have never had a dislike for the so-called 'gross appetites' as something not worthy of cultivation, which, I suppose, is the main reason why George and his compatriots hate themselves so much – no, despise themselves. They are forever elevating Spirit or Intellect above the Body. Have you seen them dance? Most of their dances are an abstraction of bodily movement into a symbolic language. Ah, Mozart, Wagner! I believe the only compliment one can pay this sort of music is that it is 'sublime'. It is created by people already reaching out of their bodies, who hate the very funky smell of their orifices.

For instance, I think George lost his will to govern, to rule, even to be master, when he first laid his eyes on Zaza, the African maid. The day he found himself in Zaza's bed, naked beside her naked-ness, no longer the lofty master but already reduced to the status of an invalid needing the care and warmth which only this dark stormy body seemed able to provide, he became inconsolable with a phoney grief. He began to despise himself and all that he had ever held dear. To Francisca, his wife, he became most insufferable and cruel; he drank himself to idiocy; he became quarrelsome, domineering, and I believe sought to expose himself to public ridicule as a way of atoning for his sins and punishing the Flesh which had led him astray.

He forgot only one thing. In South Africa the laws against racial mixing are very strict; one can be forgiven for anything but diluting what the popular imagination conceives as the pure racial strain. Therefore I can only come to the conclusion that the way George carried on in public with Zaza was because of this sub-conscious desire to be arrested and punished. It was his way of getting his own back against the Flesh which he could neither re-nounce nor crucify. That, as you can see, was the first advantage he gave me over his person.

You might say that the trap which Zaza and I laid for him was very well conceived – even brilliant – but this I doubt. It was as simple as crushing an eggshell. On the other hand I would say that the only other advantage I'm prepared to acknowledge was the opportunity which George and his kind offered me to know so much about them. The whole educational system they created was designed to teach me more about George than George was likely ever to learn about me. It is very little surprise that I came to know all the points of George's strength and weakness. George was no more a closed book to me than an earmarked volume is to one who has thumbed through it for years.

George fell then, as you might say, in a Biblical sense. He saw a black woman he desired. Instead of upholding the necessary but mistaken notion of his race, that he was superior, he quite outrageously succumbed to the weakness of the Flesh. That was his downfall.

You may very well ask, where do I come into this? How I came to be George's prisoner was a very simple matter. In fact the details, such as they are, would appear to be of less importance to many people. Still, I know your kind: a generation raised and nourished on Facts. That, if I may warn you, was George's passion too. Facts. None the less I am obliged to give you the facts of the matter. In the year I went to work for George I was arrested on the very ridiculous charge of 'vagrancy'. In those days instead of letting you serve a term of imprisonment they used to contract prisoners out to country gentlemen as 'cheap convict labour'. Of course, it was a form of slavery called by another name. Anyway, that, briefly, is how I came to be beholden to George as my master and keeper until the very nasty moment of change.

Picture me as I was then – a spry, rakish figure, young, cultivated, possessed of a felicitous mind. I was what is known to the Influx Control Department as a 'native of no fixed abode'. To this somewhat appropriate description they added a minor detail that I had 'no visible means of support'.

I was rather proud of this official entry, as a matter of fact, conjuring up as it did, a life of complete irresponsibility quite different from George's well-ordered life, evoking a picture of a man without any firm address, without filial ties, a man constantly on the move, a bird of passage, so to speak, like a sailor. I only needed a girl in every port to complete the image. If George's downfall was due to the weakness of the Flesh, mine is likely to be due to a flighty imagination and an unreliable sense of humour.

I was lucky, in a way, to have had some makeshift education given to me. I considered a spell at the Fort Hare University College as no mean achievement. In those days I had a great reputation as something of an 'intellectual' – a thinker of no mean enterprise. White friends who knew me as a bookworm and with a gargantuan appetite for books, friends many of whom used their own cards to borrow books for me at the 'Whites Only' Johannesburg Library, found it difficult to stomach the fact that I had no visible means of support. They were generally depressed by the fact that I often had to dodge the Influx Control Squad which often rounded up unemployed vagrant Africans in the streets of Johannesburg.

Normally I hung outside the Von Welligh Street Beerhall, waiting for profitably employed friends to come round and buy me *mqombothi*. I ambushed them at the gates, turning my coat pockets out in the hope of shaming them by my indigency. In the evenings I used to repair to Aunt Peggy's where I met a better class of drinker: expensive showgirls, teachers, politicians, and businessmen.

3

Many times Helene used to say to me: 'Mulela, I beg you to tell me, how can you throw away such a big opportunity to be of help to your people? A man of your brains ought to be more than a clown at European cocktail parties – yes, performing, for that's what you are doing – and tickling the egos of the petit-bourgeoisie!'

It shames me to admit that at such times I had only time to notice how fine and smooth Helene's neck was. Helene's bones were the finest bones I had ever had the privilege to witness in a woman, black or white. I wish her mouth hadn't been so tight and scornful. Though her greyish blue, introspective little eyes were the fascination of all the men who had ever known her, she tended to harden them unnecessarily when she talked to me. I think Helene wanted to save me, if only I would consent to be saved!

Her milk-white thighs were firmly resolved against wasted opportunities.

All in all, I hated white parties. They never really got started
until too late in the night when everybody was already too drunk
to be really amusing. To begin with these parties seemed to
meander, they seemed to stumble and falter in pretentious, stilted
conversation. There would be girls there standing with their
backs straight up against the wall, stiffly and firmly holding their
glasses against or between narrow, prideful, fearfully restrained
breasts, talking with wet trembling mouths to young men who
were only too anxious to flee them, to return in triumph to their
mothers, their cradles. These, then, were the people who wished to
know, as they put it, what had happened to their glorious young
lives.

I remember the careless middle-aged spinsters, the academics and
the sombrely inquiring hostesses who wished to know whether it
was all true what they had read about the 'exciting goings-on in
the black townships around Johannesburg'. Strange that they
should have always assumed that I knew what they meant by 'goings-on'. Whenever I asked what these might be they simply
smiled in disbelief at my pretence not to know. You may not believe this, but once at a party in Lower Houghton a callow young
man followed me into the bathroom to whisper shyly in my ear:
'Tell me,' he said, 'how many times a night is it possible –' Then
he seemed to lose his breath or nerve – I don't know which.

I tell you those parties were a bore. The girls used to catch a
glimpse of me talking to someone I genuinely liked; then they
would circle me, proffering their shy gawky bodies as a sacrifice
though it was clear that no one could avail himself of their gen-
erosity in such a brightly-lit lounge. I can hear their voices, even
now, like a chime of bells in the gay wispy night.

'Come on, Mulela,' and they would press their pliant bellies
against me, 'show me the *Kwela*! Oh, I think your dancing is
smashing!'

Or: 'Mulela, please stop it. For God's sake what will the people
think, Mulela. Of course, they can see us through the door!'

Or: 'Mulela, I hope you don't think this is personal. I mean, honestly, if I felt that way about you I'd say okay, let's go home right away. It's just that I don't feel that way about you. I just like talking to you.'

Or: 'Mulela! Mulela! Why don't you take me right here and now. Rape me! I know you want to! Oh, you're so fierce and cruel!' That was usually 3 a.m. when the end of the party was near and the whiteman's burden was perhaps too heavy for their frail shoulders.

No, on the whole I preferred black parties, mostly shebeen cocktails with their motley habitués of hi-fi boys, payroll robbers, nice-time girls and unscrupulous politicians. In those days when I had no idea where the next penny was coming from, the African politicians were a great boon to me. To earn a little pocket money I used to write their speeches which they delivered in the square in front of the City Hall, with hundreds of stunned white citizens listening to them in great admiration, though I venture to say that had they had the time to think through the bombast they would have been very unhappy about the sentiments expressed.

I had long noticed that African politicians preferred involved syntax, long rolling periods and ornate mellifluous phrases in order to carry the masses with them. They distrusted speeches which seemed to convey something concrete and practical. Most of all African politicians distrusted action; hence their dislike for concise sentences. However, to be fair I also ought to explain that this love for flowery language stems from the African's traditional love for poetry. Africans have a great admiration for language. Therefore the Saturday afternoon meetings in front of the City Hall satisfied the need to let off steam about apartheid as well as the hunger for poetry.

For hours I used to sit down and think up words which would carry a lot of wind in them, the more colourful the better. I used to pile up subordinate clauses on top of one another right up to the climax of a back-breaking main clause, where the speaker would linger with an air of relieved dignity, usually for the applause.

As a consequence of all this I became quite popular with politicians and in the process made some money. I even thought of setting myself up in business as a speech-writer. The more apartheid laws the Government passed the more protest meetings were held and the more speeches were needed. I considered myself something of an artist, really, a wordsmith, turning out the kind of prose which combined true literary merit with a dramatic appeal to the masses.

Sometimes it was quite amusing, though, to be asked by fledgling African Communists as well as 'pirate' businessmen turned politicians, to write speeches for them. Sometimes I had to turn out these texts simultaneously. At such moments it was a matter of not letting the left hand know what the right hand was doing. For the Communists I had a ready stock of abusive phrases like 'tools of the colonialist powers', 'war-mongering imperialists', and 'capitalist parasites'. For the equivocating black moderates I peppered the speeches with such innocuous nonsense as 'far be it that our children shall say . . .' or the more dependable 'so that all, irrespective of race, colour or creed, can live in peace!' This always brought out a swell of applause.

Only once did I get things horribly mixed up. I was working on two speeches, one for Babalala, the young Communist, and the other for a moderate sort of African politician who didn't want to get into too much trouble with the Government, which meant sacrificing valuable trading concessions in the white areas. The latter was the kind of man for whom I enjoyed writing speeches. Fence-sitting in a revolutionary situation seemed to me a very dangerous thing to do; but being a modern sort of person I had a great love for irony and ambiguity. Since these African politicians had to take great care not to offend the Government while at the same time remaining popular enough with the masses to have bargaining power with the White Council, I often had to write long ponderous speeches which had the air of being weighty and vaguely radical without having real teeth in them.

Anyway, while working on the text of this speech, for some funny reason I got it mixed up with Babalala's, the young Communist, and I livened it up with such resounding Marxist phrases as 'the inherent contradictions in the capitalist system which must result in its total collapse. . . .' This, the worthy politician delivered to a stunned Directors' Meeting which rose in an uproar and practically delivered the poor man to the Johannesburg Security Police.

This was my last speech-writing job, for I was arrested soon thereafter for 'vagrancy and suspicion', and contracted to George Hollingworth, Esquire, as convict labourer.

Well, here is George Hollingworth, Esquire, a man reduced to the dust of infamy and ignominy. George was then a tidy, industrious man, working at an electronics factory; if no longer happy he had it well concealed. That is, until Zaza's arrival. You have to see Zaza to realize the kind of impact she must have made on a happily married man like George, a man with reasonable urges and also reasonable dislike for dark flesh. In fact, it would be a peculiar understatement to say that Zaza arrived; she stormed this place. A small darkly vivacious woman of twenty-four, delicately muscled, slim as a bamboo shoot, she smelled of a well-kept vineyard, and beneath the simple denim skirt and sweater she concealed the kind of body which seemed too dark, almost bluish with sexual menace.

Yes, I remember very well the day Zaza arrived. George was reading the evening newspapers, sitting, as usual, in his favourite armchair, talking to Francisca in the kitchen, while I busied myself with tending the flowers in the front porch. It was in that soft amber cocktail hour when the world seems at its mellowest that Zaza walked into the sitting-room of the Hollingworths, her sly, incautious body spreading havoc in the still subtropical air, her small tormented mouth almost vinegarish with unearned scorn.

George rose, steadied himself and sat down. 'Why don't you knock before you come in!' he shouted. 'Who are you anyway? What do you want?'

'My name is Zaza,' said our dark Venus and her mouth grew wreathed with the world's tortuous concerns. 'This is Mr Hollingworth's house, isn't it?'

It seemed at the time that the place was too noisy with questions which would not be settled until later. 'I'm to be your housemaid!' said Zaza. 'The Bureau sent me.' And that, as I said, was the beginning of all the troubles which, as the song goes, were to fall over George's head like a shower of rain.

4

We will go in now and see George. I hope you are not squeamish. His body is not very nice to see. It has undergone terrifying changes, which is a matter of regret to all of us.

Of course you'd like to hear the end of the story. I knew you would like to hear it. Agree, we are all vultures, we all like to hear other people's misfortunes. Still, there is nothing to lose. To cut the story short then, George, who had always been remarkably tidy and industrious, always up at dawn to be at the factory in time, began to exhibit disturbing changes. The symptoms were familiar. Loss of appetite, cyclic changes from extreme depression to extreme elation, a dreamy countenance, and total absent-mindedness. He began to lose interest in his job; he was often in the house, presumably not feeling well, though that didn't prevent him from hanging about the kitchen where Zaza was working. He was always needing Zaza for one thing or the other, which kept the girl running in and out of George's room all day long. As we had already expected, George was soon offering Zaza presents: he was buying her clothes, soft silken underwear, bras and nylon stockings. He bought her jewellery and all manner of trinkets. It was obvious to me that in time the gift to African womanhood would be George himself – this splendid European manhood which his kind believe to be invested with the mystique of wealth, power and prestige. By then Zaza and I had a plan – the trap – very well laid. It was time for me to get out of jail and instead to instal the new inmate: George Hollingworth, Esquire.

I have often thought that the main reason for George's fall – the reason for the rapid disintegration which sets in whenever his kind want something badly and feel thwarted – is the illusion they entertain that however badly treated, the slave not only loves them but will help them maintain their rule forever. Like small children they all want to be loved because they imagine themselves to be unutterably beautiful and irresistible. No matter how many wrongs they commit they develop fantasies of remaining forever in the arms of enslaved women, in this case the dark crooning nanny, mistress and mother, all in one, forever singing lullabies to the ageless blue-eyed boy.

Before Zaza let him spend the night with her we had a statement already prepared, waiting only for the signature admitting the crime, with an agreement for George to release the house to us and all the goods in it. The transfer was to be made through an African firm of lawyers. We made sure that the pictures were very clear and that the evidence was sufficiently incriminating. A clear case of blackmail, you might say; but then the world is not a very nice place to live in. Is it? That is what we had to learn the hard way while George nourished the illusion that the world was conquerable and lovable.

I am afraid I have had to keep George here a prisoner. I am sure he prefers it. There is nowhere for him to go. To his people his sin would seem unpardonable; his inheritance is wasted; and Francisca – well, I admire Francisca. She proves again how adaptable and resourceful women are. Women, it seems to me, will always survive empires. They are saved only by their instincts.

Before you go in to see George I meant to ask you one question which has always bothered me. How long do you think I'll last as George's jailer? Ah, never mind, I think my position is really impregnable. Yes: I think so: impregnable. I've taken every precaution. I think I have managed to avoid every pitfall and snare which brought George Hollingworth down!

Ah, there is George's wife, Francisca! Look at those gazelle limbs, the very power of those thighs. What a prize cow!

Angola

Agostinho Neto

FRIEND MUSSUNDA

Here I am,
Friend Mussunda,
      Here I am,

With you,
With the established victory of your joy
and of your conscience.

      – you whom the god of death has made !
      you whom the god of death has made, made. . . .[1]

Remember?

The sadness of those days
when we were there
with mangoes to eat,
bewailing our fate
and the women of Funda,
our songs of lament,
our despairs,
the clouds of our eyes,
remember?

Here I am
Friend Mussunda.

To you
I owe my life,
to the same devotion, the same love
with which you saved me
from the constrictor's embrace.

1. These two lines, in the native language of Angola, are part of a children's
chant in *The Nation*, 24 February 1962.

To your strength
which transforms the fates of men.

To you
Friend Mussunda, I owe my life to you.

And I write
poems you don't understand !
Can you imagine my anguish?

Here I am
Friend Mussunda,
writing poems you don't understand.

It wasn't this
that we wanted, I know that,
but in the mind, in the intelligence,
that's where we're alive.

We're alive
Friend Mussunda
we're alive !

Inseparable
still on the road to our vision.

The heart beats
rhythms of foggy nights,
the feet dance

The sounds do not die in our ears
        — you whom the god of death has made ...
We are alive !

Moçambique

J. Craveirinha

POEM OF THE FUTURE CITIZEN

I came from somewhere
from a Nation which does not yet exist.
I came and I am here !

Not I alone was born
nor you nor any other . . .
but brothers.

I have love to give in handfuls.
Love of what I am
and nothing more.

I have a heart
and cries which are not mine alone
I come from a country which does not yet exist.

Ah ! I have love in plenty to give
of what I am.
I !
A man among many
citizen of a Nation which has yet to exist.

SONG OF THE NEGRO ON THE FERRY

If you could see me die
The millions of times I have been born . . .

If you could see me weep
The millions of times you have laughed . . .

If you could see me cry out
The millions of times I have kept silent ...

If you could see me sing
The millions of times I have died
And bled ...

I tell you, European brother

You would be born
You would weep
You would sing
You would cry out
And you would die
Bleeding ...
Millions of times like me ! ! !

Translated by Philippa Rumsey

Luis Bernardo Honwana

DINA

Bent from the waist, with his hands hanging towards the ground, Madala heard the last of the twelve strokes of mid-day. Raising his head, he sighted the greenish white trousers of the Overseer between the stalks of corn, about ten paces away. He did not dare to straighten up further, because he knew he should only stop working when he heard the order translated into a shout. He rested his elbows on his knees and waited patiently.

The sun was shining directly on to his bare back, but it was better to endure it for a while longer. He counted the time by the number of sweat drops that dripped from the tip of his nose to a stone that shone on the ground at his feet, and decided that the Overseer must be very angry. He looked again at the legs ten paces away, and saw that they were in the same position. Casting his eyes beyond them, he saw a dark patch which was Filimone's body, also doubled over the tallest corn stalks, waiting for the order to stop working.

The pain in the small of his back was unbearable, and much worse now that Dina[1] had already sounded. When the muscles of his neck began to hurt him, because of the strain imposed on them in keeping his head raised, he let his arms fall until they touched the fleshy, slippery leaves of the weeds he had to pull out. He fingered them mechanically until he felt the firm resistance of the slender stem, inserted his fingers between the branches, and stiffened his body. Although the plant did not withstand the wrench with any strength, the tendons behind his knee joints throbbed painfully. Then he lifted up the plant to revive himself

1. Dina (pronounced Deena): returning migrant labourer's adaptation of dinner.

with the strong fragrance of the black soil which clung to its white roots.

As he inhaled avidly, with the roots of the plant pressed against his top lip, he looked at the hole that had been left in the ground. The day was indeed very hot, because not a wisp of vapour arose from it.

At dawn, and in the early hours of the morning, when the rich fields were still wet with the evening dew, clouds of steam arose from the smallest clods of earth, and the work was not so tiring. But when the sun was high, only vapour arose from the holes left by the plants, and even then it lasted for shorter and shorter periods of time.

He dropped the plant and listened : Nothing. Only the ululation of the breeze among the tallest leaves of the corn.

He again stiffened his body and allowed himself to lean over backwards until the plant he held in his hand resisted no longer. This was how he saved himself all but the indispensable movements. Thus the effort in pulling up a plant actually involved the neck muscles of his body, and not the flexion of his arm muscles, which he only bent from time to time to imbibe the strength from the clumps of earth which clung to their roots.

When he had pulled out the seventh plant after hearing the last stroke of Dina, Madala looked through the corn stalks again, wondering whether he had not heard the Overseer's voice. He listened attentively for a while, but only heard the muted murmur of the waves.

Madala bent forward until he experienced an excruciating pain, but by then he had a good hold on the plant, so he leaned back until it broke free from the ground. A scorpion leaped out from between its roots, but as it was not prudent to straighten up, and not having a hoe at hand, he let it escape. Rather alarmed, Madala realized that if he had been stung by that scorpion, he would have terrible pains for three days, and perhaps die on the fourth. Yes, now he was not strong enough to withstand the poison of a scorpion of that size after three days of pains.

In the early hours of the morning grasshoppers still jumped from the leaves of the plants that were pulled, but at this time only scorpions, lizards and even snakes appeared. Pitarossi had died from the bite of a snake which had attacked him when he was working on this field. None of the others knew Pitarossi, but they would all know his wife, who, after this happened, began to sleep with men who paid for her drinks at the *cantinas*.[1] At first she used to say she would only sleep with someone who gave her twenty *escudos*,[2] but now she was only interested in drinking. When there were *magaiças*,[3] she got so drunk that it was not necessary to give her anything, and then anybody, even the field workers, took her to the high grass behind the cantinas. But everybody knew that when she was like that she fell asleep at once, and only woke up when the man got up.

He was so old now, he was the only one who would not go and sleep with her. And anyway, he had known Pitarossi.

Madala pulled up two more plants and waited, his elbows resting on his knees. The sun seemed to come nearer at every instant, but it should not be long now before the Overseer gave the order to stop.

Suddenly he felt a violent constriction of the threads of his sickness. It was the first knot.

Alert for the Overseer's command, Madala had not noticed the tightening of the threads, but now, after having felt the first knot between the folds of his intestines, he stiffened his body in the vain hope of counteracting the tangling of the threads with muscular tension. However, the thread which reached down from within his throat coiled up in the region of the middle of his chest, forming a skein which rapidly slid down to his stomach. During the seconds of dread, the veins of his neck nearly exploded with their throbbing, and his body jerked convulsively. The leaves of the plant he had in his hand were crushed to pieces, emitting an oppressive odour. The second knot nearly tore out his kidneys, but not a single moan escaped from Madala's compressed lips.

1. *Cantina*: general store.
2. Twenty *escudos*: five shillings.
3. *Magaiças*: returning migrant labourers.

'Why doesn't the man tell us to stop,' murmured Madala, trying to reach the branches of a bush. 'Since Dina sounded the shadows have grown by two palms . . .'

While pulling up the bush, Madala could not prevent his knees from giving way under him, and as he could not let go of the support of the branches, he fell prostrate to the ground.

When the painful spasm of the knot came, his legs stretched out violently.

A little later, with his body sprawled over the soft dry soil, he felt the threads slacken gradually. He closed his eyes tightly, and waited for the pains to disappear.

Kneeling, and now recovered from the crisis, Madala reached out his hand towards a tuft of weeds, and pulled them up slowly.

'You're not allowed to work kneeling down . . .' he murmured as he dropped the weeds. He grasped the stem of a small bush, but before pulling it up he separated the weeds in the small pile he had just thrown on the ground, and counted them : 'One . . . two . . . three . . . four . . . five . . .'

When he had finished counting he tugged violently at the plant he had in his right hand, and lined it up with the others : 'Six . . .'

'You're not allowed to work kneeling down . . .' he whispered, while he crushed the leaves of the sixth plant with his fingers.

With a sigh he fell on to his right shoulder and rolled on the ground, pressing his chin against his knees. With a certain satisfaction he remembered the threads of his sickness, now quiescent around his organs. He lifted the remains of the sixth plant to his mouth, and began to chew with his eyes shut.

'OK, boys ! Let's go and eat !'

'Seven ! Eight ! Nine ! Ten ! . . .' Madala raised himself abruptly and pulled up four plants. Then he drew his fingers across his forehead and flicked off the drops of sweat that caused his eyes to smart when they ran down.

He did not get up straight away. It would not be a good thing for the Overseer to notice that he was in a hurry to stop work.

As he surfaced warily he experienced a last twinge and a vague feeling of faintness. N'Guiana and Muthakati were already standing up, but the Overseer said to them : 'When it's time to start you're forever scratching yourselves, but when it's time to knock off, then it's at the double, isn't it, my little bastards? Just keep on like this and I'll tan your hides for you ! ...'

Filimone, who only had his head sticking out, sank down up to his eyes when he heard the yells of the Overseer, but seeing Madala, he gained courage, and straightened up with a somewhat challenging look.

Gradually Tandane, Djimo and Muthambi emerged from the field, with their eyes fixed on the Overseer.

Djimo's body was covered with sweat, but even so Madala observed the nervous dance of his jittery muscles under his skin of the colour of river sand.

'Let's get going to the *chicafo*,'[1] commanded the Overseer, shutting the book he had in his hand. 'That will be the day when a fellow manages to write a book without these whores ...' he added, looking at the picture on the cover of the book.

The Overseer started the march, and the others followed in silence.

Madala gazed around him, feeling a certain pleasure in hurting his eyes on the fragments of sun that sprang from the smooth corn leaves. '*Cornfields are like the sea.*'

The others were far ahead, half submerged in the thick greenness of the field, walking slowly as if they were really pushing through a liquid.

Madala remained motionless : '*Molungo's*[2] *cornfields are like the sea* . . .' he insisted, as his eyes followed the gentle waving of the even surface of the fields. Madala's gaze travelled along a wave which broke far away in the distance, assailed by a thousand silver sparks – small suns turned into comets by the wind. When he could no longer bear the burning in his eyes, he turned them away.

Suddenly Madala tired of comparing the cornfields to the sea, because he realized that this idea always occurred to him when he raised himself at the stroke of Dina and cast his eyes on the vastness that encircled him : '*The sea is different* . . .,' he murmured, frowning.

1. *Chicafo* : adaptation of **scoff** (food).
2. *Molungo* : white man.

'In the sea there are no weeds to pull up . . .' he raised his little finger. 'In the sea the fish are like the birds of the air . . . .' He put up another finger. 'Yes . . . *The sea is different* . . .' he concluded, after having thought for a while.

When Madala came to the camp, the other gangs had already arrived. Some of them had already eaten. The Clearing Gang, always the first to arrive, was now dispersed in the shade. Most of the men were sleeping, recovering from their exertions during the morning. The Farm Gang must have been delayed, because their *kuka*,[1] José, was still making the fire for their *botwa*[2] of cornmeal.

Madala went to one of the old barns and sat in the shade, choosing his place among the men of the Kraal Gang. When they saw him approach, they stopped talking about women and adopted a more reverent air.

'Madala, how are things going in your Gang?' asked a voice. Madala did not reply at once, because before pronouncing any opinion he had to repeat the question to himself, and listen to the reply from his inner self.

'The sun is very hot in the fields . . .' – the voice was apologetic before the silence of Madala.

'Yes, the sun is very hot in the fields . . .' (Madala had not yet thought of the reply.)

Feeling obliged to continue to make itself heard, the voice ventured : '. . . and the Overseer is on top of you the whole time . . .'

Madala gazed at the young face of his interrogator, and tried to think up something he could say to make him understand that it was not necessary to go on showing an interest in the work of the fields. He pondered inwardly to find it.

'The Overseer is bad,' continued the boy. 'He takes a long time to let you knock off . . . I saw this when I worked in the fields. Also he doesn't let the people stand up for a bit to rest their backs . . . I saw this once . . .' Suddenly inspired, the youth turned towards the other members of his Gang – 'This isn't a lie, I swear it's not a lie. . . . Once, we were working in the fields and the Over-

1. *Kuka* : adaptation of cook.
2. *Botwa* : three-legged iron pot.

seer was there. It was very hot ... everybody knows it's very hot in the fields ... you'll see why I say the Overseer is bad. We were working in the fields. ... It was very hot in the fields. ...' The youth continued his narrative, more and more carried away by his enthusiasm, gradually directing his words away from Madala towards his companions.

Madala observed the Overseer, who, sitting on a box in one of the near-by patches of shade, was having his lunch. His dishes were spread out before him on another box which served as a table. He ate with great enjoyment and gulped down his wine.

When Madala went to the *cantinas* at the end of the month he shared some of his wine with his friends, but the Overseer never shared his wine with anybody, although he often did not finish the bottles that his wife sent him for his lunch.

The wine was a dirty reddish yellow, and the bottle was beaded with sweat. When the Overseer drank, he even closed his eyes.

'Madala' – it was Djimo – 'Madala, let's go and eat ...'

In the patches of shade, the men of the various Gangs of the property rested and ate. There were many whom Madala did not even know, but all knew him, and greeted him when they passed.

'Madala! I didn't tell you straight away, but it was only because of the Overseer. Your daughter's here, and she wants to see you.'

Maria was already coming towards them: 'Good afternoon, Father! ...'

'Good afternoon, my daughter.'

Djimo came closer to Maria: 'Maria, I went to fetch your father for you to see, but I've only told him now that you're here, because the Overseer was eating near to the place where he was sitting ...'

'Maria, how is everybody there at home? ...'

'Madala, it's better for you to go and talk to your daughter in the shade over there. There's no sun there. It's better ... Maria, go to that shade and take your father with you and talk to him. There's no sun there...'

Djimo seemed to like Maria a lot, but Madala knew that because she slept with a lot of men no one would want to marry her.

'Maria, how is everybody there at home? . . .'

'Everybody is well at home, Father. I came here to see you . . .'

'I am well, my daughter . . .'

All the men of the camp looked at Maria, their eyes wandering over the appetizing form under her *capulana*[1]

'Good afternoon, Maria ! . . .' All greeted her, hoping for a glance from her, but she responded without lifting her eyes from the ground.

Madala and Maria remained silent for a while.

Maria felt embarrassed by the way all the men were staring at her.

'Madala, don't you want to come and eat?' – it was Djimo again. 'Now it's really time to eat, because n'Guiana and Muthakati have already finished making the food. Now it's not just for the Overseer not to find out that your daughter came to see you. . . . It's really time to eat.'

'I'll stay with my daughter, Djimo.'

The Overseer appeared around the corner of the barn with a cigarette in his hand, and came towards them : 'Hullo, Maria ! What are you doing here? Are you trying to hook Madala? . . . It can't be Madala because he's too old . . . Perhaps it's Djimo . . . Maria, are you trying to hook Djimo? . . .'

'I not try to hook Djimo . . .' replied Maria, trying to speak in Portuguese.

Amused, the Overseer paused with his cigarette half way towards his lips : 'But wouldn't you like to sleep with him? . . .'

With her eyes cast on the ground, Maria did not reply.

'Madala, let's go and eat . . . the people who work in the fields or any other place need to eat when Dina time comes !'

Madala could not declare himself immediately. At that moment

1. *Capulana* : colourful cloth worn as a garment, sarong style.

he was looking at his daughter, trying to discover what she had felt when the Overseer spoke to her. Maria looked away.

'Father, I think you had better go and eat. . . .' Maria burrowed in the sand with her toes. Seeing that her father was aware of her nervousness, she rapidly pulled back her foot. She crossed her arms over her chest and hugged her back tightly with her hands.

Madala came nearer to his daughter and tried to look into her eyes which were shadowed by her lowered lashes. 'What makes you think that?'

Hearing the hollow voice right next to her face, Maria shrank even further away, almost turning her back on her father. 'Well, nothing, there's nothing . . . that makes me think that . . .' She remained silent for a while, but went on more animatedly, 'I don't know, Father, but I think you should go and eat!'

Madala turned Maria round bodily until he faced her, with his knees bent exaggeratedly, trying to see the eyes completely hidden behind the lids. 'Do you think so? . . .'

'You must go and eat, Father.' With her eyes closed, Maria spoke more audaciously.

'But I have no hunger in my stomach!' Madala stretched his arms in a gesture of surprise. 'You must see I have no hunger in my stomach . . .'

Maria said nothing.

'And don't you want to eat, my daughter?'

'I ate at the *cantinas* before coming to see you. When I was passing the *cantinas* a friend saw me and called me inside. This friend bought me some things and said, "Here you are, this is for you to eat", and I began to eat.' Maria opened her eyes, but closed them again at once.

'And aren't you hungry any more? Don't you want to come and eat with my Gang?' Madala's voice was anxious.

'No, Father, this friend gave me plenty of things to eat, and now I'm not hungry. I'll stay and wait for you here while you eat.'

Djimo reproached Madala: 'Madala, your daughter is quite right about what she says . . .'

And Madala gave in. 'All right, I'll go and eat, and you wait for me here ...'

Maria opened her eyes when she sensed that her father had gone away.

Madala broke a piece of *coi*,[1] dipped it in the dish of *m'tchovelo*[2] and raised it to his mouth. The others followed suit. They ate in silence. The *m'tchovelo* was delicious, full of rich fat.

From the place where he was sitting Madala could see Maria, half hidden in the shade of the barn. Although he was looking in that direction the whole time, he did not see the Overseer arriving.

Maria answered the questions of the Overseer without lifting her eyes from the ground.

Madala regretted that he could not hear what they were saying, and for this reason he asked his inner self what a man would say to a woman when he wanted to sleep with her.

The Overseer seemed to be angry with Maria, but sometimes he spoke sweetly. He took out a packet of cigarettes from his pocket, opened it, took one out, lit it, and put out the match, blowing a cloud of smoke at it. He kept his hand raised, waving the matchstick in the air as he spoke.

When he finished smoking his cigarette, he turned his back on Maria and disappeared around the corner of the barn. A little later Maria went off in the same direction.

All the time that the Overseer had been talking to Maria she had not lifted her eyes from the ground.

There was very little *coi* left, but Madala was sure that no one's hunger had been fully appeased. The last piece was for n'Guiana and Muthakati, the *kukas* of the Gang. The remains of the *m'tchovelo* were for them too.

After sucking and licking his fingers, Madala rubbed them and ran them through his hair. Now that the meal was over, he rose.

1. *Coi*: moulded ration of cornmeal porridge.
2. *M'tchovelo*: gravy made with ground peanuts.

The others followed suit.

There was still some time before they would have to submerge themselves in the fields again, so Madala looked round, searching for a place to rest.

The men from the Kraal Gang went away and Madala returned to the place where he had been before. The youth who had spoken to him a while ago now eyed him with a deliberately ironic expression: 'Madala, your daughter is at the back there, talking to the Overseer . . .'

Elias, the foreman of the Kraal Gang, did not like this provocation: 'When people don't understand certain things they should keep quiet . . .' He spoke without addressing the youth directly.

The silence became oppressive, and Madala groped with his hand for a plant he had felt next to his left foot. Grasping the branches in his fingers, he wound a good portion of the flexible stem around his wrist, and pulled with determination. The bush broke free from the soil with a dull explosion.

Djimo came near. 'Madala, would you like me to do something that will please you?' Madala did not reply. Behind Djimo, on the path that led to the fields, the Overseer walked ahead. Ten paces behind, Maria followed him.

Madala followed the pair with his eyes. He searched on the ground for something he could not find. His fingers closed around an imaginary plant.

Maria waded into the green sea of corn, and splashed haphazardly through the tender shoots on the borders of the field, trying to place her feet in the footsteps of the man. The green thickness already reached her knees, but she continued. However, she walked more slowly, though resolutely, to overcome the current.

Now far into the field, the Overseer stopped and turned towards Maria. She also stopped, some yards away.

'Madala, can't you really think of anything that would please you that I could do for you without any trouble?'

Madala saw the Overseer try to retrace his steps to where Maria was, and then stop as if he had changed his mind after a few paces.

He walked as if he were crossing a river.

Madala thought he should say something to Djimo, but he did not remember to repeat the question to himself, so he did not know what to say.

The Overseer was signalling to Maria, but she seemed not to understand. The plant that Madala held in his hand resisted his pull. For this reason, Madala's wrist trembled.

The Overseer sank into the field. Moments afterwards, Maria waved her arms, clutched on to the fragile corn plants and eventually disappeared as well. At the place where they had submerged the leaves of corn stirred for a while, but soon the waves subsided.

Djimo's tone of voice betrayed a certain nervousness: 'Madala . . .' But the nervousness disappeared at once. Djimo gave an order : 'Madala, don't look over there !'

Inside Madala, something crumpled, but it was not the thread of his sickness.

In the green confusion of the far end of the field, Maria did not see the Overseer at once. She thrashed about wildly, trying to free her legs. An arm strongly encircled her shoulders.

The hot, acid breath of the man came close to her face.

Maria's *capulana* came loose after a short struggle, and the cold sensation of water became more vivid to her. She shivered and shrank away.

She felt on her naked thighs the warm and rough caress of the calloused hands of the man.

Madala looked around. No one looked directly at him, but all the men in the camp had placed themselves in positions in the shade from where they could watch him. Only the youth of the Kraal Gang, who had interrogated him a while ago, still wore his insolent expression.

The silence was ominous. José, the *kuka* of the Farm Gang, coughed insistently, but still the silence was maintained.

In the green twilight of the depths of the field, the pallid skin of the Overseer acquired a greenish tinge.

His face, hard, contorted with desire, momentarily filled the eyes of Maria.

The fiery breath of the man penetrated her half-opened lips, and she was drawn, intoxicated, into a vortex. Maria closed her eyes without rancour, and abandoned herself to the waves.

A vague warmth came from the submarine currents, mingled with the crisp algae of the bottom of the field, and bubbled gently in Maria's womb.

A gasped sigh smothered the rough possession.

One by one, Madala crushed the little leaves of the robust imaginary plant he had in his hand. A kind of sob escaped him when he realized that the threads of his sickness had so undermined his organs that he had no strength left to pull up a plant which clung more obstinately to the ground than those he pulled up in the fields.

'Don't cry, Madala . . .' – it was Djimo.

N'Guiana and Filimone were the first of the Hoeing Gang. José and Maleísse followed, because, although they now worked in the Clearing Gang, they used to belong to Madala's Gang. In an instant all the men in the Hoeing Gang and many other Gangs had crowded around Madala.

No one looked directly at Madala. No one spoke. After a while the whole camp was standing up.

Madala began to fondle the now naked branches of the imaginary plant.

'Maria, why did you come here?' – the Overseer's voice was hoarse. Crushed by the weight of the man, the breath came from Maria's chest in slow, measured gasps. The voice of the Overseer reached her in a murmur of faraway waves.

'Why you do this . . .?' she mumbled.

'Hm? . . .'

'Why? . . .' Maria shook off the man brusquely.

'Hm? . . .' The Overseer's hand closed lazily over Maria's breast.

'Didn't you like it . . .?' The man jumped aside. 'Hm? . . . didn't you like it?' He straightened his clothes and turned towards Maria. 'Hey ! . . . It's finished ! . . . Wake up ! . . .'

Maria's eyes shone in the half light of the depths of the field. 'Like this no good . . . Night time it's more better !' and there was panic in her voice. 'Now Madala saw ! . . . Madala saw ! . . .' she moaned, 'but you say it's only for us for talk about coming night time . . .'

'Come on, girl, the party's over. I'll give you the dough just now.'

Maria felt the hard ground of the field against her back.

The Overseer was the first to appear above the surface of the green sea. He thrust with his arms against the sweep of the tide, and advanced towards the path to the camp.

When Maria rose to the surface she was at once surrounded by the prolonged sighing cry of the sea. She shook some lumps of soil from her *capulana* and returned to the camp.

Along the path she had to raise her hands now and again to defend herself from the waves that the Overseer's passage provoked.

The men of the Kraal Gang drew aside for Maria to pass. The silence was maintained.

Maria smelt of the sea.

The features of the youth of the Kraal Gang who had become irritated with Madala were completely altered. Lines of hatred substituted the cynical mockery of a while ago. At the fourth attempt he managed to emit some sounds: '. . . Madala . . . the sun is very hot . . . where you work . . .'

Madala thought that before he considered whether the words were right he should say something: 'Yes, my son. The sun is very hot in the fields . . .'

But this did not succeed in breaking the silence. Maria did not raise her eyes. Standing, all the men of the camp looked down at the ground, still as posts.

'. . . Madala . . .' the voice of the youth continued with difficulty. 'Madala . . . tell us what we must do ! . . . Speak, and we'll finish with all this now. . . . They can kill us, but we're not afraid to die. . . .'

A murmur of approval rose from the compact mass of men at the camp.

Madala raised his eyes and slowly surveyed the incensed features of his workmates.

'. . . Madala, we all saw what he did to your daughter, even right in front of you ! . . . Say something, speak, Madala ! . . .' The supplicating eyes of the youth searched avidly for a trace of revolt in Madala's eyes.

Madala's inner self was dormant.

The Overseer appeared around the corner of one of the old barns and looked about for Maria. When he caught sight of her he tossed a silver coin into her lap.

'Here's what I owe you . . .' A lighted cigarette hung from his lips, which were twisted into a self-satisfied smile.

Maria freed her hands from her *capulana*. Somebody coughed. Maria retracted her hand nervously. She crossed her arms over her chest and hugged her back with her hands.

'Well, Maria?' The Overseer's eyes were filled with surprise.

Maria threw her body against the barn wall and turned her face away.

Madala watched her with his sad look. She closed her eyes.

'Why you do this?' she whispered dully.

The Overseer put his hands on his hips and let out a brief guffaw. 'But what's the matter with you, girl? Don't you want the money? Are you afraid of getting paid?' He stopped, waiting for Maria's reply. But he continued: 'Are you afraid the boys will find out that you're a whore?'

Maria hugged herself more tightly, and, digging her nails into her back, whined: 'Madala saw us, Madala saw . . .'

'And what's the matter with that?' The Overseer stretched out his arms, emphasizing his surprise, then folded them on his chest.

'Madala, he my father !' Maria spat out the words with fury.

The men of the camp, stiff as posts, scrutinized the Overseer's face.

They cut him to pieces in silence.

'What!' the Overseer finally managed to pronounce. The blood rushed suddenly to his sallow face. 'I didn't know you were Madala's daughter . . .' He gestured, suffocating. 'I didn't know. . . . True as God, Madala, I swear I didn't know . . . I didn't know you had a daughter . . . so pretty . . . I . . . I'm a friend of hers . . .'

The silence of the men of the camp throbbed with tension.

'Madala . . .', the Overseer approached Madala. 'Madala, if you like, you needn't work this afternoon. Stay here at the camp and talk to your daughter.'

Madala turned his sad eyes towards the ground. His fingers, ignorant of the volume of the invisible plant, closed violently.

The silence seemed to drive the Overseer to desperation. With an abortive gesture of conciliation, he stammered hoarsely: 'Shit! How could I have known?' He turned towards the men of the camp, extending the question to them.

The men of the camp remained mute and darkly unyielding.

'Shit!' roared the Overseer, full of terror.

'Madala . . . I'll give you some money, and you go with your daughter to the *cantinas*.' The Overseer searched anxiously for some vestige of animation in Madala's deadened features.

Madala bowed his head a little lower.

'Madala . . .' stuttered the Overseer. His hand was suspended in the middle of a gesture, and fell. 'Shit!' He retreated towards the corner of the barn and disappeared.

The youth of the Kraal Gang lifted up his voice. 'Madala, we all saw what he did to your daughter right in front of you!'

Mutely, the whole camp supported the youth.

Maria raised her hands on her back and sobbed.

Madala buried his head in his chest.

The Overseer appeared around the corner of the barn with a bottle of wine in his hand. 'Hey, boys,' his voice was firm. He faced the camp and yelled, 'Let's get to work, it's time! Come along, it's already half past one! Clearing Gang! Maleísse! Elias! Alberto! . . . Clearing Gang boys? . . . Clearing, hey! . . . You, clear the bush at the side of the river! . . . Farm Gang! Get going, Farm Gang, get rid of the worms on the cabbages! Kraal! Kraal Gang! Take the cattle to drink . . . Hoeing Gang! Follow me! Come on, Hoeing Gang, get going to the fields . . .'

Still standing, the men of the camp remained immobile.

Madala's fingers became suddenly conscious of the imaginary plant. They opened and began to fondle it.

'Well, boys? Can't you hear? The gong's struck! Dina's finished!' The Overseer shouted with increasing irritation. He looked at the bottle he had in his hand. 'Madala! . . .'

Madala rose.

'Can't you hear me? I've already told you to get going! . . . Get going, you swine! . . .'

Madala accepted the bottle that was handed to him.

'Swine! Bastards! Get to work, you bastards! . . .'

All the camp looked at Madala. The youth of the Kraal Gang took a step forward: 'Madala! . . .'

With an infinitely hard expression Madala cast his eyes upon the anxious faces surrounding him.

The bottle was beaded with sweat, and the wine was a dirty reddish yellow. Madala swallowed it in one gulp, allowing a good part of it to wet his beard and run down his neck. Then he gave back the empty bottle to the Overseer.

'You bastards! Get to work, I tell you! . . .'

The posts oscillated, faltering.

The silence was utter defeat.

Maria watched everything, very apprehensive.

The Overseer brandished the empty bottle, holding it by the neck. 'Black bastards!'

The youth of the Kraal Gang spat at the feet of Madala: 'Dog!'

Madala ignored the insult. He turned his back and started on the path to the fields. N'Guiana and Filimone followed him.

Djimo turned to the other labourers: 'Let's go . . .'

'Hurry up! Hurry up! . . .' the Overseer roared. 'Hurry, you swine!'

The men of the camp, headed by Djimo, began their return march to work.

'Hurry up!' The Overseer lunged.

The bottle broke at the first blow, but the youth of the Kraal Gang did not move. The second blow split his scalp open. The Overseer's boots crushed into his face with fury. 'Son – of – a – whore!'

Madala leaned forward and twisted the stem of a bush around his wrist. He gave a small pull to see if it was firmly embedded. Then he allowed his body to lean backwards until it came out. He placed it carefully on the ground, lining it up with the pile he had already pulled up around him. He looked ahead between the corn stalks until he saw the form of Djimo. Filimone, n'Guiana, Mutha-kati, Tandane and Muthambi were also near – Madala could distinguish them. With a hoarse sigh he went back to his work.

Above its strange fish, the surface of the green sea was swept by a soft breeze. The gentle waves it stirred up broke, ebbed and flowed, and broke again, murmuring the secret of sea shells.

Translated by Dorothy Guedes

Kalungano

DREAM OF THE BLACK MOTHER

To my Mother

Black mother
Rocks her son
And in her black head
Covered with black hair
She keeps marvellous dreams.

Black mother
Rocks her son
And forgets
That the earth has dried up the maize
That yesterday the groundnuts were finished.

She dreams of marvellous worlds
Where her son would go to school
To school where men study.

Black mother
Rocks her son
And forgets
Her brothers building towns and cities
Cementing them with their blood.

She dreams of marvellous worlds
Where her son would run along the street
The street where men pass by.

Black mother
Rocks her son
And listening
To the voice from afar
Brought by the wind.

She dreams of marvellous worlds,
Marvellous worlds
Where her son will be able to live.

Translated by Philippa Rumsey

Rui Nogar

POEM OF THE CONSCRIPTED WARRIOR

He went there
Afraid
Of being afraid.

(Oh Our Lady of Anything
In my village
I left my wife behind.)

He went there
With the shame
Of feeling ashamed.

(Perhaps I might even kill children;
I have two children, oh Lord . . .)

He went there
Involuntarily
He went there
And the courage was not his own
And the hate was not his own
Not his own
Not at all
But he went
Infected with blood lust
He killed killed killed
Until one day
Oh ! irony
On that day
There was sun
There was hope
There was his wife
There were his children his mother a letter

There was so much
But all crumbled away
All
In the treacherous cackling
Of the grenades
With yellow beaks
And red tails ...

Translated by Philippa Rumsey

Biographical Notes on Authors

CHINUA ACHEBE: Born in 1930 in Eastern Nigeria where his father taught in a school under the Church Missionary Society. He was educated at Government College in Umuahia, which features much in his novels. Graduated as a B.A. at the University of Ibadan. Mr Achebe began a career in broadcasting in 1954; he worked for the B.B.C. and in 1961 he became First Director of External Broadcasting. His first two novels, *Things Fall Apart* and *No Longer at Ease* (Heinemann, London, 1958 and 1960), have been translated into German, Italian, and Spanish.

CHRISTINA AMA ATA AIDOO: Born in Ghana and graduated B.A. at the University of Ghana, Legon, in 1963. Her short stories have appeared in *Black Orpheus*, and her verse in the Ghanaian literary journal *Okyeame*, and other anthologies. She now does research and lectures in the Department of African Studies in the University of Ghana.

GEORGE AWOONOR-WILLIAMS: Born in 1935 near Keta in the Toga Region of Ghana. His father came from Sierra Leone and his mother from Togoland. His secondary education was at Achimota, and he graduated from the University of Ghana. Awoonor-Williams now works for the Ghana Film Industry Corporation and edits the journal *Okyeame*. He has published a volume of poems *Rediscovery* (Mbari Writers' and Artists' Club, Ibadan, 1964).

SYLVAIN BEMBA: Born in the Congo, he rose to prominence when *La Chambre Noire* won joint first prize in a contest organized in 1964 by the French magazine *Preuves* in Paris for the best African short story in French. Mr Bemba is chief editor of L'Agence Congolaise d'Information, Brazzaville, Congo.

ANTOINE-ROGER BOLAMBA: Born in Congo-Leopoldville. He has published poetry and articles in *La Voix du Congolais*, a journal of which he was the editor. His poems have been published as a volume entitled *Esanzo* (*Présence Africaine*, 1956).

KWESI BREW: Born in 1928, Cape Coast, Ghana; he is a graduate of the University of Ghana. His poems have been published in *Voices of Ghana*, a radio anthology; Accra's literary journal, *Okyeame*; and in the Penguin *Modern Poetry from Africa*.

DENNIS BRUTUS: Born in Southern Rhodesia and went to live in Cape Province, South Africa. He graduated in arts at Fort Hare University College and then taught English and Afrikaans in Port Elizabeth. Because of his official position in an organization that protested racialism in sport and campaigned for the exclusion of South Africa from the Olympic Games as long as she practised apartheid in sport, he was banned from teaching and subsequently from his university law studies. He cannot be published in South Africa because of the banning order, nor can he be quoted in that country. He served an eighteen-month jail sentence as a political prisoner in Robben Island. He has published *Sirens, Knuckles, Boots* (Mbari, Ibadan, 1963), most of which is protest poetry.

JOSÉ CRAVEIRINHA : Born in 1922 at Lourenço Marques, Moçambique, where he has been working as a journalist. His poems have appeared in several journals and in an anthology.

BIRAGO DIOP : Born in 1906 at Dakar, Senegal. Qualified as a veterinary surgeon after schooling at a lycée in Saint-Louis. He lived for many years in Upper Volta as a veterinary officer. His volume of poems, *Leurres et Lueurs*, was published by *Présence Africaine* in 1960. He has also adapted several African tales to French under the titles *Les Contes d'Amadou Koumba* (Fasquelle, Paris, 1947), *Les Nouveaux Contes d'Amadou Koumba* (*Présence Africaine*, 1958).

DAVID DIOP : Born in 1927 at Bordeaux of a Senegalese father and a Cameroonian mother. Killed in an air crash off Dakar in 1960. Throughout his short life Diop was in poor health and was often in hospital. Moved frequently from his childhood onwards between France and West Africa. Was a regular contributor to *Présence Africaine* and had several early poems in Senghor's anthology. He published *Coups de pilon*, a book of poems (*Présence Africaine*, 1956).

MBELLA SONNE DIPOKO: Born in 1936 in Douala, Cameroun, and grew up on the Murgo River. In spite of the rigorous Protestantism of his uncle, with whom he lived, Dipoko took a lively interest in tribal dances and rituals. Attended secondary school in Eastern Nigeria 1952–6 and returned to Cameroun to become a clerk in the Development Corporation in Tiko. Joined the then Nigerian Broadcasting Corporation in 1957 and was stationed in Lagos as a news reporter. He has been in Paris since 1960, where he is reading Law and writing poetry. His poetry has been published in *United Asia*, Bombay, and *Présence Africaine*, Paris, and various other journals.

SARIF EASMON: Born in Sierra Leone, he is a medical practitioner in Freetown. He has published several short stories and a play, *Dear Parent and Ogre*, which won first prize in a play-writing contest organized by *Encounter* magazine in London four years ago.

CYPRIAN EKWENSI: Born in 1921 in Minna, Northern Nigeria, and lived near Onitsha, Eastern Nigeria. He went to school in Ibadan; Achimota College, Ghana; School of Forestry, Ibadan; and studied pharmacy at London University. His career has been as varied as his education: lecturer in English and science; lecturer in pharmacy in Lagos; pharmacist with the Nigerian Medical Corporation; Director of Information with the Federal Ministry of Information, a post he still holds. Among Mr Ekwensi's publications are *People of the City* (Andrew Dakers, London, 1954); *The Drummer Boy* (1960); *The Passport of Mallam Ilia* (1960); *Jagua Nana* (Hutchinson, London, 1961); *Beautiful Feathers* (Hutchinson, 1963). His short stories have been published in several anthologies.

LUIS BERNARDO HONWANA: Born in November 1942 in Lourenço Marques, Moçambique, and as one of eight children grew up in a village outside the capital. His father was an interpreter for the Portuguese administration. Lack of money prevented him from finishing secondary school as a full-time pupil. During the break he worked as a cartographer in government, and later contributed to a literary page of a local newspaper. His interest in journalism grew and he worked in turn as a reporter and as an editor – in the latter capacity for two newspapers in Beira, the second largest city in Moçambique. His short stories and reviews have been published in several journals, and Publicações Tribuna of Lourenço Marques brought out a volume of his short stories under the title *Nós Matámos o Cão-Tinhoso.*

PAULIN JOACHIM: Born in 1931 in Cotonou, Dahomey. He did his secondary schooling in Dahomey and Gabon, and graduated in *Études de Droit* at the Catholic University of Lyon, France. He was awarded a diploma in journalism at L'École Supérieure de Journalism in Paris. Joachim was political editor for *France-Soir* in Paris for three years, and is now Editor-in-Chief of *Bingo*, a monthly magazine in French published for French-speaking Africa. He lives in Paris. Joachim has published a volume of verse, *Un Nègre raconte* (Editions Bruno Durocher, Paris).

KALUNGANO: A pseudonym.

JOSEPH E. KARIUKI: Born in 1931 at Banana Hill, near Nairobi, Kenya. He received his primary education at one of the pre-emergency independent schools, and his secondary education at Alliance High School. In 1953 Kariuki graduated as B.A. from Makerere College, Kampala, and received the education diploma in 1954. He taught English in two high schools and then went to Cambridge for his B.A. Honours on a government bursary. During his stay in Britain he wrote verse, some of which was broadcast from the Overseas Service of the B.B.C. He is now Principal of Kenya Institute of Administration.

MAZISI KUNENE: Born in 1930 in Durban, South Africa. He graduated M.A. at Natal University and in 1959 went to the School of Oriental and African Studies, London, to work on a dissertation on Zulu poetry. He now does full-time political work. He writes Zulu poetry and plays and wants to write an epic to give poetic expression to the philosophy of life as understood by the Zulus. Some of his verse, translations from his Zulu poetry, appears in *Modern Poetry from Africa* (Penguin Books, 1963), and in South African journals.

ALEX LA GUMA: Born in 1923 in South Africa. He is now under house arrest twelve hours a day in his Athlone home in Cape Town, because of his political activities. He has published two novels: *A Walk in the Night* (Mbari, Ibadan, 1962), and *And a Threefold Cord* (Seven Seas, Berlin, 1964), as well as several short stories published in journals and anthologies. He is one of the four South African writers represented in the volume *Quartet*, edited by Richard Rive.

CAMARA LAYE: Born at Kouroussa, Guinea, and educated at Conakry and Paris. He now works as a civil servant in Guinea. He tells the story of his childhood in *L'Enfant Noir* (Plon, Paris, 1953); this, and *Le Regard du Roi* (Plon, Paris, 1955), have been translated by James Kirkup under the titles *The Dark Child* and *The Radiance of the King* and published by Collins, London. Camara Laye has also published short stories in *Black Orpheus*.

AKÉ LOBA: Born in August 1927 at Abobo Bacule, a small village just out-side Abidjan, Ivory Coast. As one of a family of twelve children he helped his father in the family plantation until he was eighteen. His father de-cided to send him to France to acquire more knowledge of agriculture. He worked as a farm labourer in Brittany and Beauce, but when his father died and lack of funds prevented him from continuing in agriculture, he took up a job as a factory hand in Paris. He attended courses in the evening, and his stay in France eventually lasted fifteen years, during which time he married and had two children. He wrote two novels. He is now back in his native land and directs an information service for agricultural non-cooperatives.

TODD MATSHIKIZA: Born in 1920 in Queenstown, South Africa. His father was a church organist. Attended St Peter's Secondary School, Johan-nesburg, and subsequently trained as a teacher at Lovedale, near Fort Hare College. Mr Matshikiza, himself a pianist, has composed much African choral music which has been widely performed by South African Negro choirs. More recently he composed the music for the jazz show *King Kong*, which has been performed in London by a South African Negro cast. He followed this with another musical, *Mkumbane*, which was staged in South Africa. He worked on a monthly and a Sunday paper as a jazz critic and social columnist before he left with the *King Kong* cast and lived in London with his wife and two children. He broadcast for the B.B.C. and wrote and published *Chocolates for my Wife* (Hodder and Stoughton, 1961). It is a book of sketches of the writer's life in South Africa and England. Mr Matshikiza now works for Zambia Radio in Lusaka.

EZEKIEL MPHAHLELE: Born in December 1919 in a slum location, South Africa. He attended St Peter's Secondary School in Johannesburg and after three years there took a teacher's certificate at Adam's College, Natal. He worked in a blind institute as a clerk-shorthand-typist for four years. He later taught English and Afrikaans at one of the largest high schools in Johannesburg. Banned from teaching by the Government as a result of organizing resistance against its policies regarding African education, he emigrated to Nigeria in 1957. There he taught in a grammar school and then joined the Department of Extra-Mural Studies at the University of Ibadan, teaching English language and literature. He then worked in Paris, directing the African programme for the Congress for Cultural Freedom. He now lectures in English Literature at University College, Nairobi. Mr Mphahlele has published several short stories, including two volumes: *Man Must Live* (Cape Town, 1947) and *The Living and the Dead* (Black Orpheus, Ibadan, 1960). In 1959 his autobiography, *Down Second Avenue*, was published by Faber & Faber, London; it has been translated into German, Hungarian, Czech, Serbo-Croat, Bulgarian, French, Swedish, and Japanese. He published *The African Image*, a book of political and literary essays (Faber & Faber) in 1962, and has finished another volume of short stories for which he is seeking a publisher.

JEAN-BAPTISTE MUTABARUKA: Born in 1937 in the eastern region of Ruanda, and educated among very traditional Tutsis. His father has always owned large herds of cattle. He has schooled under Catholic Fathers in the Congo (Leopoldville). Mutabaruka states that although he was born of Catholic parents, he took part in traditional religious ceremonies. Although not drawn towards such tradition it interests him to the extent that he wants to grasp its significance. Now an exile in Burundi.

AGOSTINHO NETO: Born in 1922 at Icola e Bengo in Angola. Practised medicine in his country after graduating in Lisbon; he was involved in a movement for the 'rediscovery' of the indigenous culture of Angola. In 1960 Neto became president of the MPLA (movement for the liberation of Angola). He was arrested the same year and served a jail sentence in Lisbon; he escaped in 1962. His poetry has been published in Portuguese and Angolan journals.

ABIOSEH NICOL: Abioseh Nicol Sierra Leone was educated in Nigeria and Sierra Leone. He later studied at British universities. He was awarded the Margaret Wrong Prize and Medal for Literature in Africa in 1952. His short stories, articles, and poems have appeared in English and American publications.

LEWIS NKOSI: Born in 1938 in Natal, South Africa. He worked for *Drum* magazine and *Golden City Post* in Johannesburg, as a reporter. In 1961 he left South Africa to study journalism for a year at Harvard University on a Nieman Fellowship. He has broadcast for a transcription centre in London, where he now lives, and now works as a free-lance writer. He has published a play, *The Rhythm of Violence* (Oxford University Press, 1954), about race relations. He recently acted as host moderator, interviewing African writers in various countries for a series of television programmes on African literature, for the National Educational Television, New York.

RUI NOGAR: A pseudonym.

ONUORA NZEKWU: Born in 1928 in Kafanchan, Northern Nigeria. A teacher by profession, he joined *Nigeria Magazine*, of which he is now editor. Nzekwu has published two novels, *Wand of the Noble Wood* (1961) and *Blade Among the Boys* (1963); both are published by Hutchinson, London.

GRACE OGOT: Born in 1930 in Central Nyanza Province, Kenya. After her secondary schooling she trained as a general nurse and midwife in Uganda and Britain. She subsequently worked in Maseno Hospital, Nyanza, as a midwifery tutor and nursing sister. She later worked under the Students' Health Service in University College, Makerere, Uganda. After service in the Homecraft Training Centre in Nyanza, as headmistress and community development officer, Mrs Ogot worked with the B.B.C. for fifteen months as script-writer and announcer for its Overseas Service. She is now public relations officer for Air India Corporation of East Africa and Nairobi. Her short stories have appeared in journals including *Transition*, Kampala, *Black Orpheus*, Ibadan, and *Présence Africaine*.

FERDINAND OYONO: Born in the Cameroons, he writes in French. He worked in the United States and is now his country's Ambassador to Liberia. Like Mongo Beti, his countryman, Oyono has written novels in which he laughs both at the colonial administration and white missionary and at some of the foibles of his own people as victims of colonialism. His novels to date, published by Julliard, Paris, are: *Une vie de Boy* (1956); *Le Vieux Nègre et la Medaille* (1956) to be published by Heinemann Educational Books Ltd, as *The Old Negro and the Medal*, in 1967; *Chemin d'Europe* (1960). *Le Pandemonium*, his latest novel, is due out soon.

LENRIE PETERS: Born in 1932 in Bathurst, Gambia. Educated in Gambia, Sierra Leone, and Trinity College, Cambridge, where he graduated in Medicine in 1959. He is now studying surgery at Guildford. He is an amateur singer and broadcaster, and has completed a novel. His first volume of poems was published by Mbari, Ibadan in 1964.

JEAN PLIYA: Born in Dahomey, he became a teacher. He is now a deputy in the Dahomeyan parliament.

RICHARD RIVE: Born in 1931 in Cape Town, South Africa. Graduated as B.A. in the University of Cape Town; he is now teaching in a high school there. He began writing short stories while in high school. His stories have appeared in several languages, and some have been published in a volume, *African Songs* (Seven Seas, Berlin, 1963). He has compiled short stories by three South African coloured writers (including himself) and one white, under the title *Quartet* (Crown Publishers, New York, 1963); and *Modern African Prose*, an anthology published by Heinemann. In 1962 Mr Rive undertook a tour of many parts of Africa and Europe to study literary trends, under the sponsorship of the Farfield Foundation, New York. His first novel, *Emergency*, was published by Faber & Faber, London, in 1964.

LÉOPOLD SÉDAR SENGHOR: Born 1906 at Joal, an old Portuguese coastal settlement in Senegal. He is of the Serere tribe. His father was a groundnut merchant and a Catholic in a land predominantly Moslem. Senghor passed brilliantly from the local lycée and at the age of twenty-two went to the Lycée Louis le Grand in Paris. Later he completed his *agrégation* at the Sorbonne, the first West African to do so. In Paris he met Césaire, Damas, and other black poets and intellectuals from the Caribbean area. Prominent as an intellectual and political leader of West Africa for many years, he has been at various times a teacher at the École Nationale de la France d'Outremer, a member of the Council of Europe, a Deputy for Senegal in the French National Assembly, and a minister in the French Government. In 1960 installed as first President of the independent Republic of Senegal. Senghor is the principal African advocate of *Négritude* and the only African poet who has yet produced a substantial body of work. Has published *Chants d'ombres*, poems (Paris, Éditions du Seuil, 1945), *Hosties noires*, poems (Éditions du Seuil, 1948: reissued with *Chants d'ombre*, 1956), *Chants pour Naëtt*, poems (Paris, Seghers, 1949), *Éthiopiques*, poems (Seuil, 1956), *Nocturnes*, poems (Seuil, 1961), *Langage et poésie négro-africaine* (published in *Poésie et language*, Maison du Poète, Brussels, 1954), *L'Apport de la poésie négre* (in *Témoignages sur la poésie du demi-siècle*, Maison du Poète, Brussels, 1953), *Esthétique négro-africain* (*Diogène*, October 1956).

OUSEMANE SOCÉ: Born in Saint-Louis, Senegal. Socé wrote *Karim* – a novel about his native country – in 1935 (Nouvelles Éditions Latines, Paris). His second novel *Mirages de Paris* (Nouvelles Éditions Latines) followed in 1955.

KULDIP SONDHI: Born in 1924 in India. After having schooled in India his family emigrated to Kenya. He received much of his higher education in the United States, where he graduated in aeronautical engineering, but he works in Mombasa, Kenya, as a constructional engineer. He began writing plays and short stories ten years ago, and in 1963 his play *The Undesignated* won first prize in a Kenya Drama festival; he has just finished a novel. Sondhi says he finds creative writing much more difficult than engineering.

WOLE SOYINKA: Born in 1935 at Abeokuta, Western Nigeria, and educated at Ibadan. Attended the University of Ibadan and later Leeds University where he graduated in English Honours. He worked at the Royal Court, London, where his play *The Lion and the Jewel* was produced. After returning to Nigeria in 1960 he wrote another play, *A Dance of the Forests*, which won the *Observer* competition and was produced for Nigerian Independence in October 1960. Three plays of his were published by Mbari, Ibadan, in 1963, and *The Lion and the Jewel* and *A Dance of the Forests* were published in single editions by Oxford University Press in 1964. He has been directing a theatre group in Nigeria, and his poetry has appeared in *Black Orpheus*, Ibadan, and in other journals.

FELIX TCHIKAYA U'TAM'SI: Born in 1931 at Mpili, Middle Congo. Went to France with his father, then deputy for Moyen Congo, in 1946; studied at Orléans and Paris. He has published four books of poetry: *Le Mauvais Sang* and *Feu de Brousse* (Caractères, Paris, 1955, 1957); *À Triche-Cœur* and *Épitome* (Oswald, Paris, 1960, 1962).

CAN THEMBA: Born in 1923 in Pretoria, South Africa. He obtained a distinction in English in his B.A. degree at Fort Hare University College. He edited a now defunct popular magazine in Johannesburg and then served on *Drum* magazine, Johannesburg, as a reporter and then assistant editor. He has published several short stories in various journals and anthologies. He is now teaching in a secondary school in Manzine, Swaziland.

AMOS TUTUOLA: Born in Abeokuta, Western Nigeria, in 1920, his father is a cocoa farmer. Amos Tutuola had six years of interrupted education and trained as a blacksmith. He served in the R.A.F. as a metal worker in the last war, and now works in the Labour Department of the Nigerian Government in Lagos. Mr Tutuola recreates Yoruba myth and legend in his novels and stories. His best-known novels include *Palm-Wine Drinkard*; *My Life in the Bush of Ghosts*; *The Brave Huntress*; *Feather Woman of the Jungle* (short stories); all these were published by Faber & Faber, London.

JOSEPH ZOBEL: Born in Petit-Bourg, in the south of Martinique, in 1915. His first novel, *Diab'la* (Ce diable d'homme), is set in a fishing-town, Le Diamant, where in 1937 he was Secretary to the Department of Bridges and Highways. In 1938, while supervising at the Lycée Schoelcher, he published some short stories in a local newspaper. When, during the war, Martinique joined Free France, the Governor of Martinique made Zobel Press Attaché to his Government. Meanwhile he published the novel *Les*

Jours immobiles and the volumes of stories *Laghia de la Mort ou Qui fait pleurer le tam-tam?* In 1946 Zobel left for France: Institute of Ethnology, Sorbonne, Course in Dramatic Art. In 1950, while teaching at the Fountainbleu Lycée, he published *La Rue cases-nègres*, a novel which won the Prix des Lecteurs, awarded by a jury of a thousand readers. In 1953, *La Fête à Paris*, novel. Passed French Radio Actors examination and took part in many radio plays, and persuaded many producers to give poetry a greater place on the radio. Zobel has lived in Senegal since 1957 where he has been in charge of National Broadcasting, and directed the Cultural Services which he himself founded. In 1964 and 1965 he published *Le Soleil Partagé*, short stories, and *Incantation pour un retour au pays natal*, poems. He has made a record, *Joseph Zobel dit trois poèmes de Joseph Zobel*.

More about Penguins

If you have enjoyed reading this book you may wish to know that *Penguin Book News* appears every month. It is an attractively illustrated magazine containing a complete list of books published by Penguins and still in print, together with details of the month's new books. A specimen copy will be sent free on request.

Penguin Book News is obtainable from most bookshops; but you may prefer to become a regular subscriber at 3s. for twelve issues. Just write to Dept EP, Penguin Books Ltd, Harmondsworth, Middlesex, enclosing a cheque or postal order, and you will be put on the mailing list.

Some other books published by Penguins are described on the following pages.

Note: *Penguin Book News* is not available in the U.S.A., Canada or Australia.

A Short History of Africa

Roland Oliver and J. D. Fage

For some years now there has been an urgent need for a
concise history of Africa. Although much has been written
on different regions of Africa and different periods of her
long development – colonial histories of the European
powers, current affairs articles on the emergent countries,
studies of Africa's prehistory – there has been nothing that
offers the general reader an overall view of African history
from the earliest times to the Pan-African meetings at
Monrovia and Casablanca. Drawing on archaeology, oral
tradition, language relationships, social institutions, and
material cultures, the editors of the *Journal of African
History* now present *A Short History of Africa* which not
only assembles the most authoritative views of their
colleagues into an absorbing narrative, but also contains
some original conclusions that take the study of Africa a
stage further.

a volume in the Penguin African Library

Modern Poetry from Africa

Edited by Gerald Moore and Ulli Beier

This modern poetical geography of Africa is unique. It
draws on sixteen countries to present the work of black
poets writing in English, French, and Portuguese, although
all the poems, many of which appear for the first time here,
are presented in English. As a sample of contemporary
African writing they reveal an interesting blend of public
and personal statements.

Poetry composed in African languages has been left out,
because no two editors could possibly have covered the
enormous field. This omission, however, does not impair the
clear picture of emotional, social and political pressures
(fashionably termed *Négritude*) as they are reflected by
Africa's imaginative or committed poets today.